HANDLING AND STORAGE OF FOOD GRAINS IN TROPICAL AND SUBTROPICAL AREAS

First printing 1970
Second printing 1975

FAO Agricultural Development Paper *No. 90*

HANDLING AND STORAGE OF FOOD GRAINS IN TROPICAL AND SUBTROPICAL AREAS

by

D.W. Hall

FAO Consultant

Agricultural Engineering Service
Agricultural Services Division

FOOD AND AGRICULTURE ORGANIZATION OF THE UNITED NATIONS
ROME 1970

The information contained in this manual is based on data prepared for Informal Working Bulletin No. 24 in the series available from the Agricultural Engineering Service of the Agricultural Services Division of the Food and Agriculture Organization of the United Nations. While it represents knowledge obtained from organizations concerned with technical problems of handling and storing produce, it is not possible for FAO to assume responsibility for statements contained herein.

Printed in Italy

PREFACE

This manual presents technical data on some of the principles of handling and storing food grains in relation to local practices in the tropics and subtropics, particularly with reference to the storage of cereals, legumes and oilseeds. It has been written primarily as a practical aid to agricultural officers and extension staff; produce and marketing officers (inspection); public health officers, teachers (training colleges, etc.); and especially to those who may be engaged in preparing simple extension material for use by welfare officers, warehousemen, traders and farmers in the tropical and subtropical countries.

The subject is so broad that it has been necessary to select and emphasize technical details of particular relevance to the provision of instructions for farmers and traders. At the same time, the manual is intended to provide helpful information for officials having varied interests and for scientists who have little practical experience of storage problems in the tropics. Thus some repetition of basic information occurs in the different chapters.

This work is based on valuable information provided by specialists in Africa and in 11 countries in other parts of the world, and by organizations concerned with stored products problems. Some of this information appeared in the FAO Informal Working Bulletin No. 24. The collator is Dr. D.W. Hall, Director, Tropical Stored Products Centre, Tropical Products Institute, Ministry of Overseas Development, Slough, England. The writer wishes to acknowledge the collaboration received from the staff of the Pest Infestation Laboratory, Agricultural Research Council, and of the Infestation Control Laboratory, Ministry of Agriculture, Fisheries and Food. He is also indebted to members of the staff at the Tropical Stored Products Centre at Slough who assisted in the compilation of data.

CONTENTS

Appendices

LIST OF ILLUSTRATIONS

Figure

COLOUR PLATES

Acknowledgement is due to the following institutions and individuals:

Miss Jane Burton (Figures 19-23), Cyanamid International, New Jersey, U.S.A. (Plates A and B), Mr. D. Farry (Figures 31-33), Mr. C.T. H. Fisher (Figures 28 and 39), Mr. J.A. Freeman (Figure 46), Mr. P.H. Giles (Figure 35), Dr. S.M. Henderson, University of California, U.S.A. (Figures 6 and 10), Honeywell Inc., Minneapolis, U.S.A. (Figure 62), Infestation Control Laboratory, U.K. (Figure 22), Institut africain pour le développement économique et social (Figure 50), Dr. W.F. Jepson (Figure 46), Mr. S. Kockum (Figures 30, 37 and 41), Drs. Leprigue and Lefebre (Figure 36), Prof. Baeta Neves (Figure 34), Mr. I. Pattinson (Figure 52a), Pest Infestation Laboratory, Slough, U.K. (Figures 5, 9, 11-16, 38, 40, 42-44, 47, 48b, 49a, 51, 53-55, 57b, 59-61, 63), Mr. A.C. Ross and Major J.H. de W. Waller (Figure 26), Tropical Stored Products Centre (Figures 2-4, 8, 17, 18, 27, 29, 49b).

1. INTRODUCTION

Storage and marketing of food grains, if carried out efficiently, will be a major contribution to the solution of world hunger. This is more widely recognized now, especially in the developed areas, than it was a few years ago, but in the developing parts of the world little attention has been paid to this aspect of the problem.

In the tropics and subtropics there are some 70 developing nations with a population of about 2 000 million which is expanding annually, and what is termed malnutrition is widespread and persistent (U.S. Economic Research Service, 1961). The problem of improving the present diets of human beings in specific areas of the world is almost always considered in terms of increasing food production. In tropical countries in early stages of development, increasing agricultural productivity would appear an obvious aim, not only with respect to cash crops, the sale of which can provide money to buy food, but also to local food crops, linked with local marketing economics. The process of improving total food production is slow and costly. An overall food increase of 75 percent by 1980 or some 200 percent by the beginning of the 21st century is considered necessary.

While this situation is striking, it is in fact even more critical than these figures suggest. It is based on agricultural production data and therefore on the assumption that the caloric and nutritional potential of harvested produce is fully utilized by man. Unfortunately this is not so because, between the time a crop is harvested and its consumption by man or his domestic animals, considerable quantities of food are wasted or eaten by pests, particularly insects and rodents; also, losses in quality (nutritional and/or commercial potential of the produce) occur whenever these pests and microorganisms (fungi and bacteria) have been able to grow on produce or when methods of drying or processing destroy the nutrients. In some countries, losses after harvest (i.e., during storage, processing and marketing) may be as high as 50 percent, and in some cases higher.

The first step is to save what has been grown and harvested for human beings by protection against pests, and by improving local processing methods to retain inherent natural nutritional value of produce. What man has reaped must be protected; at the same time future yields must be improved.

In many of the developing parts of the world people live in relatively isolated communities, each producing its present food requirements plus small quantities of food or other agricultural products to provide money for clothes, bicycles, sewing machines, taxes, small quantities of meat, etc. Experience has taught the grower that, if produce is stored, it goes bad. This has two effects: a sufficient quantity is grown to feed the family for about three or four months; immediately after harvest (sometimes before it has been dried thoroughly), when there may be a temporary glut of food and prices are low, produce is sold to traders; moreover in many areas the farmers are in debt to the traders and any produce surplus beyond their own food requirements is immediately sold to meet the accumulated debts. Thus one of the major contributory factors responsible for the economic nonviability of farming areas is the farmer's inability to handle and store food efficiently so that he can sell good quality produce when it is scarce and commands a high price. The standard of living of a rural community depends not only upon the range of foods grown, the capacity to grow in quantity, but also upon the facilities for efficient handling, drying, storage and marketing.

In the course of time, local governments, marketing organizations, etc., have come to associate low quality standards, including infestation, as unfortunate but unavoidable criteria associated with food products in the tropics, particularly those for local consumption. In the past, standards of conservation of produce in the newly developing countries have been low principally due to:

1. educational standards of the local population;
2. shortage of money;
3. absence of organized internal marketing systems (particularly a lack of wholesalers);

4. lack of information among farmers and government officials concerning prices of produce, quality, and purchasing procedures in local markets;
5. lack of organization of agriculture to ensure continuity in supplies of produce of uniform quality to support local processing industries;
6. inability of local population to pay for quality (including the more highly processed foods);
7. lack of demand of buyers in developed countries for produce of the highest quality;
8. dearth of scientific data on the behaviour of plants, animals, chemicals, and building materials under local tropical conditions;
9. absence of extension and research staff to use and modify known techniques.

In many tropical countries the authorities are unaware of the actual quantities of produce lost between harvest and consumption. Current knowledge of modern handling and storage techniques is derived from industrialized countries, which are mainly in the temperate regions of the world. This knowledge has only limited application under the climatic conditions of tropical countries, particularly in the monsoon areas. For this reason the following points have been recommended by the International Rice Commission (1960-62) for inclusion in regional programmes of rice research:

1. basic research to ascertain requirements and technical means for safe storage in the tropics;
2. technical and economic analysis to determine the field for useful application of small farm storage, medium storage and large storage facilities at central points;
3. study of traditional storage facilities aimed at obtaining low cost structures particularly suitable for small depots.

This data must be obtained from the developing countries for all types of produce.

Greater effort is required in each country for the careful and efficient handling of produce to bring about improvements in poor, unhygienic conditions in which produce (including feed) is stored; this, in turn, requires the appointment of competent staff to assist

2

TABLE 1. – NUTRITIVE VALUES OF SOME MAJOR FOODS (FIGURES RELATE TO 100 GRAMMES OF EDIBLE PORTION)

	Calories	Protein	Fat	Carbo-hydrate	Calcium	Iron	Vitamin A	Thia-mine	Ribo-flavin	Nicotin-amide	Ascorbic acid
		.... *Grammes*			.. *Milligrammes* ..		.. *I. U.* ..	.... *Milligrammes*			
Maize, whole	*363*	10.0	4.5	*71*	12	2.5	—	*0.35*	*0.13*	2.0	—
Millet, finger, whole	*336*	6.0	1.5	*75*	*350*	5.0	—	*0.3*	*0.1*	1.4	—
Rice, lightly milled, parboiled	*354*	8.0	1.5	*77*	10	2.0	—	*0.25*	0.05	2.0	—
highly milled, parboiled	*352*	7.0	0.5	*80*	5	1.0	—	0.06	0.03	1.0	—
Sorghum, whole	*355*	10.4	3.4	*71*	32	4.5	—	*0.5*	*0.12*	3.5	—
Wheat, whole	*344*	11.5	2.0	*70*	30	3.5	—	*0.4*	*0.1*	*5.0*	—
Bean	*326*	*20.0*	1.5	*58*	*120*	*10.0*	—	*0.3*	*0.1*	2.0	—
Cowpea	*340*	*22.0*	1.5	*60*	90	5.0	20	*0.9*	*0.15*	2.0	—
Groundnut, dry	*579*	*27.0*	*45.0*	17	50	2.5	—	*0.9*	*0.15*	*17.0*	—
Cassava, fresh	153	0.7	0.2	37	25	1.0	—	0.07	0.03	0.7	*30*
flour	342	1.5	—	*84*	55	2.0	—	0.04	0.04	0.8	—
Plantain	128	1.0	0.2	31	7	0.5	*100*	0.05	0.05	0.7	*20*
Potato, sweet	114	1.5	0.3	26	25	1.0	*100*	0.1	0.04	0.7	*30*
Yam, fresh	104	2.0	0.2	24	10	1.2	20	0.1	0.03	0.4	*10*
flour	*317*	3.5	0.3	*75*	20	*10.0*	—	0.15	*0.1*	1.0	—
Molasses, cane	*276*	—	—	*69*	*300*	*10.0*	—	0.05	0.05	1.5	—
Sugar cane stem	60	1.0	—	14	10	1.0	—	0.02	0.02	0.1	—
Oil, palm	*900*	—	*100*	—	—	—	*1 000+*	—	—	—	—
Fish, dried	*309*	*63.0*	6.3♀	—	*3 000*	*8.5*	—	0.1	*0.2*	*6.0*	—

SOURCE: PLATT, B.S. 1962.

NOTE: Figures in italics indicate the nutrients for which the food is a major source; no significant dietary evaluations.

farmers and traders in efficient handling of good quality produce, to improve on existing storage conditions, and to ensure that deterioration from infestation and condensation does not occur during transportation due to lack of effort on the part of owners of road vehicles, railway authorities, harbour authorities, inspection staff, shipping agents and ship owners.

Food and its importance

Food which is essential for human beings and animals contains the following essential components:

1. *carbohydrates* which provide the body with energy and may also be converted into fat;
2. *fats* which provide energy and may also be converted into body-fat;
3. *proteins* which provide material for growth and repair of body tissue; also they provide energy and can be converted into fat;
4. *minerals* which provide material for growth and repair and for regulation of processes within the body;
5. *vitamins* which are used in chemical processes within the body, required in small amounts and unsynthesizable by the body from raw materials.

Most foods contain some of all of these components but in different proportions (Table 1); thus there is a predominance in cereals, root crops and sugar of carbohydrate, in meat, milk, cheese, eggs, fish, peas, nuts and beans of protein, in oilseeds of fats, and in fruit, vegetables, and dairy produce of minerals and vitamins. The proper maintenance of health and the efficient functioning of the body depends on the consumption of appropriate quantities of all the nutrients. Effective storage of pulses, cereals and oilseeds will contribute to providing a balanced diet.

2. TROPICS AND SUBTROPICS

In broad terms, the world consists of two regions: one where the human population has more than 2 300 calories of food per day available to it and the other where less than that number of calories of food per day is available. The area of lower daily calorie intake lies mainly between 40°N to 40°S while that of higher daily calorie intake lies between 40°N to 60°N.

Reference has been made to the importance of balanced diets. Figure 1 gives a broad comparison of the proportion of different types of foodstuffs in the diet in terms of calories consumed per head per day in a few countries in these two areas of the world. This indicates that in developed countries (e.g., in Europe, North America, Australia and New Zealand) enough food can be produced or purchased to ensure that a well-balanced diet is available to the population. In the developing countries (e.g., in Africa and Latin America, India and a number of other Asian countries) a daily intake of less than 2 500 calories, composed mainly of carbohydrates with only a small proportion of the essential proteins and minerals, is the typical diet of millions of people, a diet resulting in the undernourishment of about two thirds of the world's population.

The tropical belt is the area which lies between the Tropic of Cancer and the Tropic of Capricorn and contains about one quarter of the land surface of the earth and about one third of the world's population. The subtropical belts lie on either side of this, within latitudes 40°N and 40°S.

The tropics and subtropics include the least densely populated continent, Africa, which has only 8 persons to the square kilometre compared with 85 persons for Europe (including the U.S.S.R.) and 59 for Asia (Drogat, 1962). The Indian subcontinent, which has a population and area similar in size to that of Europe (excluding the U.S.S.R.), has about 17 persons to the square kilometre compared with 91 persons for Indonesia.

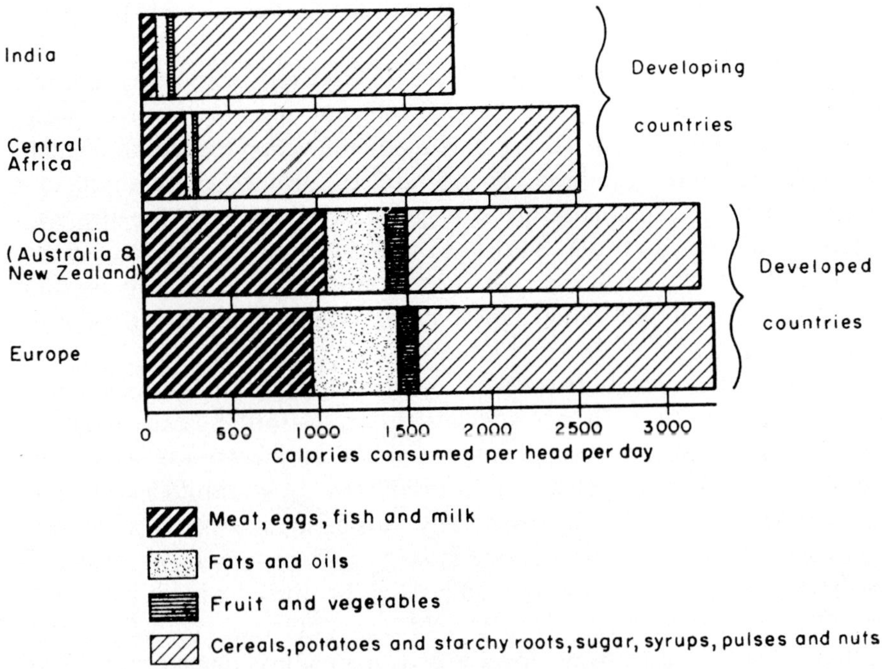

FIGURE 1. Comparison of estimated daily per caput calorie supplies in terms of food types for developed and developing areas.

Seven types of climate are distinguishable, each of which has its impact on the pattern of food supply and consumption in the areas concerned and particularly on drying and storage problems after harvest. These climates may be defined as equatorial, tropical, desert, humid subtropical, mediterranean, temperate, and highland, which have characteristic natural and cultivated vegetation potentials.

Agriculture is gradually becoming geared to local requirements in a number of countries in the tropics and subtropics. The gross agricultural product for many countries is not accurately known, due partly to the prevalence of subsistence farming with millions of small, widely scattered units, and in some areas to the practice of shifting cultivation and in others to that of harvesting small quantities for immediate consumption; moreover, in certain areas in Africa and Latin America cassava, a delay harvest crop, may be left in the ground from about 9 to 36 months after planting depending on local food requirements, and in some cases may not be harvested at all.

The existence of a monetary incentive geared to meeting marketing requirements, either within a country or in international trade, constitutes the basic drive for expansion of crop production which, in turn, depends on the expenditure of money on research and extension work. Expenditure on agricultural research for the production of more food has been infinitesimal in relation to the magnitude of the problem. In most countries it is seldom as high as 0.5 percent of the value of the gross annual production of food and export crops.

How much is being spent on protecting the harvested crop from deterioration? In considering this question it is necessary to distinguish between produce for export, that grown for local consumption, and that which is imported. In most countries produce for export is handled by especially established boards or government departments which finance storage and pest control measures designed to minimize losses. Imported produce, which is usually handled by commercial firms, is seldom protected against deterioration. In the same way, locally grown produce deteriorates in the farmers' and traders' stores because money has seldom been made available for employment of staff to study local storage problems and demonstrate improved handling and storage methods.

It is not uncommon for at least 75 percent of the population of countries in the tropics and subtropics to be engaged in agriculture. Throughout the rural areas and as a rule in urban areas as well (except perhaps in the major cities) there is an almost complete dependence on the local staple foodstuffs, although in countries which export cash crops (e.g., groundnuts, cotton, rice) imported food can be purchased.

With the steady increase in urbanization the number of people growing their own food is becoming smaller. Thus the food requirements of the towns may to some extent have to be met by imports, and this may have a crippling effect on the economy of the country. Also, the number of economic development schemes using large labour forces has increased greatly in recent years, and these labour forces require bigger rations than those normally available to the farmer or villager. In urban areas the high proportion of total income spent on food, estimated by FAO (1961a) at about 65 percent, is indicative of a poor standard of living, and it is difficult to avoid the attendant danger of inflation resulting from increases in food prices unless agricultural production is increased and sound storage practices and properly organized marketing are established.

Under these circumstances the importance of protecting all food products from deterioration cannot be overstressed. One indication of the magnitude of the problem is given in Table 2, which presents data (FAO, 1966) on cereal production in the tropics and subtropics; this produce as well as the quantities imported from temperate countries must be properly handled and safely stored.

TABLE 2. – PRODUCTION FIGURES FOR CEREALS IN AREAS OF THE TROPICS AND SUBTROPICS, INDICATING POTENTIAL STORAGE REQUIREMENT (FAO, 1966)

	Maize	Sorghum and millet	Paddy	Wheat	Barley and rye
	Thousand metric tons				
Africa	14 920	18 240	5 730	6 230	3 010
Asia	16 510	19 920	154 480	31 780	11 270
Latin America	19 050	1 180	7 470	13 050	13 740
Oceania	200	219	170	10 280	1 235

Local diets

The major food crops grown in tropical and subtropical areas are maize, sorghum, millet, wheat, paddy (rice), beans, peas, groundnuts, palm kernels, coconuts, cassava, yams, plantains, fruits and vegetables. Dietary patterns follow closely the dictates of local climate, soil, etc. Data provided by FAO (1966) gives the major areas of production of cereals (wheat, maize, sorghum, rice), legumes (groundnuts and soybeans), root crops (cassava), fruit and meat.

There is a heavy dependence on cereals and root crops, and according to FAO (1961a) this dependence is of the order of 60 percent in some countries and between 70 and 85 percent elsewhere. A comparison of the percentages of different types of foodstuffs in typical diets of local populations in a number of areas is given in Table 3.

TABLE 3. – COMPARATIVE PERCENTAGES OF DIFFERENT TYPES OF FOODS IN TYPICAL DIETS OF LOCAL POPULATIONS IN SELECTED AREAS (FAO RECORDS)

Foods	Latin America	West Africa	India	Southeast Asia
Cereals	27.8	70.5	49.2	40.5
Roots and tubers	14.5	3.9	4.3	13.1
Legumes	1.5		10.9	8.8
Fruits and vegetables	19.8	2.7	11.3	22.8
Animal protein (meat, fish, milk and eggs)	28.6	22.1	17.2	10.5
Sugar; oils and fats	7.8	0.8	7.1	4.3

Where root crops and cereals are important crops in agriculture, diets provide sufficient calories. The importance of good storage of cereals, pulses and oilseeds is apparent in view of the part which these crops play in local diets.

In general, there is an obvious seasonal pattern of food consumption which in some areas includes a preharvest period of extreme shortage or "hungry season." This is usually the result of a combination of factors including: insufficient production; lack of storage; possibly excessive use of grain for other purposes in the period of abundance immediately after harvest, such as making beer during festivals, etc., or a long dry season and unreliable rainfall. During this hungry season the daily intake of food may fall to below two thirds of what is required. Many families have to rely on plantains, yams, root crops, or whatever can be found in the way of other roots, berries, dried local leaves and seeds collected from the bush (which in many cases must have the poisons they contain removed by washing and maceration) or mice, snakes, lizards, etc. (Although the meat provided by hunting local animals is a welcome addition of protein to the otherwise meagre diet, it may also cause endemic disease due to the ingestion of parasites.) Other families sell cattle to buy grain at the market at a time when cattle prices are low and grain prices are high. An excellent discussion of the impact of the hungry season on the peoples of western tropical Africa has been given by Johnston (1958).

Four distinct nutritional problems are relevant in this context:

1. seasonal food shortages occurring before the normal harvest period due primarily to severe climatic conditions or ravages by pests;
2. nutritional deficiencies — particularly seen in children, whose protein and nutrition requirements are greater than those of adults, in areas where local production of animal protein (e.g., dried fish, meat), green vegetables and fruits is insufficient; related also to overall shortage of food or perhaps lack of information on the minimum food requirements of children;
3. inadequate use of the nutrients in food through lack of knowledge of food potentials;
4. postharvest handling of food causing loss of valuable food after harvest due to lack of knowledge of proper methods of storage and handling.

When food is imported it is the responsibility of governments to ensure that local methods of unloading from the ship, storing, transporting and inspection are adequate and are carried out efficiently to avoid spoilage through exposure to too high temperatures, to rain and high moistures, to insects and rats, or due to rough handling and use of transport vehicles in a state of disrepair.

Food as a cash crop

Exports of agricultural produce are important to many countries in the tropics and subtropics. For example, such exports from the African continent have averaged at least $3 400 million per year.

Although in some countries there are dietary shortages of vegetable protein and fat, there are considerable exports of beans, peas and vegetables from these regions. Maize, rice, groundnuts, cocoa beans, palm kernels (and oil), pulses, animal feed and copra are major exports from the tropics and subtropics.

In most countries, the only produce for which marketing is highly organized is produce for export. World demand for such produce provides a financial incentive to the country on the basis of which production is expanded and marketing is organized through produce boards or departments. The result is a substantial increase in the purchasing power both of the farmer and the state.

In some countries these special organizations are semigovernmental in nature and are established by legislation. They have the following objectives:

1. to secure the most favourable arrangements for the purchase, marketing and export of produce;
2. to assist in the development by all possible means of the agricultural and educational needs of the farming community.

These boards have statutory powers to buy, store, process and sell produce overseas, or locally if necessary. The purchase price at farm level is controlled as also are the minimum quality standards of produce purchased and the regulation weights, marks, etc., for shipping.

3. LOSSES OF STORED FOOD

Losses of growing crops are immediately apparent because there is less produce to harvest. On the other hand, losses of stored food are not always apparent and the extent of deterioration in the quality of produce is seldom fully appreciated.

Deterioration of stored food may begin while the crop ripens, i.e., before harvesting. Bacteria, fungi and termites attack various parts of plants, while beetles and moths fly out of farm buildings, etc., and infest produce as in the case of unharvested heads of grain. Rodents which can devastate whole areas by chewing at the stalks of plants also damage heads of grain, cocoa pods, and stems; birds (e.g., *Quelea* sp.) also attack unharvested cereals.

Handling and drying practices and methods of transportation may be responsible for reducing quality, and storage conditions may result in the development of microorganisms as well as chemical changes within produce.

Deterioration of products in the form of weight loss, chemical changes in protein, carbohydrate and oil content and of contamination by chemical toxins, insect fragments, and due to rodent urine and faeces is common in the tropics and subtropics. In many countries the presence of insects and other contaminants in stored food has become an accepted phenomenon. According to one belief produce in store for a few weeks " spontaneously generates " insect life. Infested stored produce is also believed to have " matured " and therefore to be better than freshly harvested produce, so that there are now many merchants and consumers who are accustomed to, and therefore accept, products of inferior or poor quality.

As FAO and international conferences are now pointing out, in many countries the extent and levels of losses after harvest have not been fully assessed, but those assessments which have been made of the quantities of food which are damaged and lost indicate that there is a serious wastage.

An FAO estimate of worldwide annual losses in store has been given as 10 percent of all stored grain, i.e., 13 million tons of grain losses due to insects or 100 million tons to failure to store properly (Wolpert, 1966), but losses in the temperate regions of the world can be expected to be lower than in the tropics and subtropics. In the United States, grain storage losses each year have been stated (Pawley, 1963) to be between 15 and 23 million tons (some 7 million due to rats and between 8 and 16 million due to insects) and a breakdown of the quantity and quality of losses together with the dollar value has been given by the U.S. Department of Agriculture (1965). In Latin America it has been estimated that there is a loss of 25 to 50 percent of harvested cereals and pulses; in certain African countries about 30 percent of the total subsistence agricultural production is lost annually, and in areas of Southeast Asia some crops suffer losses of up to 50 percent.

Although these figures must be considered in relation to many millions of tons of food production in each country (see Table 2), it must be emphasized that such losses do not involve every commodity in all countries in the tropics and subtropics.

Current losses of about 30 percent are apparently occurring throughout large areas of the world. Prevention of these losses would result in:

(*a*) more food for consumption by the farmers;
(*b*) more food available for farmers to sell;
(*c*) higher living standards for farmers;
(*d*) more food available for nonfarming population;
(*e*) higher quality and competitiveness of export commodities in world trade;
(*f*) sounder economy for the country and improvement of its international standing.

Levels at which losses occur

Losses occur at different stages in the movement of food from the field to the consumer. There is deterioration while the product is growing in the field; before harvest and after, while it is in the producer's hands; again in the traders' transport vehicles and stores;

while it is being processed (e.g., by millers); and, finally, in the port transit sheds and on ships.

In the past, an assessment of losses occurring immediately prior to harvesting was not seriously considered, although one estimate records 20 percent of crops planted being eaten or spoiled by rodents and insects (Anon, 1967). Similarly, only a few records exist of losses due to harvesting methods; Connell (private communication) has indicated that such losses of rice in Guyana are valued at some $ 50 to 57 per hectare. An assessment of losses in producers' stores has been based on surveys which have had to be limited to a small proportion of the total quantity stored in the country; also examinations of the condition of products in any one store have been based on small samples which are unlikely to have been truly representative of the whole consignment. Moreover a difficulty arises from the practice by some farmers of drawing produce from their stores over a period gradually while others leave the products untouched between harvests.

In traders' stores assessment of losses is fraught with sampling errors. Among the more advanced traders the weight of products taken into store is compared with the weight at the end of the storage period; trading practices have been built up to ensure that weight losses recorded are minimal and do not affect the financial profits from trading transactions. Various methods may be used to achieve this aim, such as the inclusion of a quantity of material other than food in the sack (including dust, insects, earth, stones and water) which is passed on to the purchaser.

Large trading organizations such as some produce boards handle millions of tons of commodities worth large amounts of money and, within minimum trading standards, attempt to control the quality of the commodities handled. In the past, however, little detailed attention has been given to the quantity of water purchased with the product and to the presence and multiplication of many species of insects within sacks of produce during storage. Cleaning and rebagging produce in new sacks improves its general appearance by removing signs of water damage and rodent urine on the sack, visible mould on the surface of the product, and many of the stages of insects living on the outside of the grains. It does not, however, restore the quantity of produce eaten or the quality which has been reduced by contamination by microorganisms, insect and rodent excreta, or by the presence of toxic chemicals resulting from the development of microorganisms, particularly certain strains of fungi.

In the past the organizations responsible for the handling and storage of produce in transit sheds and ship holds have given little attention to the provision of facilities which would reduce losses in quality and quantity of products. Transit sheds have been designed with a view to making possible quick movement of produce without considering the possibility of incorporating a system which would also:

(*a*) prevent rodent infestation;
(*b*) prevent cross infestation of insects from one parcel of produce (e.g., palm kernels, groundnuts) to another (e.g., flour);
(*c*) minimize temperature gradients and the movement of air of high humidity through the warehouse and so prevent the development of moulds and other microorganisms;
(*d*) enable insect disinfestation techniques to have maximum effect.

Attention must be given to conditions in holds before produce is loaded onto ships if further deterioration from cross infestation, condensation and odour absorption is to be prevented. Current practices of carrying insurance against insect infestation or the presence of aflatoxin above a certain level, or of allowing for "ocean loss" in the trading agreement may deal conveniently with the financial aspect of trading but it is no substitute for ensuring that the maximum quantity of produce of highest quality is made available by one country to another.

Types of losses

Losses to harvested produce may be of quantity or quality and may occur separately or together. Thus produce which by its appearance shows clearly that either its quality could have been better, or more of it might have been available, may be said to have deteriorated. The higher the quality demanded or the lower the acceptable tolerance, the greater is the loss potential (Figure 2).

A consignment of rice consisting mostly of broken grains or of grains which are either discoloured or chewed by insects is of lower quality than undamaged whole grains of normal colour for

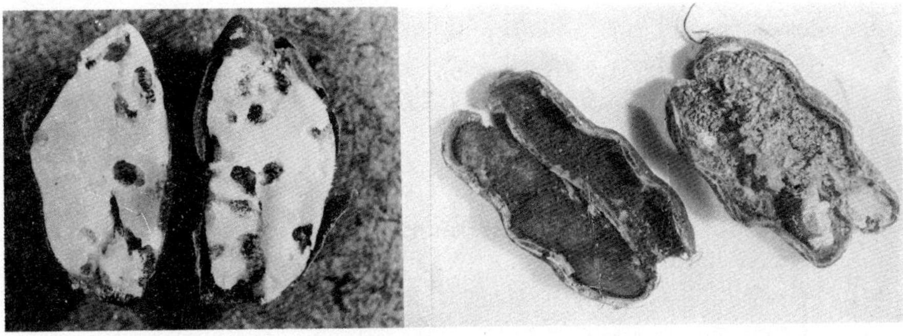

FIGURE 2. Examples of types of damage to produce. Left, partial loss of kernel due to insect pests and contamination of remainder; right, complete loss of food due to infestation.

the same variety of rice. A sample of maize meal which is dark in colour, of coarse texture and rather rancid in flavour is of low quality. A grain or kernel seed may be chewed by an insect or rodent so much that only half of the original amount of food harvested remains; the portion which is left may, of course, be of good quality but it may have been contaminated by frass and secretions and therefore have a higher acidity than an uninfested, unbroken grain or kernel. A consignment of groundnuts, chickpeas, etc., containing a percentage of black or discoloured kernels is of inferior quality and may command only a low price or may even not be purchased (by discoloration may be due to the method of drying, or to contamination by mould spores which, during their development, produce chemicals within the kernel which can be toxic to animals).

The various ways in which produce deteriorates between time of harvest (in some instances before harvest) and consumption result in changes in the appearance of the products which are normally detectable by the human senses, e.g., sight (appearance); sound (the sound of the produce when shaken in a tin); smell; flavour; and touch (the feel obtained by pressure of the nail on the grain).

A study of the factors involved in the deterioration of produce indicates that particular consideration has to be given to a wide range of factors including:

1. chemical changes in produce;
2. growth of microorganisms on produce;

3. development of insects and mites on produce;
4. feeding on produce by rodents;
5. human mishandling of produce, affecting quality and causing loss through spillage;
6. use of poor containers and stores;
7. exposure of products to extremes of temperature and moisture.

Losses are manifested in several ways:

(*a*) weight loss;
(*b*) food loss;
(*c*) quality loss;
(*d*) monetary loss;
(*e*) loss of goodwill (i.e., reputation);
(*f*) seed loss.

Loss of weight

Weight losses result from evaporation of moisture; from component parts of a product being eaten by insects, rodents and birds; and from allowing quantities to spill from the container in which the produce is transported or stored. In some instances weight loss (due to insects, for example) may be converted into a slight gain in weight due to reabsorption of moisture from the air (or from water deliberately added to products to increase weight and earn more money for the owner). Birds peck holes in bags and the amount of produce eaten plus that which pours out of the bag (especially with small grains such as sorghum and millet) can result in a loss of some 70 percent of the original weight of the bag. Rodents chew holes in bags, causing an excessive amount of spillage which becomes contaminated with rodent excreta, dust, etc.; the quantity of produce contaminated by rats is considerably greater than what they eat. In India (Anon, 1967) it has been estimated that at least 3 600 tons of cereals and rice are lost annually in Bombay alone due to rodents. To these losses must be added the loss in weight from bags which burst during handling and transportation. Some organizations allow for a 2 percent loss in weight from this cause.

In a number of countries, produce is sold by the farmer and trader on a volume basis (for example, in cigarette tins or in kerosene tins [1]) and weight changes are therefore of little interest. Although weight and quality may not yet be integral parts of the life of local farmers and traders, the weight system is used universally by produce boards, government departments and commercial organizations exporting produce.

To determine weight loss it is essential to know the weight of every unit of produce at the beginning and again at the end of the storage period. When products are contained in bags, a weight allowance has to be made for the bag; a tare figure (based on the weight of a dry bag) of some 1.1 kilogrammes is used.

Assessment of weight losses occurring in producer storage is often based on data obtained from scientifically controlled experiments. In the Democratic Republic of the Congo, for example, it has been reported that after 12 months' storage, loss of weight resulting from insect attacks on sorghum was 50 percent, on beans 20 percent, and on groundnuts 15 percent (CCTA/CSA, 1957). Previously published data from tropical countries has been summarized by Parkin (1959) and Howe (1965b) but there is a shortage of data from nonexperimental conditions.

Weight losses also occur at markets; in traders' stores and at large collecting centres (including ports); and in warehouses controlled by produce boards, port authorities, etc.

Since very few appropriate surveys of market conditions have been carried out, losses in such markets are generally not known (See Tables 4 and 5).

In warehouses controlled by autonomous boards, for example, weight losses are recorded regularly. Standard pack weights for each commodity are used or the actual weight established at shed entry is used as the bill of lading weight. It is the practice in some areas to allow a franchise of some 1.9 percent (about 1.6 kilogrammes per net standard pack of 82.7 kilogrammes) to cover loss in weight between time of purchase and time of shipment or landing; this practice is intended to compensate for loss of moisture through the jute sack and or oil exudation in the case of some oilseeds.

[1] A cigarette tin holds 0.3 litre; a kerosene tin holds 18 litres; the latter is equivalent to 11.5 kilogrammes of dry maize and 15 kilogrammes of wet maize.

TABLE 4. – DATA RECORDED FOR WEIGHT LOSSES TO PRODUCTS DURING STORAGE IN A NUMBER OF COUNTRIES

	Commodity	Loss		Level of storage	Period of storage	Cause	Source
		Percent	*Millions tons*		*Months*		
Ghana	Legumes	9.3	0.006	FTC	12	I	Hayward, L.A.W., 1964. Personal communication to FAO Plant Production and Protection Division.
Upper Volta	Legumes	50–100		FTC	12	I	Hayward, L.A.W., 1964.
Nigeria	Legumes	10		T	6	I	Hayward, L.A.W., 1964.
	Wheat	34		F	24	I	Ahmadu Bello University, Institute for Agricultural Research. 1963.
Somalia	Grain	20–50		FTC	12	RI	Bethke,, S. 1963. FAO report.
South Africa	Legumes	50		FTC	12	I	Hayward, L.A.W., 1964.
Tanzania	Legumes	50		FTC	12	I	Hayward, L.A.W., 1964.
Malaysia	Rice	17		C	8–9	A	Wright, F.N., 1963.
India	Rice		11.0	FTC	12		Central Food Technological Research Institute, 1965.
	Food grains	20.0		FTC	12		Johnston, J., 1966, personal communication.
	Food grains	5.0	2.8	F	12		Wolpert, V., 1967.
	Grain	4.0	0.2	C	3–4		Pingale, S.V., 1964.
	Wheat	8.3		C	12		Pingale, S.V., 1964.
	Food grains	9.3		FTC	12	A	
Japan	Rice	5		FTC	12	I	Kiritani, K., 1964.
United Arab Republic	Rice	0.5			12	IR	Kamel, A.H., 1951, personal communication.
United States of America	Maize	0.5	5.9		12	I	U.S. Department of Agriculture, 1965.
	Rice	1.5	0.04		12	I	U.S. Department of Agriculture, 1965.
	Sorghum	3.4	0.41		12	I	U.S. Department of Agriculture, 1965.
	Wheat	3.0	1.6		12	I	U.S. Department of Agriculture, 1965.
Thailand	Paddy / Maize	10		F		I	Boon-Long, S., 1965, personal communication.

F - farmer storage; T - trader storage; C - central storage depots; R - rodents; I - insects; A - all causes.

TABLE 5. – FIGURES OF LOSSES OF PRODUCE DUE TO INSECT PESTS AT DIFFERENT LEVELS OF STORAGE (NONEXPERIMENTAL) IN AFRICA

	Commodity	Apparent loss		Storage period	Major pest	Country
		Damaged grains/kernels	Weight loss			
		.... Percent		... Months ...		
Producer storage	Beans	38–69	6	6	Pulse beetles	Uganda
	Beans	3.6		4	Pulse beetles	Zambia
		80.7		12	Pulse beetles	Zambia
	Cowpeas	13.0		4	Pulse beetles	Zambia
		81.6		12	Pulse beetles	Zambia
	Maize		20+	8	Weevils	Ghana
	Maize	30–50		5	Weevils	Dahomey
	Maize	30		5	Weevils	Togo
	Maize	45–75	20+	7	Weevils	Uganda
	Maize	90–100		12	Weevils and moths	Zambia
	Maize cobs	5–10		12	Weevils	Ivory Coast
	Sorghum, unthreshed	3–78	1–26	9	Weevils	N. Nigeria
	Sorghum, unthreshed	2–33	0–13	6	Weevils	N. Nigeria
	Sorghum, unthreshed	2–62	3–13	14	Weevils	N. Nigeria
	Sorghum	11–88	6–37	26	Weevils	N. Nigeria
Trader storage	Beans	35–44	6	12	Pulse beetles	Uganda
	Maize	20			Beetles	Togo
	Maize		5–10	6	Beetles	Uganda
	Maize	16.7	4	3	Beetles	Uganda
	General produce		10–15	12	Beetles and moths	Tanzania (Zanzibar)
Central depot	Maize		5–6	11	Weevils and moths	Rhodesia
Storage	Maize		12–19	24	Weevils and moths	Rhodesia
	Maize	35–38	10	9		Uganda
	Wheat	5 8.	2	6	Weevils	Kenya

SOURCE: Data based on personal communications by specialists to FAO.

This is a variable factor depending on the initial moisture content of the product, the length of time in storage prior to shipment, and the conditions of storage. When stocks are low so that shipment is prompt, the bags will not have lost their full franchise. Generally, buying agents of produce boards are paid on the basis of check-weights at time of entry into the board's stores or at shipment; a bonus is earned for any weight in excess of the gross weight per bag and agents are debited for shortages below that figure. In the case of these large trading organizations percentage loss in weight is recorded as being very low. Reports of weight losses greater than 0.5 percent to 1.5 percent (Tables 4 and 5) are unusual. Normally, losses over 1.5 percent are checked by relating the average outturn weight from the ship with that taken at time of shipment. Time of shipment is obviously a factor in the variability of losses encountered, e.g., in the rainy season cotton lint absorbs moisture and later dries out, while bales shipped from the tropics in the dry season and discharged into a damp atmosphere record a gain. However, the experience acquired over many years in the commodities trade makes it possible to keep financial loss to a minimum and to attain quality which seems acceptable to the buyer.

Existing data on weight losses, although somewhat sketchy and in certain instances conflicting, are sufficiently realistic to warrant serious action involving the necessary expenditures to minimize the wastage which occurs at present. Tables 4 and 5 give examples of the data presented for a number of countries.

In India, especially since 1954, numerous studies of local losses have been carried out. A number of relevant records are given in Table 6.

Assessment

The reduction in weight registered over the storage period does not always provide an accurate record of the actual weight loss of produce. The tare allowance on a bag (dry weight of bag) and the variation in moisture or oil content of the bag fibres have been mentioned above. In addition, reabsorption of moisture by the product in the bag from the humidity in the atmosphere, from water either deliberately added or from condensation on the fabric,

TABLE 6. – DATA ON WEIGHT LOSSES OF PRODUCE IN INDIA

	Weight loss	Cause	Storage period	Level of storage	Source
	Percent		*Months*		
Paddy	1–3	Condensation		T	Doyal *et al.*, 1961. Communication to the Rice Commission of India.
Paddy and milled		Insects			Ghose R.L.M. *et al.*,
rice	1.5	Insects		C	1960.
Rice in husk	2.7	Insects	10	Bulk C	Pingale, S.V., 1954. Ph. D. Thesis (unpublished).
Rice in husk	6.2	Insects		Bag C	Pingale, S.V., 1954.
Rice	5	All	12	FTC	Garg, O.P. and Agrawal, N.S., 1966.
	10	Inadequate machinery	12		
Grain (rice and wheat)	4	All	3–4		Pingale, S.V., 1964.
Wheat, untreated	8.3	All	12	C	Pingale, S.V., 1964.
Food grains for seed	5	All	12	FT	Wolpert, V., 1967.

the building or the container with which the product is in contact should be taken into account. Another factor is the composition of the contents of the weighed bag which may include dust and insects. The weight of dust (more hygroscopic than cereal grains or oilseed kernels), which may consist of powder from the product, insect and rodent frass, stems, leaves, grass seeds, stones and earth, plus the weight of any insects present, should be deducted from the weight of the product which is sold. It has been shown that this extraneous matter is a major factor in causing heating and creating favourable conditions for insect activity (United Nations, 1962a). Moreover, it may account for a 100 percent increase in weight loss; e.g., in Malawi 3 000 bags of maize infested with insects after two years in storage showed an apparent weight loss of 7 percent which increased to a 14 percent actual loss when the dust and insects were removed (CCTA, 1958; similarly Prevett, 1959) obtained a 25 percent apparent weight loss in parboiled paddy during one year in Sierra Leone, or an actual loss of about 41 percent due to infestation.

In Kenya, careful assessment made by Kockum (1958) led him to estimate the average loss of crib-stored maize in 1952 at 9.6 percent of the weight in four months, rising to 23.1 percent in six months. In the untreated part of an experimental crib of cob maize the number of damaged grains increased from 1.1 percent at the start to 91.0 percent after 10 months' storage. The application of insecticide treatment to some 10 percent of the crop since 1953 has resulted in an estimated saving of about 15 percent in weight. Similar data has been recorded by Pingale (1964) for wheat storage in India and by scientists in other countries, e.g., Davies (1960a) in Uganda.

Various experiments have been carried out to determine the correlation between percentages of insect damage and weight loss; the levels of insect density in stored produce can be very high: under reasonably good storage conditions in the tropics infestations yielding 80 to 100 live weevils per 500 grammes of produce after only six months in storage have been recorded. In Uganda, in a maize experiment in a bamboo crib, J.C. Davies calculated that a 10 percent bored sample represented a weight loss of 2.4 out of 91 kilogrammes or 2.7 percent, and that the percentage of bored grain in crib-stored maize (untreated) in Uganda frequently varies from 45 to 75 percent. Ten samples of maize from stocks of a large commercial enterprise in Uganda averaged over 35 percent bored (storage period in excess of nine months), while top samples from silos on government stations were over 38 percent bored after nine months. Samples taken from bag stacks in store at a plantation in Uganda showed three-month-old maize to be 16.7 percent bored and crawling with insects. These figures represent weight losses of between 3.5 and 10 percent. In India, Venkat Rao *et al.* (1958) found that the percentage of sorghum grains holed by weevils was two to three times the percentage loss of weight.

Figures on beans show a similar situation resulting from attacks by pulse beetles. Much of the crop in Uganda, when stored in reasonable conditions, is over 50 percent bored after six months in storage. Davies (1959) has quoted figures of from 38 to 69 percent after bin storage for six months and from 35 to 44 percent after bag storage for a year; 50 percent of the damaged samples revealed weight losses of between 6 and 7 percent. Similarly in India, Venkat Rao *et al.* (1960) found that after four months of storage 62 percent of *Dolichos lablab* beans were holed by *Callosbruchus*, but that weight loss was only 15 percent. After six months 94 percent of the seeds were holed. Jotwani and Sircar (1964) weighed garden peas which had been attacked by *Callosobruchus*. Peas with a single adult beetle emergence hole were 12 percent lighter than sound peas, and in those with two, three and four holes loss of weight was, respectively, 22.5, 32 and 35.5 percent.

Food loss

Weight loss during storage not due to a loss of moisture is a measure of food loss. This type of loss may result from exposure of the product to extremes of temperature and humidity during drying, processing and storage; from the development of fungi; or from the attack of insects, rodents and birds. Very few detailed investigations have been carried out on these problems.

Overexposure to sun destroys certain vitamins and causes oxidation of carotene. High temperatures during artificial drying cause loss of thiamine content in rice; during parboiling (which involves steeping paddy in water and then subjecting it to steam) there is a redistribution of thiamine in the grains, so that milling of parboiled paddy results in a loss of 45 percent of the thiamine content compared to about 80 percent loss with raw paddy (Kik, 1943; Nelson, 1951).

The physical conditions prevailing during the storage of brown rice cause a reduction in thiamine content reported as amounting to about 75 percent loss over four years of storage when in bags (Kondo and Okamura, 1932) and about 8.6 percent loss when stored in bulk in silos (Kondo *et al.*, 1941).

A comparison of the reduction in nutritive constituents of different foodstuffs under various storage conditions is required. There are considerable data available showing that insect infestation is responsible for severe losses of nutritive values in food. In general, figures could be quoted for food value loss on the basis of existing weight loss data.

The effect of insect infestation on the nutritional value of produce varies with the composition of the products affected and the species of insect (depending on its feeding habits). Weevils, which feed mainly on the carbohydrate portion of a maize grain, remove a considerable amount of the calorie potential but little of the protein and vitamins which are mainly in the germ and bran. In legumes, in which the protein and vitamins are more evenly distributed throughout the grain, infestations of beetles, which can be responsible for consuming up to 50 percent of peas and beans of which some 25 percent of the dry matter is crude protein, can cause a loss of about 12 percent of the available protein. It can be seen from previous tables that up to 81 percent of cowpeas and beans in farmers' stores are damaged by insects after 12 months' storage, intensifying loss of protein potential in areas where protein deficiency diseases are prevalent.

When grains are attacked by insect species which feed selectively on the germ leaving the endosperm almost untouched, food loss is not apparent; weight loss is also very small compared to the loss of vitamins, etc. It has been shown recently (Proctor, private communication) that in the larval stage the moth species, *Cadra cautella*, feeds on the germ of hard wheat but with soft wheat the endosperm is also eaten. This would seem to be due to the hardness of the endosperm as compared with the germ in hard wheat. With beetles, the lower the moisture content of the grain attacked, the more specific will be the feeding on the germ. (These aspects are of course related to the germinative capacity of seed grain or malting barley.)

In the case of insect species of which the young stage (larva) is not confined within a grain, feeding is general and therefore considerable quantities of the outer bran layers of the grain as well as the endosperm are eaten. Pingale *et al.* (1957) report that losses of thiamine in rice stored for eight months were 10 to 15 percent greater in infested than in uninfested samples.

Loss of quality

Loss of weight and loss of food represent loss of quantity of products; in addition, the quality of the remaining produce has to be taken into account.

Quality of produce is assessed in different ways according to the circumstances considered important by the local population and the traders concerned. In general it is assessed and the products are graded on the basis of appearance (uniformity of size and colour, texture, and dirt content); but smell and flavour are included as quality criteria, particularly for such products as spices and beverages. In particular instances, chemical data such as oil content, acidity, moisture content and the presence or absence of toxins are included.

Legislation dealing particularly with loss of quality in the produce of developing countries is summarized in Appendix B.

In some countries the system of buying is on a weight per volume basis intended to show up low quality grains such as those which are immature, small, shrivelled and diseased. A decision based on a criterion of good or average quality is made, establishing the weight of grain or seed winnowed by machine per 36.4-litre capacity bushel for a particular country or area. The bushel weight of grain which the average farmer should be capable of producing is then decided and an allowance is made, in some countries of 2.5 percent, for each 0.5 kilogramme above or below the standard set; assuming the standard weight per bushel is set at 19 kilogrammes, then:

> if A offers 100 bushels weighing 20 kilogrammes each, he receives payment for the equivalent of $100 + (2 \times 2.5) = 105$ bushels;
>
> if B offers 100 bushels weighing 18.5 kilogrammes each, he receives payment for 97.5 bushels.

The buyer has to protect himself against bad quality due to mixed grains, etc., and this he usually does by hand-picking a sample.

Harvesting under conditions which ensure that the produce is undamaged (i.e., not bruised, cracked or broken) followed by immediate and efficient drying to a safe moisture content for storage will ensure that chemical changes within the plant cells are negligible; respiration of the grains or kernels will be almost imperceptible. Thereafter, provided insect and rodent infestations are prevented and equable climatic conditions are maintained during storage and transportation, quality should remain satisfactory.

Damaged grains or kernels deteriorate through chemical changes within their cells. Thus hydrolysis and oxidation of oil in plant cells results in an increase in acidity (e.g., free fatty acid content or ffa) which may develop to the point of rancidity (Pingale, Rao and Swaminathan, 1954); the available quantity of high quality oil requiring minimum processing is reduced, increasing processing costs if edible oil has to be manufactured. If groundnuts are damaged or broken during shelling, increases in ffa occur; Howe (1952) showed the comparative increase in ffa of whole, split and broken nuts stored for over 12 months in Nigeria to be about 4, 9 and 17 percent respectively.

By damaging dry produce insects reduce the quality of food. The effect of infestations of the beetles *Tribolium castaneum* and *Trogoderma granarium* on groundnuts is shown in Figure 3. The samples of damaged whole groundnuts which had been exposed to attack by these two beetle pests were cleaned of adhering insect frass and dust (which has a very high ffa content) as far as practicable, so that the increases in acidity recorded in Figure 3 refer to the condition of the remaining portion of nut. By comparison, the increase in ffa of oil from whole and from half and broken nuts which had also been damaged by insects has been reported by Hayward (1955) to be as high as 16 percent and 28.5 percent respectively. Associated with increased quantities of insect frass is increased lipolysis, and the activity of lipase (as with enzymes generally) accelerates with increase in temperature.

Reduction in ffa can be of considerable benefit to a marketing board which sells on the basis of oil content and ffa because a premium is collected or a penalty paid for shipments of oilseeds depending on whether quality is above or below contract specifications (normally under 3 percent ffa).

Increase in acidity is not confined to oilseeds. Cereals after prolonged storage, but particularly when ground into a meal or flour or when infested by insects, show an increase in ffa content. As soon as good, uninfested maize is milled into a meal there is an increase in fat acidity (Figure 4). If prior to milling the maize has been attacked by adults of *Tribolium castaneum*, the initial ffa of the resultant meal is much higher than that of uninfested meal, and the ffa rises to a much higher level. Figure 5 indicates the response of a community to the sale of maize meal milled from

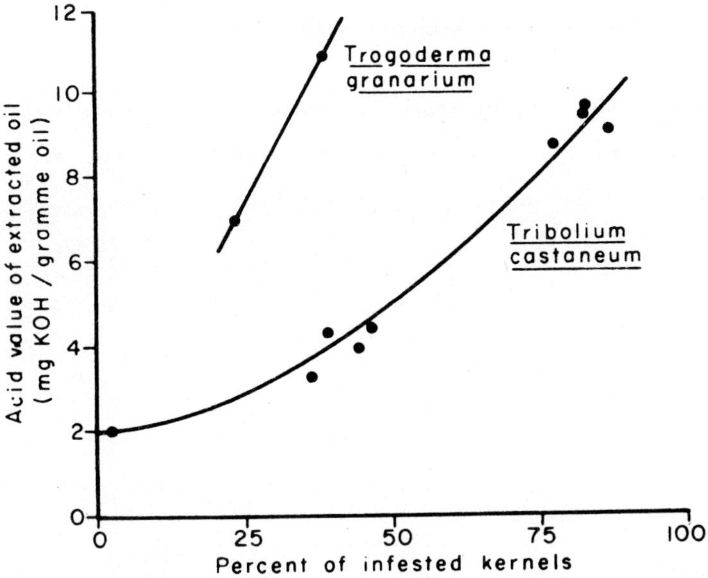

FIGURE 3. Increase in fat acidity of groundnuts following infestation by two species of beetles.

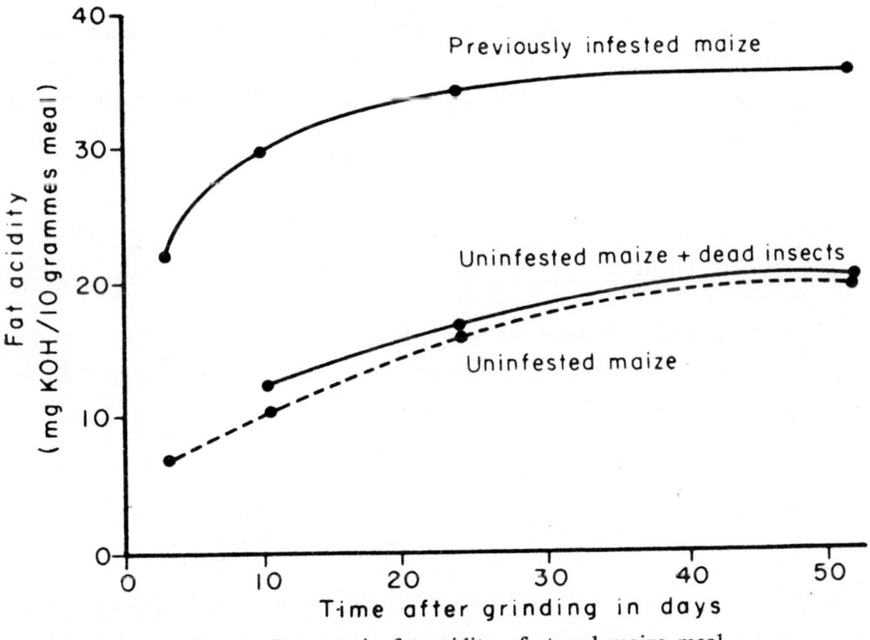

FIGURE 4. Increase in fat acidity of stored maize meal.

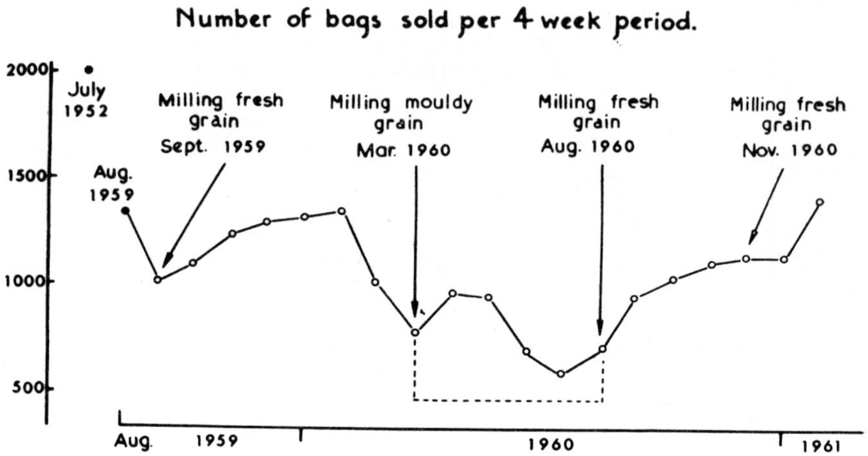

FIGURE 5. Consumption of maize meal in relation to milling maize after storage and with increased free fatty content.

infested stored maize compared with that from newly stored maize. The addition of dead insects to uninfested maize before milling did not affect the fat acidity (Davey, 1961).

When bacteria and fungi develop on produce, chemical changes occur; there is also spoilage by protein-decomposing halophilic bacteria and through the interaction of the metabolites of the fungal spores and hyphae on the cell tissues. Certain strains of fungi can produce chemicals (mycotoxins) which, if present in the produce when fed to animals, may cause death. Aflatoxin is such a chemical (United Kingdom, 1962) and research since 1959 has shown that several toxins produced by fungi on a number of foodstuffs are responsible for carcinoma conditions of the liver in animals (Barnes, 1967).

Insect and fungi infestations may also be responsible for discoloration, in some instances to the extent of charring of products, due to the phenomenon of heating.

Contamination by filth

The contamination of foodstuffs by extraneous matter has been given the descriptive term filth contamination. It is appropriate to use this term to include unnecessary matter associated with produce (i.e., foreign to the product concerned) such as stones; earth; shells or husks of plants; fungi; insects and their fragments and excreta; hairs and droppings (e.g., of goats, sheep, chickens, rodents); string; bottles and metal. All of these have been recovered from bags or bulks of produce prior to its being eaten or processed for consumption. Products contaminated by these "foreign bodies" have deteriorated in quality. It may be sufficient to refer to the existence of microorganisms of various kinds (gram-positive spore-forming anaerobes and aerobes, such as *Clostridium botulinum* and *Staphylococcus* spp. and gram-negative nonsporing rods of *Salmonella* spp.), on stones and soil, and to the urates, bacteria, worms, etc., in animal droppings to illustrate the need for better hygienic standards in quality of produce.

The harvesting of produce together with lumps of earth and the effect of exposing products to contamination by dust, stones, animal droppings etc., while drying on the ground or on matting spread on the ground have to be minimized through improvement of local practices and particularly through controlled purchasing and marketing.

In the United Arab Republic, it is reported (Tainsh, personal communication, 1963) that farmers and merchants estimate the dirt content of freshly winnowed grain as follows:

"A section of reed is filled with the grain, levelled off at the top with a finger, the grain is poured into the cupped hands and large pieces of earth and straw are picked out, the dust is blown away, the cleaned grain is poured back into the reed and when the reed is held up toward the sun, being translucent shows the new level of the grain and the measure of the value previously occupied by the dust."

Sieving or washing produce is sometimes carried out to eliminate fungal and insect infestation; while this may remove the majority of the insects moving freely between the grains and the mould on the surface, it does not remove insects (at all stages) and moulds inside the individual grains. Insect infested grain, oilseeds, spices, etc., when ground into meal or processed as a powder produce flour, meal or cakes (e.g., wheat flour, maize meal, cocoa powder, ground spices, etc.) contaminated with insect fragments and secretions. How are these contaminants detected? The insect fragments can be detected by flotation methods (MacMasters, 1962) and counts have shown that in the United Kingdom good quality wheat flour contains about two fragments per 220 grammes of flour. In striking contrast, the number of insect fragments in samples of maize meal examined in the United Kingdom during a limited survey by staff at the Pest Infestation Laboratory on the conditions of the buildings in which maize is milled in eastern, western and central Africa was up to 47 500 fragments per 10 grammes of meal (Raymond, Spickett and Ward, 1954).

On the average, one flour beetle shatters into about 150 fragments in a hammer mill (Davey, 1961), while between 800 and 1 200 fragments are produced when a grain containing an insect is passed through a reduction roll.

The levels of contamination by insect fragments vary in the different ground commodities and a study of the type of infestation gives an indication of the handling and storage conditions, etc., to which the product has been subjected between harvesting and milling.

Monetary loss

Knowledge and the facilities for drying products thoroughly and storing them successfully provide the farmer with means to overcome a situation which forces him to sell immediately after harvest when prices are low; between the preharvest and postharvest periods market prices may fluctuate by a factor of two. Similarly, a knowledge of the range of market prices within an area would help the farmer to send his products to the most favourable market, so as to obtain maximum monetary return for them. It is not unknown for produce to fetch three times more money in one area than in another; for example, differences in produce prices exist in adjacent areas in Ghana and the Ivory Coast. At present the farmer's inability to sell when food is least plentiful prevents him from obtaining money and restricts the quantity grown to very little more than is needed to feed the farmer's own family. Consequently ability (however small or great) to increase production is limited, which in turn prevents the area or country concerned from adequately feeding the urban population. In this way, the farming community loses money and the country loses income because it has to import food to fill the gap.

The trader also loses financially when products and sacks he has purchased deteriorate in store. In some instances the quantity of produce taken into store is not recorded accurately and loss of quantity through drying out, oil exudation, burst or shortweight bags due to rodent and bird damage or to thieving mounts up to wipe out profit in commodity trading.

Rodent damage to sacks in certain areas has been estimated at 3 percent, which to a trader handling the products means a loss of about $1 per 100 sacks plus the wastage or produce spilled from the sacks which in turn may account for short weight of about 10 percent. Even recorded losses of 1.5 to 2 percent at central depots on a moderate sized trading account of about $15 000 000 involve a by no means insignificant (i.e., $300 000) loss of money. When viewed in terms of a country's agricultural production or total export of produce financial losses are considerable.

The figures of losses recorded in Tables 4, 5 and 6, when considered in terms of the current value of each commodity give an indication of the large monetary losses which occur. Hayward (1963) has recorded the figure of £250 000 saved for each reduction of 1 percent ffa, which gives a guide to current losses of oilseeds.

For the individual trader who is forced, through legislation where necessary, to take the measures required to clean storage premises and disinfest produce in countries concerned with raising hygiene standards, the expenditure of money on such measures often seems uneconomic. This is because such expenditure is not always set against previous losses which, as has been indicated, may not have been realized. Economic incentives for quality are essential if hygiene standards of products are to be improved. Hayward (1963) has stated that in Nigeria pest control measures costing $448 000 have effected a saving of $840 000 worth of groundnuts equivalent to $2.8 million worth of oil. Recently in India on the basis of estimates of a loss of some 1.5 million tons from rodent attack and about 3.8 million tons occurring on the threshing floor, in transit, during processing, during storage and due to moisture, insects, and birds the Government has been urged to set up central and regional organizations to coordinate action, including a national educational campaign.

Insurance

In world trading circles insurance is carried against the possibility of the quality standard not being met on outturn at the port of unloading. Insurance costs money but in some circles may be considered a cheaper method of dealing with deterioration in quality than by paying for measures to remove the causative agents of deterioration and thus retain the high natural quality of the product.

The charters under which ships are hired may often include terms relating to infestation. Some charters not infrequently include a clause providing that the owners shall pay fumigation costs within the first six months of the charter unless it can be shown that the infestation for which the fumigation is necessary results from cargo carried during that period. In a talk to the Insurance Institute of Liverpool in 1963, Dr. J.A. Freeman referred to the following important aspects of this matter.

"Generally all contracts in respect of shipment of cargoes are subject to the Hague Rules of 1921, which are incorporated into the terms of bills of lading or required by national legislation. Under these rules a shipowner is bound to provide a ship which is not only seaworthy but also cargoworthy. The presence of weevils or other insects remaining in the holds after discharge of a previous cargo could be regarded as violating this obligation if the ship was presented for loading a fresh cargo of a kind which could be attacked or contaminated by these insects.

"The owners of goods may insure themselves under most marine cargo policies against losses due to infestation discovered in the goods on arrival. Cases have been reported of premiums as high as 30 percent being charged and it has been known for some insurers to decline further business because of considerable claims in recent years resulting from infestation by the tropical warehouse moth. It must be recalled, however, that insurance does not compensate for all the losses, since the importer often has to recondition the produce in an attempt to render it acceptable for sale. It is interesting to note that some insurance companies may agree to reimburse the assured against actual cost of sifting sacks of produce, of brushing or reconditioning such sacks and relevant additional incidental expenses including cost of fumigation but will not tolerate liability for depreciation or loss of market. In some instances the premiums charged are higher than the cost of disinfestation treatments.

"Also, there is the extra money paid in some docks for the discharge of heating, dirty or infested cargoes."

Recently, in connexion with the probable incidence of mycotoxins in produce entering international trade, insurance is being offered against consignments containing more than 0.005 ppm of toxin and premiums of $3.60 per $100 food value may be charged.

LOSS OF GOODWILL

The concept of a country having a good or bad name for quality of produce in international trade is comparatively new. However, with the advent of nationhood for many countries in Africa, there is and will continue to be growing pride in the ability to provide produce of high quality. In this field, however, with some countries having to export or import produce through other countries, it is essential that all countries within a continent maintain equally high standards of hygiene and quality of produce.

Local traders not only between but within countries are gradually becoming alert to the benefits (financial and otherwise) to be expected if they build up a business based on quality and strict warehouse hygiene standards. Local governments are beginning to provide specialist staff and information to assist the local trader in this development. A similar process is going on at the farm level through the facilities provided by farmers' improvement schemes. Although to date these farmers have been directing their efforts at growing more food, later they will be turning attention to handling and storage practices and, with the aid of local government staff, to improving their reputation for high quality produce.

Thus industrial organizations in the developed parts of the world will increasingly place reliance on the good name of produce from areas of the tropics and subtropics and will inevitably purchase from those areas which can provide products of the highest quality uncontaminated by toxins, insects, etc.

SEED LOSS

The importance of the availability of good seed is recognized by all farming communities and, irrespective of the level of farming, seed is given special attention. Despite this, considerable losses of seed occur mainly due to lack of information about the factors causing poor germination and to poor facilities for safe storage.

Loss of seed results from both external and internal factors, most of which are discussed in Chapter 4. Physical factors such as light, moisture and temperature are important in causing losses. When the seed coat is damaged respiration of the grain increases especially at normal oxygen concentrations and causes loss of viability. Chemical factors in the hereditary makeup of the seed as well as chemicals used to control deterioration due to the presence and development of microorganisms have to be considered. The extent of the effect of insecticides and fumigants not only on germination but also on growth of rootlets and the strength of the resultant plant is important; Caswell and Clifford (1960) have shown that with maize, fumigated with chlorinated hydrocarbons, the higher the moisture content of the grain the more seedling growth is reduced.

Seed loss is apparent through reduced germination, abnormal growth of rootlets and shoots, and reduced vigour of the plant.

Standard packs

Commercial handling of produce for export, storage and transportation is usually organized in such a manner as to minimize economic losses and operate on a profit-making basis.

Double handling, such as that required in bagged transportation, is costly due to the labour involved, breakage of bags and spillage of produce. With small grains such as sesame seed and sorghum, a torn bag means the loss of a considerable proportion of the contents. Changes to stronger and more expensive bags, a reduction in the weight of the standard pack, extra care in handling and the introduction of semibulk or bulk handling techniques are sometimes only adopted slowly.

Produce for export is handled in such a way as to comply with quality standards laid down by legislation (Appendix B). Market boards operate on such standards and on this basis examples of recorded commercial losses are given for some commodities:

Groundnuts. In bags (each of which has a tare weight of 1.1 kilogrammes) shelled groundnuts stow at about 1.8 cubic metres per ton. Standard pack may be 80 to 86 kilogrammes gross. Outturns rarely show a loss.

Soybeans. In bags (tare 1.1 kilogrammes), stow at 2 cubic metres per ton. The standard pack is 84 kilogrammes gross. Loss is about 1 percent.

Cottonseed. In bags (tare 1.1 kilogrammes, cost of bagging is $5 per ton), stows at 2.5 cubic metres per ton. The standard pack is 73 kilogrammes gross. Nearly always gains weight partly through absorption and partly due to haphazard standardization at the packing source.

Cocoa beans. In bags (tare 1.1 kilogrammes), stow at 2 cubic metres per ton. The standard pack is 65 kilogrammes gross. Loss is rarely in excess of 0.5 percent at the end of season when constant sampling by inspectors has reduced the bag contents by about 0.5 kilogramme.

Palm kernels. In bags (tare 1.1 kilogrammes), stow at about 1.8 cubic metres per ton and the standard pack is 82 kilogrammes gross. Although the bills of lading covering kernel shipment are raised on the basis of 82 kilogrammes, the bags may be standardized at 84 kilogrammes, allowing about a 2-kilogramme franchise for expected oil exudation between time of bagging and unloading at the port overseas. When shipment is prompt (for example, when stocks are low at the ports), the bags are unlikely to have lost 2 kilogrammes, although they are billed as if they had. At time of shipment a bonus may be paid to the trader on check-weights which show any excess over 82 kilogrammes; (in the same way, the trader is debited for shortages). Any bags weighing under 81 kilogrammes may be refused and returned for standardization. Bag tares, although calculated at the weight of a dry bag, can increase by as much as 200 grammes from oil absorption. At outturn, gains of the order of 0.5 percent or losses of 5 percent have been recorded. An average loss for a year's shipment has been recorded as 1.6 percent. In some countries, the actual weight established at shed entry is used as bill of lading weight instead of the standard pack system. Losses vary according to the time lag between shed entry and shipment.

The standards which are currently being worked out by the Joint FAO/WHO Food Standards Programme (Codex Alimentarius) will have a marked effect on national food laws and regulations. This programme will facilitate international trade in foodstuffs and exporting and importing countries will need to consider adopting the Codex Standards when they are finally established.

4. FACTORS AFFECTING FOOD VALUE AND DETERIORATION

Many factors are responsible for the deterioration of produce after harvest. The composition and behaviour characteristics (internal forces) of food grains vary, and grains are constantly being exposed to external forces including physical factors such as temperature and humidity; chemical factors such as oxygen supply; biological agencies such as bacteria, fungi, insects, rodents; and man with his methods of handling, storing, transporting and disinfesting products.

The primary factors have been considered as scientific and socioeconomic (Hall, 1955), and can be divided into two major and a number of subcategories:

Scientific

- Physical
  - Temperature
  - Moisture
- Biological
  - Produce (properties)
  - Microorganisms
  - Insects
  - Rodents, birds
  - Man
- Chemical
  - Breakdown of produce
  - Pesticides
- Engineering
  - Structural
    - Bag storage
    - Bulk storage
  - Mechanical
    - Conveying produce
    - Application of pesticides

Socioeconomic

- Finance
- Farming method
  - Indigenous
  - Nonindigenous
  - Plantation
- Storage and marketing method
  - Producer
  - Small trader
  - Autonomous board
  - Government
- Politics

Properties of food grains

As has been previously indicated, produce consists of carbohydrates, proteins, vitamins, minerals, fats, fibre and water. The relative proportions of these constituents vary with the type of produce (see Table 1) and also the treatment to which the produce has been subjected during handling and processing. Susceptibility to deterioration depends mainly upon the following properties common to produce.

Respiration

When unprocessed, grains are usually alive; they breathe and produce heat, moisture and carbon dioxide. In Figure 6 representative respiration rates for a number of grains are given, from which it will be seen that oilseeds breathe at a progressively faster rate than the more fibrous cereals; the rate is reduced approximately one half by each 10°C reduction in temperature.

It should be noted that respiration is a self accelerating process. The moisture produced can increase the moisture content of the grain which in turn can cause an increase in respiration rate; also the heat produced can raise the grain temperature in turn increasing respiration rate.

Normally the rate of respiration of grain in good condition for storage is extremely low. Oxley (1948) has reported that the removal of the embryo from wheat grains has little effect on respiration; he also points out that respiration is centred almost entirely in the pericarp due to the presence of microorganisms under the outer covering of the grains (i.e., subepidermal fungi).

The respiration mechanism is specially important in grain storage. Henderson (personal communication, 1963) has brought out several points: if grain with a moderate to high moisture content is stored immediately after harvesting it will breathe at the rate shown in Figure 6. The moisture and heat resulting from the process will create conditions which foster mould growth, and spoilage may start within a period of hours. Ventilating the mass by a fan, a process called aeration discussed elsewhere in the manual, can be used to solve this problem. Grain stored in the sun and covered with plastic sheets or canvas becomes heated; the surface

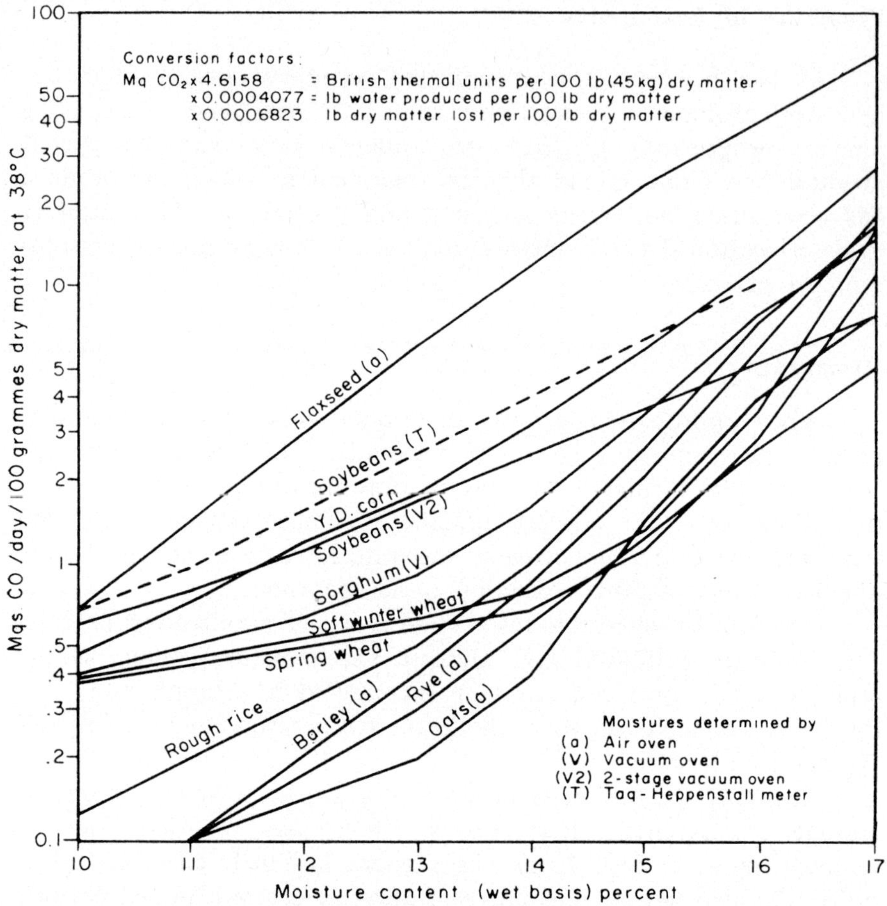

FIGURE 6. Comparative rates of carbon dioxide production by some cereals and oilseeds at 38° C.

of the grain may spoil quickly due to the faster respiration rate resulting from the higher temperature. Moisture and heat contributed by the microorganisms and insects present further accelerate the process.

MOISTURE

Produce contains moisture which is present in grains or kernels in two main forms: water of composition and adsorbed water. The amount of " free water " present is critical to the rate of deterioration of produce.

There is an exchange of moisture (water) with the surrounding atmosphere, to maintain a balance which always exists between the moisture in the produce and that in the atmosphere.

Moisture is moved from one location to another according to either a temperature gradient or variable vapour pressure. Moisture may be transported by warm air which rises and, aided by convection current, carries moisture to areas of lower temperature where the moisture is condensed on the lower temperature surfaces. Movement of moisture out of individual grains occurs due to higher vapour pressures in the grain than exists in the surrounding air.

CONDUCTIVITY

Food grains have low thermal conductivity. Thus heat produced in the produce is accumulated; also, outside temperature fluctuations do not readily penetrate grain stored in large quantities.

FLOW

Grains have a characteristic flow property which is unlike that of liquids. Each type of produce has a natural angle of repose of about 30° but this varies somewhat according to the size, shape, moisture content and cleanliness of the grain.

PRESSURE

Grains stored in a container exert pressure, both vertical and lateral, on the sides of the container but these pressures are unlike those characteristic of liquids, since these components are unequal. For very small storages the following guides may be used: lateral pressure varies with depth of grain and increases steadily until the depth of grain is about 2.5 to 3 times the diameter of the column of grain. Vertical pressure rises rapidly in depths of grain up to about 6 metres, thereafter the rate of increase becomes less rapid. The pressure will vary with the moisture content of the grain because of changes in the coefficient of friction, which is greater at lower moisture contents.

The volume occupied by grain is also affected by its moisture content; for example, grain at 22 percent moisture content occupies 0.22 cubic metre of space per ton more than grain at 12 percent.

More specific data on loads imposed by stored grain is presented in Appendix G.

Physical and chemical nature of surface

Undamaged shells of groundnuts, sheaths of maize cobs and husks of paddy grains reduce penetration by most species of insects and also protect the grains inside from damage during harvesting, drying, etc. Areas of these protective parts of a grain may be weakened however (although not ruptured) by the attack of sucking bugs (Jassidae, Pentatomidae) during ripening, or of termites and/or fungi prior to harvesting; such areas are split fairly rapidly during harvesting, threshing and drying. Incomplete closure of the sheath (around cob maize) or of the husk (around a rice grain) or separation of the seed coat on one side of the grain due to varietal or growing conditions, occurs and facilitates deterioration. Brauer and Genel (1960) have shown that there is a relationship between the percentage of exposure of maize grains (a consequence of maldevelopment of the sheath due to hereditary factors) and attack by insects and fungi.

Storage of the unthreshed grain is often more successful than storage of threshed grain because of the physical damage to the seed coat which occurs during threshing (i.e., removal of grain or kernel from the plant) particularly to the weakened or imperfectly closed areas. In 2 kilogrammes of combine-harvested paddy in Guyana, Breese (1964) found some 3 000 damaged grains out of 30 000. Breese (1963) states that research workers in stored products have failed to appreciate the extent to which larvae of insects, particularly *Rhizopertha dominica F.*, can exploit extremely narrow cracks in husks of paddy grains. Immature or "green" grains are readily attacked by this insect because the husk is loose and may gape slightly. He also makes the point that the weevil *Sitophilus oryzae* can only feed and lay in a paddy grain when there is a split or opening in the husk wider than the insect's snout, i.e., more than 0.12 millimetre. Apparently sound grains of paddy, when examined carefully (microscopically), can be seen to have cracks in the husk. With completely sound paddy grains, penetration by the adults of certain beetles and moths, is not observed, even at high moisture content.

Some varieties of threshed grain have better storage properties than others because of the type of endosperm, or the thickness, hardness, brittleness and resistance to splitting of the seed coat. Hardness affects the rate of damage by insects, as is clearly shown by comparing damage to palm kernels and coffee beans with that to groundnuts and cowpeas. Differences in susceptibility within a grain type are less obvious; both hard and soft wheats are very susceptible to infestation although flint maize is less quickly damaged than dent maize, and recent work by Doggett (1958) and Davey and Elcoate (1962) has shown that within sorghum varieties degrees of hardness affect susceptibility (the harder the grain the fewer the eggs deposited).

Khalifa (1962) has indicated that the rate of loss in weight is probably associated with grain size, the rate of loss increasing with grain diameter. Although grain shape and size can be shown to be factors in the choice of oviposition sites by certain species of insects in laboratory experiments, under storage conditions they seem to be outweighed by other factors.

With respect to the important role of moisture in the susceptibility of grains to attack by insects and fungi, the more moisture is present the softer the grain and the more readily it is penetrated.

Susceptibility to infestation is also more or less directly related to the chemical or nutritional value of the food grains (subject to the effects of the factors already mentioned). Thus absence of essential vitamins and sterols reduces susceptibility (for example, white flour compared with wholemeal flour or white rice compared with brown rice), but many insects are able to overcome the lack of nutrients in the food by manufacturing their own (due to the presence of symbiotic organisms within them). High sugar or oil content and toxic components in soybean, castor bean and maize germ are apparently unattractive to insects, as is high tannin content in the seed coat.

Temperature

The prevailing temperature conditions in the tropics and subtropics are characterized by maximum shade temperatures of 38°C to 43°C and minimum temperatures of 30°C to 35°C in the hot dry areas and by maximum shade temperatures ranging from 21°C to 35°C in the warm wet areas. These conditions are important for the following reasons:

1. High temperatures (21°C to 43°C) speed up the life processes of all organisms (i.e., chemical reaction increases with increase in temperature).
2. Natural drying can be effectively carried out during long periods of high temperature when relative humidity is low.
3. Produce containing a certain amount of heat is put into store and the heat is retained during the storage period; problems due to condensation on the surface of the stored produce will therefore occur in areas where there are wide fluctuations in temperature (such as differences between day and night temperatures or between high and low altitude areas).

Temperature is a determining factor in the development of all organisms and its effect is correlated with the amount of moisture present; the relative amount of moisture in the atmosphere decreases when the temperature is raised.

Under very damp conditions grain respiration increases to the point where germination occurs. The lower the temperature the greater the retarding influence on respiration rate. When grain temperature rises above 66°C, not only is germination damaged but there will almost certainly be damage to the gluten value of wheat for baking quality. The lower the initial moisture content from which artificial drying takes place the less detrimental is the effect of high temperature on germination, etc. (This is important when considering the output of an artificial drier.)

Fungi have different rates of growth at different temperatures. This is illustrated in Figure 9 which shows results obtained at controlled relative humidity equilibria for two species, *Aspergillus flavus* and *A. chevalieri* (Austwick and Ayerst, 1963). For each species of fungus there is a temperature tolerance variability with extremes ranging from very low temperatures of about 2°C to a maximum temperature of about 63°C. (Bacteria will develop up to a temperature of about 71°C.)

Insect development also accelerates with increase in temperature up to about 42°C. At that level most species of insects, if exposed for a long enough period, will die. Temperatures below 15°C considerably retard insect reproduction and development and, if prolonged below 10°C, will cause the death of most insects.

Increase of temperature above the level at which food grains are initially stored is an indication of deterioration. It has been shown that because of the low thermal conductivity of grain, increase in temperature within a parcel of food grains is due either to the respiration of the grain itself or to the development within the grain of insects, fungi or bacteria. Increase in metabolic activity is accompanied by an increase in carbon dioxide production and in some storage containers the concentration of carbon dioxide can replace temperature increase as an adequate measure of metabolic activity.

When a temperature of 50°C is reached, food grains are killed and their respiration stops, but further changes and destruction continue from the development (and respiration) of fungi and bacteria until the temperature reaches about 80°C (Figure 7).

Temperatures of products are seldom measured during storage even at large collecting centres where warehousing is "big business." During recent years some special investigations have been carried out on stacks of bagged produce to obtain an overall picture of temperature gradients and to assess the relationship between temperature gradients and condensation in stacks of bagged produce under different climatic conditions. Temperature measurements inside stacks of bagged produce can be carried out either by placing thermocouples, thermistors or distant-reading thermographs in position while the stack is being built or by using a thermocouple spear which can be pushed through bags to the required depth of a stack (or into bulk). In certain circumstances, for instance where groundnuts are stacked, it should be possible to obtain a record of temperature by using glass thermometers taped to lengths of stick for insertion into the heap. Additional information on temperature measuring equipment is presented in Appendix I.

Since microorganisms are sensitive to temperature, it is possible to consider using extremes of temperature to kill them. In the

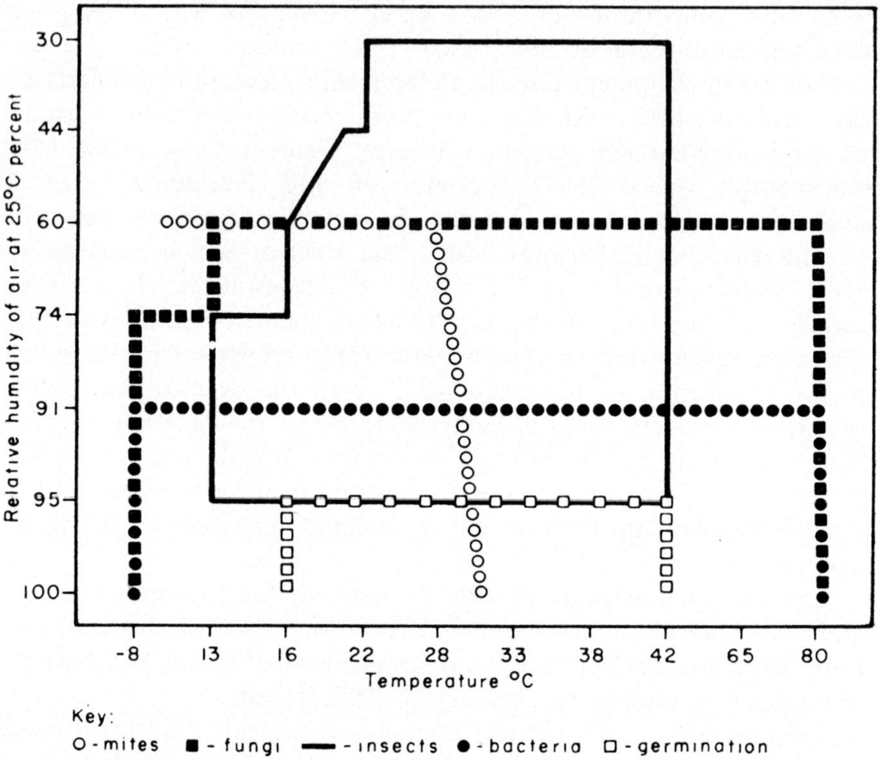

FIGURE 7. General limits of temperature and relative humidity for the multiplication of biological agencies.

tropics where ambient temperature conditions for the development of such organisms are nearer the optimum than the minimum, it has been suggested that the temperature inside warehouses or storage containers should be raised above the present average so as to create conditions unfavourable to development. This might be attempted by the use of " lenses " in the roofs of stores or of solar heat traps of one type or another. Any increase in temperature which may be obtained by such means, however, is likely to be less than is required to reach the thermal death point throughout the contents of the store. Thus, by falling short of this point, conditions favourable to rapid development of insects and fungi are created which also make working conditions difficult and unpleasant for human beings. Normally the beginning of lethal high temperature is only a few degrees above the optimum for rapid increase of these pests; there are indications however that sublethal high temperatures may have an effect on the fertility of insects since sterile females are produced under such conditions. If the temperature throughout a product (i.e., inside each grain of maize or paddy) can be raised to 66°C and maintained for 4 minutes (or 60° for 10 minutes, or 49°C for 20 minutes) all insect stages will be killed. Attempts at creating much lower than ambient temperature conditions by using mud or concrete walls instead of metal, or by painting metal (e.g., aluminium) silos white have shown that temperature conditions inside the container are between 10°C and 15°C lower than in unpainted metal silos (Prevett, 1962a). With most food grains, cooling the air to a temperature level which does not permit the development of microorganisms or prevents the occurrence of chemical reactions is seldom economic and products must be dried to low moisture content levels for control.

In the tropics, the possibilities of ventilation at night in order to lower the temperature of produce may be considered where the dewpoint is low, but in warm/wet areas great care is required to limit such air movement to those times of day when the relative humidity permits drying.

The main use of heat is in the removal of moisture from food grains to attain a level at which they will store successfully. In the drying of grain by use of artificially heated air, the grain is subjected to a stream of air heated to not more than the highest safe temperature for that particular grain. These safe temperatures vary with the type of grain, its moisture content and the end use of the grain. Current investigations indicate the advantages of drying by using large volumes of air a few degrees above ambient temperature (between 25°C and 35°C) as compared to the method of using low volumes of high temperature air (from 46°C to 95°C). It has been shown by Craufurd (1962) and others that the upper temperature limit for drying parboiled paddy is 35°C while maize has been dried at about 95°C.

Moisture

Moisture is the key to the safe storage of produce. Biological activity occurs only when moisture is present, with the minimum quantity required for such activity varying according to the organisms concerned. It is well known that for germination of seeds a considerable amount of water or moisture is required, for example, legumes when soaked in water for 24 to 48 hours begin to sprout (i.e., germinate) with attendant chemical changes within the grain producing a marked increase in ascorbic acid and other nutrients and changes in the carbohydrates (e.g., to sucrose, glucose, fructose). Where less moisture is present than that required to promote germination, conditions are suitable for the development of bacteria. Even less moisture is sufficient to provide conditions for the development of moulds (fungi) and mites, and still less is needed for the development of insects.

Since an increase in moisture results in increased respiration of microorganisms it also causes an increase in temperature.

Types of water

Moisture in produce is of two main types: " water of composition " which is water contained within the plant cells of which the grain or kernels is composed, and " free water " which is water present on the surface of, but not within, the cells. A proportion of the free water is less free, being adsorbed on to the surface of the cells; therefore when methods of determining the amount of moisture in produce (e.g., moisture content) are considered, it is important to standardize a specific method so as to attempt to ensure that the same degree of water removal is being considered each time the amount must be determined.

Moisture content/relative humidity

All produce has its own characteristic balance (or equilibrium) between the moisture it contains and the water vapour in the air with which it is in contact. This is known as the moisture content/relative humidity equilibration pattern. When food grains containing a certain amount of moisture are exposed to the air, moisture moves from the former to the latter as shown in Table 7 until there is a balance between the moistures in the grain and in the atmosphere.

Each food grain has a characteristic equilibrium curve, sometimes referred to as a humidity balance curve (Davey and Elcoate, 1965,

TABLE 7. – MOVEMENTS OF MOISTURE IN ATMOSPHERE AND IN GRAIN

Air with	More moisture than grain →	Grain reacts by absorbing moisture from the air
	Less moisture than grain →	Grain gives up moisture to the air

1966, 1967). The curve is obtained by plotting a graph of moisture content against relative humidity of the air; the appropriate isotherms or MC/RH equilibration curves for a range of food grains are given in Figure 8. These values must be considered only as a guide since different types and varieties of grain vary in their equilibrium values.

The precise change in equilibrium moisture content will vary from that shown in graphic presentation. The range of change is indicated by the following work: Oxley (1948) has mentioned that the temperature effect (for wheat) is about 0.6 to 0.7 percent mois-

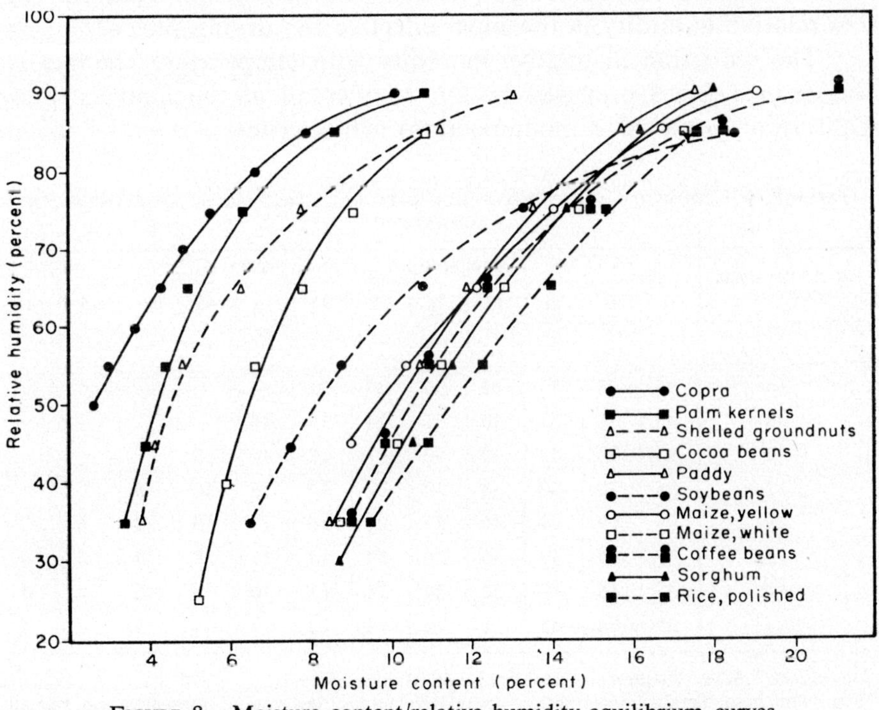

FIGURE 8. Moisture content/relative humidity equilibrium curves.

ture content decrease per 10°C temperature rise at the same percentage relative humidity of the air; results obtained by various workers suggest that 1.0 percent decrease per 10°C rise may be appropriate between 15°C and 27°C although Pedersen (United Nations, 1962b), studying wheat, rye, barley and oats, indicates decreases of 0.4, 0.7, 0.9 and 0.6 percent respectively at 70 percent relative humidity between 20°C and 30°C.

The direction of and rate of approach to the equilibrium will depend upon many conditions. If, for example, the grain is stored in such a way that air is not moved through it, then the air in contact with the grain will approach an equilibrium relative humidity determined by the moisture content of the grain; if air is being moved through the grain, as for example during natural and particularly during artificial drying, then the moisture content of the grain is conditioned by the relative humidity of the air.

The relative humidity is determined by the temperature and moisture content in the air. If the temperature is increased while moisture is kept constant the relative humidity drops. Air having low relative humidity is the most effective for drying purposes.

The reduction in relative humidity with temperature changes is shown in Table 8 prepared by Dr. Henderson of the University of California (personal communication) who writes:

TABLE 8. – REDUCTION IN RELATIVE HUMIDITY RESULTING FROM AN INCREASE IN TEMPERATURE

Air temperature, degrees C	Temperature increase, degrees C											
	0	6	11	17	22	28	33	39	45	50	55	61
					Percent							
43	95	72	55	42	33	26	21					
38	95	71	53	40	31	24	19	15				
32	95	70	52	40	30	23	18	14	12			
27	95	70	50	38	29	22	17	13	10	8		
21	95	69	49	36	27	21	16	12	9	7	6	
15	95	67	49	36	26	19	14	11	9	7	5	4
10	95	66	47	32	24	18	13	10	8	6	4	4
4	95	64	45	31	22	16	12	9	7	5	4	4

SOURCE: Dr. S.M. Henderson, University of California.
NOTE: For more detailed information on relative humidities, vapour pressures and related data refer to Appendix H: Use of the psychrometric chart in grain drying.

" If for example atmospheric air is 32°C and 95 percent relative humidity and the temperature is raised 22°C that is, to 54°C, the resulting relative humidity will be 30 percent. The table is also useful if the relative humidity of the atmospheric air is below 95 percent. For example, if atmospheric air is 27°C and 50 percent relative humidity and is heated to 49°C (temperature increase 22°C) enter the table at 27°C and 50 percent relative humidity which is located in the 11°C temperature increase column. A 22°C temperature increase would move the relative humidity to the 33°C column from which the relative humidity is found to be 17 percent. (Note that it is the heated, higher temperature, lower relative humidity air that dries the grain. The relative humidity that results from heating is used in determining equilibrium moisture values in cases where they are needed.) "

MOISTURE CONTENT FOR SAFE STORAGE

It is essential that the moisture content of food grains be known when they are accepted for storage. As has been indicated previously, deterioration in storage virtually depends on the level of moisture in products. In addition, warehouse records can not be maintained without this information.

In buying and selling food grains considerable quantities of water are paid for (e.g., a bag of maize at 12.5 percent moisture content weighing 90 kilogrammes contains about 11.5 litres of water). Thus for a given measure of produce sold by weight the greater the moisture the less food it contains.

During storage, grain may take up or lose moisture; storage weight loss will therefore vary according to climatic conditions and the type of storage involved. In Kenya recent experiments on stacks of bagged maize which were kept covered permanently with plastic sheets indicated that the saving in moisture (impossible under usual conditions of storage) paid for the cost of disinfestation measures against insect pests.

Since moisture above a particular level is necessary for the development of microorganisms it can be seen from Figure 7 that deterioration due to fungi and bacteria can be prevented only if produce with a moisture content in equilibrium with less than 60 percent relative humidity (for most species at tropical temperatures)

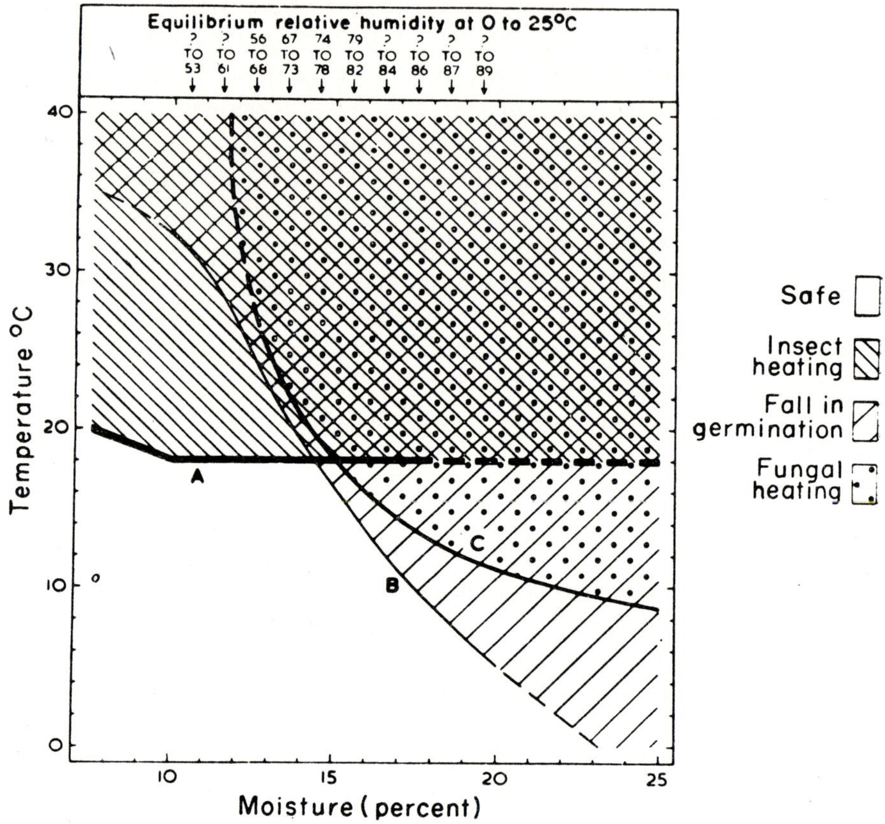

FIGURE 9. Values of temperature, relative humidity and moisture content for safe storage, insect and fungal heating and fall in germination.

A. Lower limit for insect heating
B. Lower limit for germination
C. Lower limit for fungal heating

is accepted for storage. Under these circumstances only deterioration due to attack by insects and rodents will have to be prevented. Figure 9 correlates temperature, relative humidity and moisture content values for cereals and indicates their influence on germination, insect and fungal development. As previously stated, the development of microorganisms is affected by a combination of temperature and moisture. In general, the higher the temperature the lower moisture level must be in order to reduce deterioration; conversely, the lower the temperature the higher is the permissible moisture level for safe storage.

Above 65 or 70 percent relative humidity fungi develop, producing heat and an increase in temperature which may reach 63°C giving what is termed "damp grain heating" (Sinha and Wallace, 1965). At relative humidities (RH) below 70 percent, insect infestation may develop and an increase in temperature, resulting from the respiration of the insects may occur. Temperatures may reach 42°C (for insect species except *Trogoderma granarium* which can tolerate slightly higher temperatures) giving what is termed "dry grain heating" (Sinha, 1961).

Produce having a moisture content above a level in equilibrium with 70 percent humidity should not be accepted in storage or allowed to enter trade routes. The equilibrium values at this acceptable level of relative humidity (at a temperature of about 27°C) for a range of commodities is given in Table 9. In some countries, because of difficulties in sampling consignments adequately for assessment of moisture content, the maximum acceptable level of moisture content for safe storage is about 1 percent below these figures.

TABLE 9. – MOISTURE CONTENT EQUILIBRIUM VALUES (AT A TEMPERATURE OF ABOUT 27°C) FOR A RANGE OF PRODUCE AT 70 PERCENT RELATIVE HUMIDITY, THE MAXIMUM ACCEPTABLE LEVEL FOR STORAGE FOR ANY SAMPLE

	Equilibrium moisture content at 70 percent RH
Maize	13.5
Wheat	13.5
Sorghum	13.5
Millet	16.0
Paddy	15.0
Rice	13.0
Cowpeas	15.0
Beans	15.0
Groundnuts (shelled)	7.0
Cottonseed	10.0
Cocoa beans	7.0
Copra	7.0
Palm kernels	5.0

The equilibrium moisture content of produce for a given relative humidity of the atmosphere will be different at various altitudes and therefore the safe moisture content for storage which is in equilibrium with 70 percent relative humidity should be determined at the appropriate altitude by using the reference methods detailed below in the specific areas involved.

It is also important to obtain data on the reliability of the moisture tester used to determine the moisture content. If the accuracy of a meter is 0.5 percent then the acceptable level stipulated must be 0.5 percent moisture content below the theoretical guide, e.g., under these circumstances the level for maize would be 13 percent. Even this may have to be lowered because of difficulties in obtaining representative samples.

Although the figures quoted in Table 9 may serve as a useful guide to acceptable moisture levels for storage, varieties of grains are known to vary in their storing characteristics with respect to moisture. For example, the equilibrium values of yellow and white maize differ by about 1.5 percent; varieties of paddy from low temperature areas may differ by 1 percent moisture content for maximum safe storage moisture due to varietal differences (e.g., silicon content, type or thickness of husk), or differences in harvesting methods so that the husk may be damaged more in one variety than in another. With certain products, (e.g., coffee beans) there is evidence that if the beans have not been killed during processing deterioration from mould does not occur between 70 percent and 85 percent relative humidity, but if the beans are dead mould develops above 70 percent.

Many warehouse keepers and staff have not yet realized the importance of ensuring that only dry produce be put into store if proper handling and good storage are to be obtained. The presence in a consignment of only one bag, basket or kerosene tin of damp grain can act as a focal point of high moisture and temperature in which deterioration sets in; then, through the medium of temperature gradients, moisture moves to adjacent areas thus enabling deterioration to spread to produce which was originally of good, sound quality.

In experimental work it is sometimes necessary to obtain a quantity of grain at a particular moisture content when there are only two lots of grain available and these have other moisture contents. In such cases, the following formula may be used to mix the two available equal weight samples of grain in particular proportions to give a mixture which, if allowed to equilibrate, will have the desired uniform moisture content.

W = Weight of dry grain
Q = Weight of damp grain
MC = Percent moisture content of damp grain
mc = Percent moisture content of dry grain
x = Percent moisture content of grain mixture desired

$$W \text{ (to be added)} = \frac{Q \times (MC - x)}{x - mc}$$

MEASUREMENT OF MOISTURE

Indigenous farmers always have their own methods for assessing the amount of moisture in grain. Some of these provide a fairly reliable estimate of the grain's suitability for safe storage. These methods include pressing the grain with the thumb nail; crushing the grains between the fingers; biting the grain; rattling a number of grains in a tin; obtaining the " feel " of the grain by smelling a handful and shaking it; or by plunging the hand (fingers extended) into a largish bulk of the grain (a sack or heap). With long experience a man can judge whether the grain or kernel is suitable for storage (i.e., whether it is wet, damp, dry or overdry). With these methods it can be observed that wet and damp grain compared with dry and very dry is soft, gives a dull sound, smells " off, " or prevents penetration of the hand up to the forearm. However, reliance on these senses is open to question since inconsistency can arise due to differences of opinion or when the person concerned feels ill, and especially when the price paid for commodities varies with the amount of moisture present. The latter point applies particularly at traders' stores and large collection centres where certain products are purchased on a moisture content basis.

The moisture content of food grains may have to be determined on the farms, in the stores, etc., and under laboratory conditions. The methods available for measuring moisture under these types of conditions vary; methods suitable for use in the laboratory, by which a considerable degree of accuracy can be achieved, are seldom practical under field conditions.

The percentage moisture content of a product is usually calculated as follows:

$$\frac{\text{Weight of moisture}}{\text{Weight of wet sample}} \times 100$$

Sometimes moisture content is expressed as a percentage of the dry sample; it is therefore important to check whether moisture content refers to the wet or to the dry basis.

Laboratory methods

Moisture can be determined in the laboratory by a number of methods, of which the oven drying method and the distillation method are the most accurate; these are normally used as reference methods for moisture meters used under field conditions. Both of these methods require a sample of the produce. It is essential therefore to ensure that:

(*a*) the sample is representative of the parcel being examined; sampling of the component units (e.g., bags) of the parcel and subsampling of the main sample are sufficiently large to provide the quantity of grains to be tested for moisture;

(*b*) the sample taken is kept in a sealed container (e.g., tightly fitting tin, bottle or plastic bag) between the time of sampling and that of determining the moisture content.

A. *Oven drying*

The amount of moisture in a sample of produce which does not decompose on heating can be determined by weighing a quantity of the ground produce and drying it in a forced draught air oven at a given temperature for a predetermined length of time. A well-mixed sample of the produce, sufficient to fill a bottle of 100-gramme capacity, is ground to a powder sufficiently fine for at least 85 percent to pass through a wire sieve (0.9 millimetre gauge) No. 30 mesh per 2.5 centimetre type (or a No. 20 mesh American Standard screen 0.84 millimetre gauge). The ground material is mixed with a clean spoon spatula; two counterpoised aluminium tins with lids (diameter 45 to 65 millimetres, depth 10 to 20 millimetres) are alternately filled with spoonfuls of the ground material. The tins are weighed and then heated in the oven for a certain length of time at the temperature recommended for the particular product concerned. A number of temperature and time combinations are used in different countries. The data given in Table 10 may be considered to provide a uniform approach.

TABLE 10. – DRYING TEMPERATURES AND TIMES FOR PRODUCTS WHEN DETERMINING MOISTURE CONTENT BY AN OVEN DRYING METHOD

	Temperature	Time
	... *Degrees C* ...	..... *Hours* .....
Cereals	130	1
	113	4
Pulses	114	4
Cocoa beans	98–100	2.5
Copra	103±2	3
Coffee beans	105	4
Groundnuts	103±2	3
Palm kernels	103±2	3

NOTE: If these temperatures and times are exceeded to any great extent the produce may break down, giving inaccurate moisture content determinations.

After drying the tins are removed from the oven, covered with their lids and the samples cooled by placing them in a desiccator; when cold, the tins are weighed again.

With very wet samples of produce (e.g., over 17 percent for cereals) a two-stage drying method may be used. First the unground material is weighed in a tin and is subjected to a period of drying in the oven followed by cooling and reweighing (as above). This is followed by grinding, weighing, heating, cooling and reweighing as indicated above.

In making determinations by oven drying at stations or depots in areas having widely different altitudes, care should be taken to adjust the drying time or employ a measurement factor which compensates for the different moisture content results obtained (using the same temperature/time ratio).

B. *Distillation methods*

These methods are used for products which break down easily when subjected to heat (e.g., cocoa beans containing laevulose, and spices such as cloves, chillies or black peppercorns which contain volatile oils). Two methods are in common use: the Brown-Duval and the Dean and Stark methods.

Brown-Duval. The weighed grain (100 grammes) is heated in a nonvolatile oil to a temperature well above 100°C (180°C for wheat) for a specified length of time. The water run off together with any other volatile immiscible substances is collected in a still. The amount of water which is distilled into a graduated cylinder is read in millilitres and reported as percentage moisture content. This method will give different values of moisture content for the same sample if applied at different altitudes, due to differences in boiling point of the oil at the different pressures caused by the change in altitude.

Dean and Stark. A weighed sample of grain is heated in an immiscible solvent. The solvent extracts the water from the grain and both solvent and water are condensed in a calibrated container. Since the liquids are immiscible the water and solvent separate out and the water, being less dense than the solvent, settles to the bottom of the tube where it is measured and the moisture content calculated. With distillation methods the vessels used must be cleaned before each operation (MacMasters, 1962).

C. *Rapid "oven" methods*

Since the oven methods used as reference methods are time-consuming, a number of more rapid laboratory methods operating on the same principle have been designed. They range from simple, inexpensive pieces of equipment to highly sophisticated and expensive instruments. A typical simple method consists of shining an infra-red lamp on a balance pan in which a ground sample of approximately 5 grammes has been placed. The produce is exposed to the intense heat of the lamp for a predetermined period and the loss in weight is shown on a scale calibrated in percentage moisture content.

Field methods : moisture meters

Moisture meters are required for use at farms, processing installations, warehouses, in ship holds, etc. At the larger and more highly organized depots, an accuracy of ± 0.5 percent is required whereas nearer the primary buyer and the farmer where a smaller quantity is being stored, often under conditions where the grains are spread out daily in layers to dry, an accuracy of ± 1 percent may be sufficient.

An ideal meter for use under field conditions does not exist. Such a meter would have to be:

(*a*) capable of being used on bags and bulk without taking a sample;
(*b*) portable, robust and unaffected by damp or dust;
(*c*) cheap and reliable;
(*d*) simple to operate;
(*e*) quick in giving the reading;
(*f*) unaffected by temperature.

The meters currently available are of three principal types.

A. *Acetylene type*

A weighed ground sample of the commodity is thoroughly mixed with calcium carbide in a gastight container. The moisture in the commodity reacts with the calcium carbide to produce acetylene gas, and as the gas mounts up the pressure in the container increases and is indicated on a pressure gauge calibrated in moisture content. This method, however, has a number of disadvantages and is not widely used.

B. *Hair hygrometer probes*

These probes consist of a stem and dial. Inside the stem a hair is fixed to the end of the probe and is attached at the other end via a mechanical linkage to a needle which moves over the dial. The dial is marked in percentage relative humidity and also in terms of the moisture content of some of the more common commodities. No sample need be taken; the stem is pushed into the sack or bulk of produce; the dial is rotated to open the " holes " in the stem; and the hair is given time to equilibrate with the moisture in the intergranular air. Where widely different moisture contents are involved the operation may take up to 30 minutes. Under such circumstances the device is best suited for use in small silos where the meter is left in position. Several probe type meters based on this principle are available. They cost less than $60 each and have the advantage over all other meters of requiring no temperature correction.

Since the criterion for storage is a maximum relative humidity of 70 percent, it is possible to consider using these meters to indicate the storage potential of the product rather than as an instrument to give exact moisture content values.

The following method is suggested for using a hair hygrometer moisture tester to determine whether sacks of produce contain the excess moisture necessary to support the growth of moulds.

At the time of receipt of sacks of produce:

1. Close holes of tester by revolving the head of the meter on the stem.
2. Push the probe into the centre of the sack.
3. Open holes of tester by revolving the head on the stem.
4. With the first sack:

(*a*) if the pointer moves toward 70 percent relative humidity (RH) from a position below this mark;

(i) allow the pointer to come to rest (may take 15 minutes) if the reading is below 70 percent RH;

(ii) if the pointer moves into the 70 to 80 percent range, it should be allowed to come to rest and the sack should be subjected to further drying before acceptance for storage;

(iii) if the pointer moves above 80 percent, the instrument can be removed immediately and the sack concerned must be rejected for storage;

(*b*) If from a point above 70 percent the pointer moves below this figure (which may take only a few minutes), the commodity is dry and safe for storage and the instrument can be removed immediately.

5. With subsequent sacks the probe is inserted in the next sack and the movement of the pointer is noted. It can then be decided whether the pointer should be allowed time to settle or the probe should be removed immediately from the sack, depending on the movement of the pointer in relation to the 70 percent figure on the dial.

When testing stacks of bagged produce the tester is used as described above to assess the condition of the product both at the centre and at the periphery of a number of sacks on the outside of the stack. The tester is pushed into each sack both at right angles to assess the condition in the centre of the outside sacks, and in such a way that it lies just under the surface of the sack to assess the condition of the outer three centimetres of produce in the outside layer of each bag.

If the instrument is left hanging in the store it will indicate the relative humidity of the air in the store.

These instruments should be "conditioned" once every two weeks by soaking a piece of cloth in water, wringing it out and wrapping it round the perforated end of the stem and leaving it there for about 20 minutes. The holes in the stem should be open during this time. The pointer should show 95 percent. If not, the instrument should be adjusted to this figure in accord with the manufacturer's instructions.

C. *Electrical moisture meters*

There are many electrical moisture meters available on the market. These meters measure one or more electrical properties of a commodity: the electrical properties of a product are highly dependent upon the moisture content.

Electrical moisture meters may be divided into two main types, i.e., capacitance and resistance meters.

Capacitance moisture meters are used to measure the permittivity of a sample (usually unground) held in a cell, two sides of which form the plates of a condenser; the cell forms one arm of a bridge circuit. The product must be poured into the cell in a manner which ensures consistent packing in the cell; otherwise false readings may be obtained. Capacitance moisture meters are also liable to give false readings if the sample to be tested is surface-wet. A temperature correction is needed which may be made in several ways depending on the exact design of the meter. The representative or unrepresentative nature of the sample being tested must be taken into account.

Resistance moisture meters for this purpose may be of two types, using either a compression cell or a probe. In the compression cell method a ground sample is compressed and the resistance measured on a scale calibrated in percentage moisture content. A temperature correction is required. The methods by which a probe is pushed into the sack or bulk to be measured are less accurate than the compression methods, but this loss in accuracy may be acceptable where the method is required only to give a guide to the condition of a large number of sacks. These instruments are liable to give false readings if used on a quantity of surface-wet grain, or if the sack itself is damp. A pressure correction as well as a temperature correction is needed with resistance probe methods. The advantages of these methods are that they not only allow rapid testing of a large number of sacks in a short time but, since these probe type meters measure the highest moisture content present, the presence of an undesirable pocket of high moisture content grain can be detected.

The lack of accuracy of probe type meters may be compensated for by taking the average of a large number of samples. This average may prove more representative than the results of fewer although individually more accurate readings from meters requiring a sample taken from a bulk.

The cost of portable electrical moisture meters is between $75 and $500. The price of a moisture meter is no indication of its accuracy, speed of operation, or suitability for any given purpose.

Moisture movement in storage

Spoilage can occur although precautions have been taken to put only dry grain into store. Such spoilage results from the existence of temperature gradients within a stack of bagged grain or a silo of bulk grain. Differences between the temperature of the grain and the outside air temperature (Figure 10) can be communicated to the grain through the walls of the store or silo, particularly if they are constructed of metal. Due to the low thermal conductivity of grain these temperature effects on the outside of the grain mass are only very slowly transmitted to the centre. The temperature of the grain at the centre of the bulk may rise due to the presence of insects (Figure 11) and this temperature rise will only be communicated very slowly to the outside of the grain. This shows how a temperature gradient can occur.

These temperature gradients cause convection currents in the grain, accompanied by a movement of moisture from high temperature to low temperature areas. As the air is cooled its relative humidity rises and may reach saturation point when excess water will be deposited on the surface of the cooler grain (Joffe, 1958). Localized increases of moisture content can therefore occur giving conditions favourable to the development of fungi, resulting in further spoilage of the grain.

If the external air becomes consistently colder than the stored grain and remains so for many weeks, the air within the mass develops a slow but persistent movement pattern, as illustrated by the arrows in Figure 10. The air in the silo adjacent to the outer walls is cooled, its relative humidity rises and as a result there is a slight increase in the local moisture content of the grain. The rise in the relative humidity of the air may bring the air to saturation point when any further increase in moisture content of the air or further reduction in temperature will lead to liquid water being deposited onto the grain. In due course the moisture content of the grain at the bottom of the storage container will rise sufficiently for deterioration to occur, as shown by the cross-hatched areas in Figure 10. The dry air rising through the warm central section takes up moisture from the grain. When this warm, moisture-laden air comes into contact with the cool upper surface of the grain, moisture is deposited and another potential area of deterioration develops.

Figure 10 shows an air movement pattern which occurs when the external air temperature is consistently above the grain temperature. High moisture content conditions may develop near the floor if there is no underfloor ventilation. The latter condition is

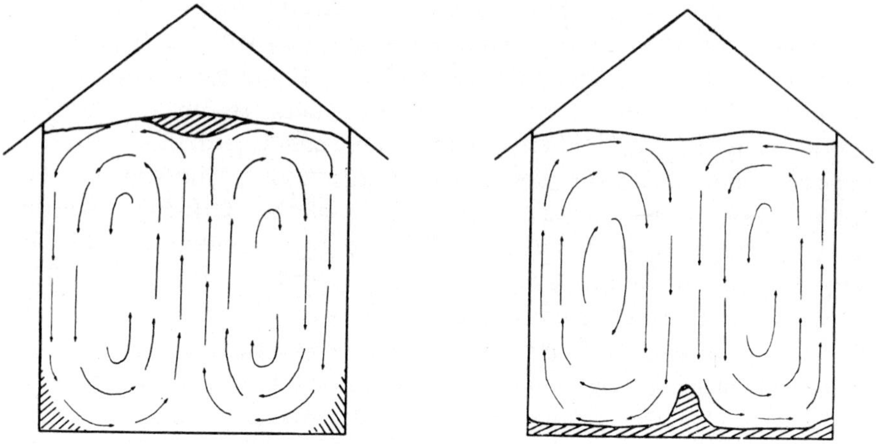

FIGURE 10. Moisture movement within bulk of grain due to differences between the temperature of outside air and of stored grain. Left, outside air temperature below grain temperature; right, outside air temperature above grain temperature.

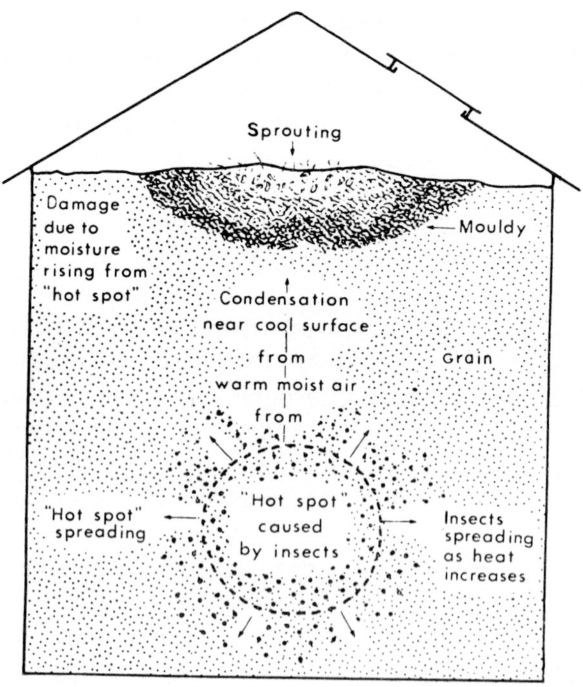

FIGURE 11. Spoilage of grain due to temperature gradients, movement of moisture and localized development of fungi and insects.

the less common of the two since grain is normally harvested in high temperature conditions and thereafter the temperature of the outside air may be expected to fall.

The lower the moisture content of produce on entry to the store the less the risk that its temperature will fall to below the dewpoint temperature. This is the temperature at which a given sample of air becomes saturated, and below which water starts to condense out. If the temperature of a surface is below the dewpoint of the surrounding air, water will condense onto it.

Condensation problems, especially in metal silos, occur in the tropics particularly in areas where the sky is clear during both day and night. Clear skies result in high daytime temperatures in the fabric which, by heating the inside of the store, causes a movement of moisture from the produce to the surrounding air space. At night radiation from the store leads to a very rapid drop in the temperature of the fabric and the water vapour in the air space condenses onto the internal surface of the store. Condensation may not be apparent on cursory inspection since the liquid water may be absorbed by grain in contact with the silo walls. Grain itself can act as a condensing surface if its temperature is reduced to below the dewpoint temperature of the air. The presence of high moisture content grain and areas of mould at the surface of produce indicate that condensation has occurred.

Metal silos should be light in colour to reflect most of the incoming radiation during the day. The major temperature changes normally required to cause condensation can be avoided by providing adequate shade to prevent large gains of energy in the grain.

If grain is uniformly dry when put into the store and is kept dry and at a constant temperature, damage due to condensation and translocation of moisture will be minimal.

Processing

Methods of processing to which food grains are subjected prior to storage affect their storability. Respiratory activity and the tendency of grain and grain products to deteriorate in storage are affected by the " soundness " of the grain. Therefore any process is to be avoided which bruises or damages the grain or leaves enough moisture within the produce to favour the agencies responsible for deterioration.

At the time of harvest food grains are protected by various types of seed coats through which moisture, oxygen and microorganisms have to pass before reaching the "naked" seed grain or kernel within. During the processes of harvesting, threshing, shelling, steeping, cleaning and milling, damage to the grain cells can occur.

With groundnuts an unbroken shell is important in reducing the rate of penetration of fungal spores to the kernel within, and in preventing damage to the kernel by insect species. The undamaged skin or testa of the groundnut kernel prevents discoloration of the cotyledons through oxidation; and grain covers also contain fairly active antioxidants so that the fats in unbroken kernels or grain are shielded from the oxygen in the air. Similarly, the tightness of the glumes of paddy (this character varies with different varieties of paddy) can prevent penetration by insect species (Breese, 1964) as is also the case with maize varieties having sheaths which completely and tightly cover the maize grains.

HARVESTING

Methods and time of harvesting are important factors in the deterioration of produce and vary with the country and the product; such factors must therefore be considered by authorities concerned with storage problems.

Knives of various types — machetes, sickles, etc. (for cereals) and hoes (or jembes), more frequently of the solid blade type than the fork type (for ground crops such as groundnuts, yams and cassava) — are used in many countries, and mechanical harvesters including binders and combines are being introduced in some areas.

With cereals, the heads are sometimes bent at an angle to the stalk and are left for a few weeks before hand picking. With groundnuts, the plants are pulled or dug from the ground and in some cases a number of groundnuts are cut by the hoe or several may be left in the soil and in both cases fungi develop rapidly. With pulses, the plants are cut and the pods are hand-picked.

When mechanical harvesters are used the plant is cut and the grain and straw are separated immediately; this often involves the application of considerable force and it has been shown that the use of combine harvesters provides a higher proportion of " green " or immature grains than hand harvested grain and in addition cracks the glumes of paddy grains providing an easy entry point for fungal spores and insects (Breese, 1964). Harvesting by combine leaves no time for the grain to dry out between harvesting and threshing; also the cutting of green weeds with the grain frequently results (during storage) in the transfer of moisture from weeds and immature seeds to the drier full grain kernels. Consequently, with the increasing adoption of combines, grain moisture hazard becomes a more serious problem.

Time of harvest is important in relation to maturity of the crop and also with respect to climatic conditions.

Harvesting before the crop matures usually means a lower yield and also a higher proportion of immature seeds which deteriorate more rapidly than mature seeds because the enzymes contained are not dormant. The longer produce is left in the field, exposed to alternate periods of wetting and drying (e.g., dew at night and hot sun by day), the greater is the degree of cracking (this is particularly true with long grain types of paddy). Under these conditions insect infestation and fungal attacks develop unhindered. With paddy it is sometimes best to reap before the grains are fully ripe and to dry in the sun, protecting from dew at night. It has been shown that, on milling, the highest yields of whole grains of rice are obtained from harvesting between six and nine days earlier than the time usually accepted (e.g., West African Rice Research Station, 1963).

In countries where the crop matures and must be harvested during the rainy season, major problems of drying must be solved. Data on the relationship between harvesting dates and the period of the rains (or high humidity) in terms indicating the specific areas within countries where such problems exist are not readily available.

Crops can become infested prior to harvesting by insects which are major pests of the stored crop. Little information is available from most countries in the tropics and substropics on the extent of this type of preharvest insect infestation. Recent investigations (in India, Kenya, Nigeria and the West Indies) indicate, however, that crops such as maize, beans, and paddy carry significant infestations of insects from the field into the store. Even a 1 percent level of infestation at time of harvest has been shown in Nigeria to result in a 45 percent weight loss through insect development in store.

Threshing and shelling

This process, whereby grains or kernels are removed from the part of the plant on or in which they have developed, if carried out by hand or by machine in such a way that cracking or breaking of the grains or kernels results, will contribute to deterioration.

Trampling, consisting of laying sheaves of paddy on the threshing floor and having them trampled by driven animals or tractor wheels or by foot, is reported to cause heavy losses since a percentage of the grain is not shed. Also, when threshing is done on a hard earth floor, earth and other impurities become mixed with the grain, prejudicing storage and processing. The beating of produce contained within sacks to effect removal of the grains or kernels is time-consuming and not always very efficient.

Many types of mechanical devices have been and are being developed to speed up threshing and/or shelling and to improve efficiency so that whole undamaged produce is obtained.

Drying

Drying is practised to prevent germination of seeds, to retain maximum quality of the grain, and to reach a level of moisture which does not allow the growth of bacteria and fungi and considerably retards the development of mites and insects. It is essential that food grains be dried quickly and yet effectively. Food grains such as oilseeds, cereals and legumes differ in their biological make-up (having shells or outer coats and also inner kernels or seeds of different textures and compositions). Since each is processed in a particular way to meet the food habits of the local population, local drying methods vary. Drying affects the quality of grains and hence their value to purchasing organizations. For some grains and trades value is attached to appearance of grains, such as colour and texture, and for other grains and trades equal importance is attached to chemical composition, such as oil content and acidity.

Air is used as the drying medium and to conduct heat to the produce, causing water to vaporize; it is also used to convey the moisture vapour away from the drying produce. The moisture-carrying capacity of the air is dependent upon the temperature and, in fact, increases with the rise in temperature (e.g., at 30°C the air is capable of holding twice as much moisture as at 16°C). The psychrometric chart shown as Figure 61 in Appendix H provides this information for every set of temperature conditions. Detailed instructions as to its uses are given in the Appendix.

Types of drying

There are two types of drying: natural and artificial. Within each type several systems may be considered. Different varieties of grains have specific drying characteristics and it is essential, therefore, to use a type of drying which will give the highest quality.

The capacity of air to remove moisture from produce with which it is in contact depends upon many factors, but principally upon the relationship between the moisture content of the produce and the relative humidity of the air. The relative humidity of the air must be lower than the equilibrium relative humidity coinciding with the moisture content of the produce; for drying to be completed the drying air must have a relative humidity below the equilibrium relative humidity at the minimum crop moisture content required for safe storage.

A. *Natural methods*

This type of drying utilizes a combination of sun and air but also requires time and some effort by man to spread and collect the produce.

In natural drying, care must be taken to avoid too rapid drying or overdrying and to minimize excessive movement of the grains which causes breakage or damage to the seed coat. Drying too rapidly causes certain seeds (e.g., pulses and spices) to swell and burst (where a capsule containing a number of seeds is involved some of the seeds may be lost) and others to bleach; with some types of products "case hardening" occurs, whereby the surface of the grains, dries out rapidly, "sealing" the moisture within the inner layers. It also causes the grains to become wrinkled and scorched (or discoloured) in appearance; the greater part of the original carotene can be lost through oxidation and the riboflavin may be destroyed. In seeds which are normally protected by a capsule, exposure of the seed to the atmosphere may result in loss of oil. Moreover, grains should not be exposed to rain and rewetting during and after the drying period because stresses set up within the grains cause cracking.

In natural drying care should be taken to eliminate dust and dirt, which represent extraneous material and accelerate deterioration by permitting an increase in moisture content and fungal contamination.

It should be noted that natural air drying does not eliminate insects. Sun-drying temperature in the tropics varies but it may be assumed that produce spread on matting in a layer not thicker than about 5 centimetres receives a drying temperature of about 36°C (higher temperature may be recorded, however) which is insufficient to kill insects present in the grains. Breese (1964) has found that at 39°C paddy dried over the range of about 16 to 11 percent is not disinfested and subsequent larval development is not affected.

B. *Artificial drying*

This involves the use of ambient temperature air and mechanical means of moving it through the produce, or air heated above ambient with or without the mechanical means of moving it through the produce.

Air is heated by burning carbon and hydrocarbon fuels, utilizing the heat supplied by internal combustion engines, and resistance heating by electricity.

In drying with direct-fired units the fuel is burned and the hot combustion gases pass through the produce or are collected by the air stream from a fan and distributed throughout the produce being dried; with this system the produce can become contaminated by unburnt fuel, fumes and soot. Work being conducted (particularly in the Federal Republic of Germany) on the residues of combustion of oil as related to potential carcinogenic hazards may lead to future legislation requiring the use of heat exchangers which would eliminate such hazards.

Contamination of the product does not occur in indirect-fired driers where hot gases pass into a heat exchanger around which the drying air circulates and picks up heat before it is distributed through the produce.

In drying crops in deep layers, excessive temperature increase at constant air moisture results in drying grain to an undesirable low level of moisture content at the bottom of the layer before moisture content in the grain at the surface is near the desired level. See Chapter 5 for details. The slow, steady rate of drying achieved by this method can yield a high quality produce for some crops such as rice.

In drying grain in shallow layers the maximum permissible drying temperatures recommended depend upon the use for which the grain is intended; examples are given in Table 11. These are

TABLE 11. - SHALLOW LAYER DRIER OPERATING TEMPERATURE CONDITIONS

Produce and intended use	Maximum recommended drying temperature
	Degrees C
Grain to be used for livestock feed	74
Grain for human consumption	57
Grain for milling and manufacturing	60
Seed grain or brewery grain	43
Rice for human consumption	43
Beans for human consumption	35

SOURCE: Dr. S.M. Henderson, University of California.

broadly recognized values not appropriate to all areas or varieties. Experience may indicate that temperatures in excess of these may be used satisfactorily. Initially, however, the temperatures listed are recommended. Minimum temperatures are always recommended when quality is a factor.

In order not to destroy grain viability, the maximum heating time for air at different temperatures is limited according to the moisture content of the grain. Pedersen (United Nations, 1962b) has given relevant data as recorded in Table 12.

TABLE 12. – RELATION BETWEEN MOISTURE CONTENT, TIME AND PERMISSIBLE HEATING OF THE DRYING AIR

Heating time	Grain moisture content (percent)			
	15	20	25	30
Minutes	.... *Degrees C*			
15	59	55	52	50
30	56	52	49	47
60	53	49	46	44
120	50	46	43	
480	44	40		
1 440	39			

SOURCE: United Nations 1962b, after Pedersen, T.T.

" Stage " drying is used with some commodities to maintain certain quality criteria, particularly with rice. Instructions for rice which is harvested at 25 to 27 percent moisture content are:

1. dry to approximately 20 percent;
2. cool to atmospheric temperature;
3. store for approximately 24 hours;
4. then repeat the drying and storage sequence for at least two more stages.

In the case of rice, cracking is said to be kept to a minimum by this procedure.

Excessive drying due to the drying air being at a low relative humidity need not occur in continuous flow driers. With batch driers, the final moisture gradient through the batch is likely to be somewhat less when working with high rather than low moisture content air at the same hot air temperature.

COOLING

Having dried the produce by subjecting it to hot air, it is essential to cool it before putting it into store. The storage of produce with a temperature higher than that of ambient temperature will lead to moisture problems and consequent deterioration. By ensuring that produce is put into store with a low temperature (commensurate with that of ambient), insect activity will be less than at a higher temperature and moisture migration will be less of a problem.

All grain which has been dried and particularly when dried in continuous flow type driers should be cooled before storage. A decrease in grain temperature will result in greater safety in storage since cooling by 4°C will produce an additional safety margin equivalent to a lowering of moisture content of 1 percent.

Aeration

The use of ambient temperature air (or air heated only slightly above ambient temperature) to aerate grain is practised in many countries. It is essential to differentiate between aeration and drying.

The principle aims of aeration are to:

1. lower grain temperature (i.e., cool a mass of warm grain);
2. equalize grain temperature through the bulk (control localized heating);
3. remove unpleasant odours or toxic gases after fumigation;
4. reduce moisture content by a very small amount.

Generally no heat is added to the air but care must be taken to avoid aeration with air at temperatures and relative humidities higher than those associated with the equilibrium moisture content of the grain, since this is liable to increase its moisture content.

WATER TREATMENTS

Water treatments (steeping, parboiling and cooking) dissolve the soluble vitamins out of grains. With rice, two quick washes can cause a loss of 7 to 44 percent of the vitamins (Nicholls, 1951). Where parboiling has preceded washing, vitamin loss is lowest (i.e., 7 to 12 percent) because the process of parboiling has toughened (or gelatinized) the starch, made the scutellum and aleurone layers (carrying the vitamins) more adherent to the starch and carried the soluble vitamins into it.

Differences in parboiling techniques (e.g., in some countries 16 hours soaking in cold water is followed by 10 to 20 minutes steaming; in others 36 hours soaking in cold water is followed by 2 minutes steaming, while in others again soaking for a few hours in hot water is followed by steaming) may influence the quality of the grains and their susceptibility to infestation by insects. Breese (1964) suggests that with the longer steaming process there is more swelling of the kernel and separation of the husk making these grains more vulnerable to attack by insects (as shown by Prevett, 1959).

Prolonged soaking is undesirable unless it is carried out at temperatures which prevent the development of bacteria (i.e., above 60°C). During parboiling, the soaking stage may be responsible for the development of off flavours due to the growth of yeast and bacteria in the water.

Cleaning

It has been known for many years that the presence of dirt, dust and other foreign material in food grains accelerates deterioration because grain which has not been cleaned is more likely to heat than sound grain of the same moisture content. The reason for this has not been clearly established but it is obvious that extraneous material will harbour greater numbers of mould spores and bacteria, and in the case of insect frass and dust will have a higher moisture content at the same relative humidity.

Where produce has been exposed to insect infestation, considerable quantities of dust accumulate (up to 10 percent in some cases) consisting of minute pieces of produce (usually with a high acidity), of insect frass and of insect bodies. This accounts for a percentage of the weight of the contents of the container and also provides focal points for the development of fungi.

In tests carried out on the quality of groundnuts it was shown that the acidity of a consignment of groundnuts could be reduced by several percent, by the process of sieving and removing the groundnut-cum-insect dust which had an acidity value 12 times greater than that of the unbroken groundnuts.

One of the simplest methods of winnowing is by throwing the grain into the wind which carries away the dead grains and chaff;

this method allows stones, earth and a certain amount of extraneous seed to remain in the grain. In some countries special screens are used in an attempt to remove clods of earth and other foreign matter but in very few countries a sieve is used at primary collecting points to remove foreign bodies which are larger and smaller than the produce which is being kept, stored or sold.

MILLING

The grinding of grains into flour can be carried out between two stones, by pestle and mortar or in hammer, plate or roller mills and the quality of the resulting flour or meal depends upon several factors.

With all milling processes the quality of grains from which the flour is to be prepared and the pretreatment of the grain prior to milling are important.

The sieving and winnowing of the grain and hand picking of damaged grains prior to milling will produce a meal of higher quality than is obtainable from similar grain untreated in these ways. Where maize is taken from store and poured into a hammer mill, maize grains, dirt, dust, insect fragments, etc. are contained in the meal. Such meal has high insect fragment counts and has high acidity which increases rapidly with storage. The development of oxidative rancidity is often a serious problem in the storage of oilseeds and of cereal milled products.

The breakage of grains into fragments and finally into flour results in particles too small for the complete development of insect species such as the weevils, *Sitophilus* species, and the moth *Sitotroga*, but provides ideal media for other insect pests.

Because of the way in which rice is usually eaten, the breakage of the grain detracts from its quality and value. Rhind (1962) in a review of the causes of rice breakage in milling shows that among the important factors are temperature and low relative humidity (i.e., below 70 percent); in addition, sharp moisture changes during drying, especially during rewetting as a result of exposure to rain or dew, maturity of the crop at harvest and high drying temperatures are listed. Rhind states, contrary to Autrey *et al.* (1955), that because of the presence of cracked grains there is breakage of these grains as soon as milling starts (in the huller and first cone especially). When breakage is related to the degree of milling there is some breakage in the early part of the bran removal and then a nearly proportional relationship between breakage and further milling (excluding parboiled grains). Craufurd (1960) has shown that milling raw paddy at 10 to 11 percent (i.e., low) moisture content reduces cracking; that with dry parboiled paddy, dried artificially and slowly, the moisture content at milling has no effect on breakage, but when dried in the sun the moisture content at milling should be 14 percent.

It is well known that in the milling of cereal grains, any system which encourages the separation of the germ and the outer layers of the grain coat (i.e., bran and pollard) removes those parts of the grain which are rich in vitamins. When paddy is milled beyond the removal of 8 percent of bran there is a reduction in thiamine from about 2.3 grains per gramme (when the scutellum layer of the grain is present) to about 0.5 grain per gramme at 20 percent removal (when the scutellum has been removed) (Nicholls, 1951).

With processed food flours, the keeping quality is dependent upon the amount of fats, minerals and vitamins they contain; microorganisms (including insects) breed or multiply most rapidly on flours containing maximum amounts of these nutrients (e.g., flours of over 85 percent extraction). Since the greater the fat content the more likely will enzyme action result in rancidity, flours prepared from oilseeds deteriorate rapidly unless specially compounded.

In the manufacture of oilseed cakes from groundnuts, cottonseed and palm kernels, the expeller process kills all stages of insects even if infested oilseeds are used; but the warmth of the newly pressed cake is particularly attractive to insects and therefore the cake readily becomes reinfested.

CONVEYING

Produce is moved from one place to another in a variety of ways, all of which may affect its quality.

Containers such as gourds, skin bags (of goat or camel), tins, baskets and sacks made of natural fibres (e.g., jute, sisal, kenaf, rice stalks, paper) are used. In certain circumstances produce is moved in bulk by several types of mechanical conveyors.

Conveyors for bags or bulk, using the principles of a moving chain, a jog trough, a moving rubber belt, a pneumatic system, etc., result in varying degrees of bumping and breakage of the grains as well as separation and reconcentration of dust. The moving or turning of grain from one silo to another is one of the oldest methods practised in the attempt to reduce spoilage. It was believed that this operation controlled insect infestation and the grain was kept in better condition. By turning grain which had started to heat, the temperature was kept to a lower level than would otherwise be possible and it was believed that this practice retarded insect development. Joffe (1963) has said that by turning maize 13 times over a period of eight and a half months it was possible to keep grain relatively cool and in sound condition, substantially reducing the number of insects present in the turned grain. In a series of laboratory experiments (Joffe and Clarke, 1963) not only adults but also preadult stages within the maize grains were readily killed by mechanical or physical disturbance. It is interesting to note the suggestion that insect infestation control may be achieved at large silo installations by running grain through an empty bin with the gate left open so that maximum mechanical shock would be applied. With certain products, of course, this would not be a practical solution since breakage of the kernels or grains would be excessive.

During the moving of grain in thin layers by a number of conveying systems it is possible to introduce certain types of automatic sampling devices either to obtain a sample for testing quality or to incorporate an automatic moisture recording system. At the same time the use of irradiation techniques to disinfest grain by passing the grain through a point source is also being investigated.

A machine called the entoleter, designed to kill insect infestation by a percussion effect, is used especially in flour mills. This machine is particularly effective with infested powder and material in which insect stages are not shielded from the impact. However, when infested grains or kernels are passed through this machine with the speed set at a level adequate to kill the insect stages outside the grains, it can not be assumed that the insects inside the grains will also be killed. Bailey (1962) has shown that adults and unprotected larvae on the outside of the grains are killed with relatively little force by percussion; but the force required to kill the stages inside the grains would shatter the grain. On the basis of these findings and his own work, Joffe (1963) suggests that the development of a commercial percussion machine for whole grain treatment at suitably timed intervals may be a promising alternative to chemical control.

Transportation of produce is effected in a variety of vehicles and vessels, in the operation of which produce hygiene has an important part to play. Cross infestation of produce occurs from infested residues in the vehicle or ship, or from several types of infested produce carried in the same part of the vehicle or ship.

Certain types of produce from particular countries are more heavily infested by insects than other produce and therefore the spread of infestation in transport vehicles can be a serious problem. It can be overcome only if all produce is disinfested before it is loaded into transport vehicles or while it is in them. Products such as animal feed (e.g., oilseed cakes, bran) and bones have a low commercial value but are an important source of cross infestation. All produce being moved from farms, mills or ports must be treated to kill the insect pests present and prevent their spread to vehicles, buildings and other facilities. The development of semi-bulk containers which are specially designed to facilitate efficient fumigation could alleviate this problem.

The structural condition of vehicles often requires improvement to minimize rupturing of sacks and prevent increased losses from spillage and quality deterioration. Moreover, the exposure of produce to the direct heat of the sun (e.g., in uncovered lorries or river craft) or to fluctuations in temperature of the metal roof or sides of vessels (e.g., ship holds) which promote condensation and soiled sacks, with consequent deterioration in quality of the produce, is very detrimental.

Water damage to bags during transportation is serious. Lorries, railway trucks (both closed and open), dhows and barges are often constructed in such a way that bags of produce carried in them become water damaged (for example, due to incomplete sealing between floor boards of railway wagons through which water is thrown up by the wheels and permeates the sacks, and to sagging tarpaulins which are not waterproof).

The number of water-damaged bags may be less than 1 percent of the total handled and this, of course, is not considered serious by the authorities since the contents can usually be rebagged into new ones. This practice is dangerous because, in these few bags having high moisture content, mould may have grown on the produce; even if this occurs for a few days only it is long enough for chemical deterioration to take place. Under certain circumstances a chemical highly toxic to animals can be produced in this short time. All bags which have been water damaged even for a few days and subsequently dried out should therefore be clearly labelled "water damaged: dangerous" and kept separate from good quality or sound produce. The mixing of water-damaged produce with dry sound produce to obtain maximum financial return is criminal and overseas buyers are likely to become aware of the situation eventually and buy from countries which can guarantee that no such practices exist.

Biological agents

The biological agents commonly responsible for the deterioration of food grains are fungi, mites, insects, rodents, birds and lizards. It is well known that these agents of deterioration differ in their rate of development and ability to cause damage under different conditions of temperature and moisture. A record of the limits for multiplication of biological agencies, i.e., fungi, mites, insects and bacteria is given in Figure 7 which has been prepared from data recorded by Roberts (CCTA/FAO, 1961b). Howe (1965b) has given a useful summary of estimates of optimal and minimal conditions for population increase of some storage insect pests; data on fungi are given in Figure 12.

FUNGI

A large number of fungi have been found both on and inside food grains; these can be grouped into internal and external microflora. A review of stored products fungi, with particular reference to the deterioration caused, has been carried out by Christiansen and Kaufmann (1965). Recent studies on moist maize have also shown that in conditions of low oxygen and high moisture, yeasts (e.g., *Candida*) can be more important than fungi (Burmeister and Hortman, 1966).

All produce is susceptible to attack by fungi and only a few of the numerous fungi species are commonly found in large numbers on any particular sample of produce; the dominant species at any one time are determined by the size of the original inoculum, the chemical composition of the product and the temperature conditions of storage.

Fungal spores develop everywhere so that every sample of produce, when tested by one of the standard plating techniques, may yield fungi. Golumbic (1965) has estimated that annual losses due to microorganisms in stored commodities run to millions of dollars. The importance of fungal attack depends on the use to which the produce will be put: mould contamination of cocoa and coffee imparts a tainted flavour; mould on barley affects malting; mould on wheat can reduce germination; and mould in palm oil and copra can accelerate the liberation of free fatty acids.

During growth some fungi produce chemicals which can be toxic to man or domestic animals. *Aspergillus flavus*, producing aflatoxin on groundnuts, is a recently well-documented example but Forgacs and Carll (1962) also give details of a number of toxicoses caused by fungi including *Stachybotrys atra*, several *Aspergillus* spp. and *Fusarium sporotrichoides*. It should be emphasized that the mere presence of a toxigenic species on a product is not in itself evidence of toxicity. Morphologically identical strains vary in their ability to produce toxins and fungi are frequently present on products as contaminants. Scott (1965) has shown that strains of 22 out of 59 species (*Aspergillus* and *Penicillium*) can cause the death of day-old ducklings. Mouldy products obviously should not be used for human or animal consumption.

Fungi in foods and feeds have been a problem for many years and reported cases of ill effects (including death) from ingestion of mouldy feeds are numerous. Poultry, mice, rats, rabbits, guinea pigs, pigs, horses, cattle and sheep have been poisoned; usually liver cirrhosis, nephrosis, neurotoxin or dermatoxin conditions have occurred. A considerable range of agricultural products have been recorded as containing toxins from the development of fungi. Fungi also have indirect effects since they encourage the development of infestation by some species of insects and mites.

The problem of the interaction of moulds and insects and mites on stored products is extremely complex. Fungi probably frequently supply nutrients which are essential to some insects and mites and which are lacking in undamaged food; however, the correlation may sometimes be due to the fact that both the insects or the mites and the fungus require moist conditions to develop. The presence of some fungi may be detrimental to some insects and mites but fewer examples of this effect have been reported.

Most storage fungi grow most quickly at some point in the temperature range between 20° and 40°C and above 90 percent RH (Figure 12) and some are practically confined to these conditions. An indication of the physical limits and optima for a number of species of fungi is given in Table 13. The fungi which grow on products stored at higher and lower temperatures or at lower humidities fall into fairly clearly defined groups. Figure 12 indicates the conditions in which each of a small number of the major species of fungi are likely to be most important. In the areas outside the line mould growth is unlikely to occur.

In general, fungi are most tolerant of low relative humidity conditions at the optimum temperature for growth, which is usually near the maximum temperature tolerance. A knowledge of the physical limits within which fungi grow makes it possible to predict the degree of drying necessary to prevent growth of specific fungi at existing temperature conditions. It can also be helpful in assessing the causes of the existence of certain types of mould damage. Thus if it is possible to determine which species of fungi are responsible for the observed damage, it is possible also to deduce the

a. *Aspergillus candidus*
b. *A. flavus*
c. *A. fumigatus*
d. *A. tamarii*
e. *A. niger*
f. *A. glacus* group, including *A. restrictus*
g. *A. terreus*
h. *Penicillium cyclopium*
i. *P. martensii*
j. Some *Cladosporium* sp.
k. *Sporendonema* sp.

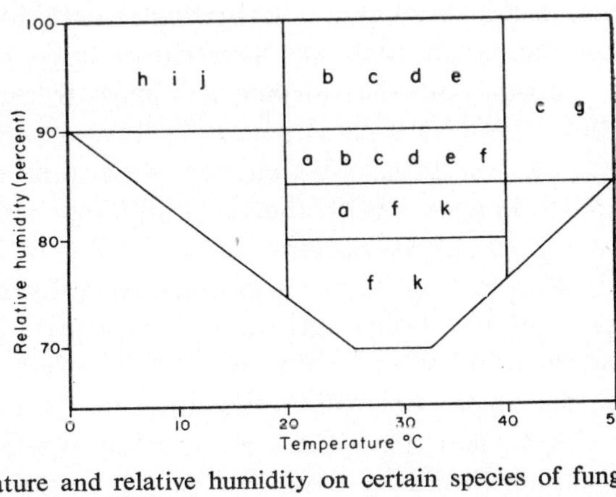

FIGURE 12. Effect of temperature and relative humidity on certain species of fungi.

TABLE 13. – PHYSICAL LIMITS AND OPTIMA FOR A NUMBER OF SPECIES OF FUNGI

	Limits		Optima	
	Temperature,	RH	Temperature,	RH
	Degrees C		*Degrees C*	
Aspergillus ruber	5–38	72	24	93
A. amstelodami	10–42	70	30	94
A. flavus	12–45	80	35	99
A. fumigatus	12–52	83	40	99
A. niger	10–45	77	35	99
Penicillium martensii	5–32	80	24	99

physical conditions to which the produce was previously subjected (e.g., during storage).

Tests of fungicides have not revealed any which have dependable action on fungi species causing damage to stored cereals and which are also free from phytotoxic and toxicological hazards (Christiansen and Lopez, 1963).

MITES

Mites (Acari) are a subclass of the Arachnida (to which spiders belong). They are distinct from insects since at the adult stages they possess eight legs and their bodies are not divided into a head, thorax and abdomen (Plate B); as a group they are generally much smaller than insects. They are extremely difficult to see, are usually detected when they are present in large numbers and are seen as a " dust " on the surface of bags or around the base of stacks. Mite pests (Astigmata) generally have a shiny translucent body and legs and mouthparts which vary in colour from pale straw to dark reddish brown. Both the body and legs bear numerous setae which have a constant pattern.

Respiration is either cutaneous or by means of tracheae which open on the body surface by spiracles. The absence or presence and the number and position of these spiracles are the main diagnostic characters on which the mites are subdivided (six orders).

A typical life cycle consists of eggs which hatch into six-legged larvae, followed by from one to three stages, called nymphs, which finally develop into the adults. Each prestage is terminated by a resting stage. For many species it is difficult to relate the male to the female because the sexes are so different in appearance. They feed on a range of stored foodstuffs but some also are known to feed on moulds.

Often found in association with these typical stored product species are somewhat larger, faster moving mites, usually brown in colour (representing the orders Mesostigmata, Prostigmata and Cryptostigmata in that order of frequency of occurrence). They are not known to feed upon stored foods and therefore are not considered to be pests. Many, however, are predacious upon stored product mites and upon the eggs and young stages of certain insect pests; others are known to feed on moulds, while the food requirements of a great many are still not known.

A number of the mites associated with stored products are important economic pests. Under suitable temperature conditions and usually in materials with a relatively high moisture content, they multiply rapidly to form dense populations which can cause serious damage or loss. Such infestations occur frequently in the temperate regions of the world. At present indications are that similar infestations do not occur in the tropics although the comparatively few available records show that stored product mites are present in tropical produce. The current view therefore is that in themselves mites do not constitute a danger to safe storage in the tropics and subtropics. This view may have to be modified as more careful inspection of produce is carried out to detect these extremely minute animals and authentic records become available. At present, it is advocated that inspection of stored produce should include examination for, and recording of, mites. They can serve as a valuable guide to the condition of the stored material since their presence usually means that the produce is too moist for prolonged storage.

Some records have indicated an interrelationship between certain insect and mite species which suggest that mites may be capable of effecting some degree of control on the insect pest involved.

INSECTS

In the tropics, beetles and moths (Plates A and B) are the main insect pests causing losses and deterioration to stored food grains.

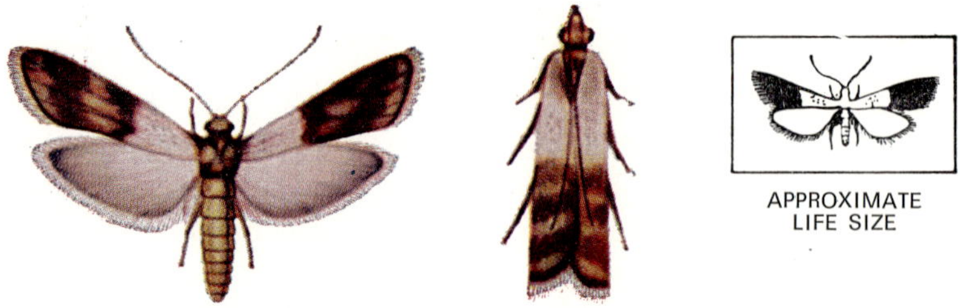

INDIAN-MEAL MOTH
Plodia interpunctella Hbn.

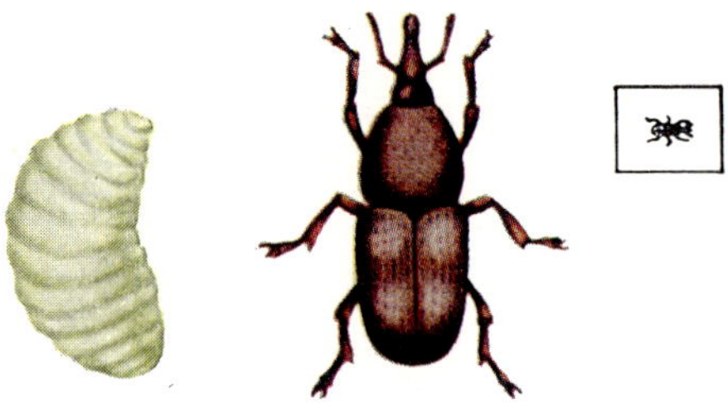

RICE WEEVIL
Sitophilus oryzae L.

GRANARY WEEVIL
Sitophilus granarius L.

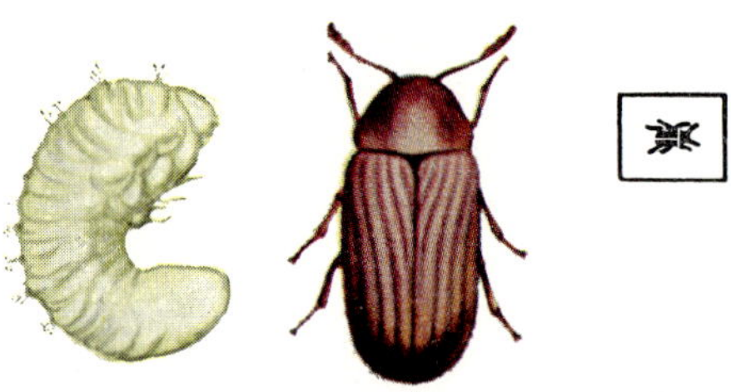

DRUGSTORE BEETLE
Stegobium paniceum L.

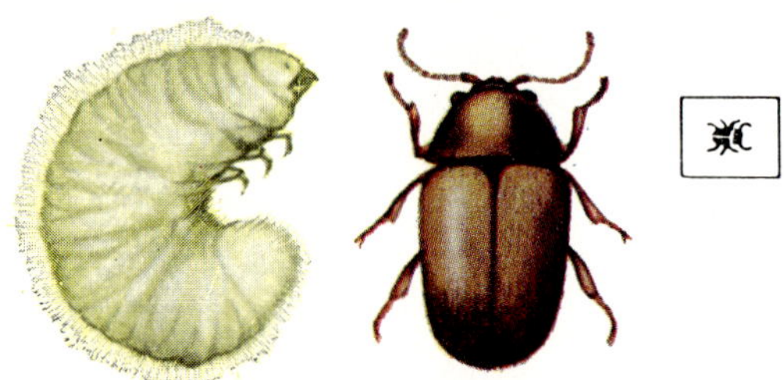

CIGARETTE BEETLE
Lasioderma serricorne F.

FLAT GRAIN BEETLE
Laemophiloeus pusillus Schönherr

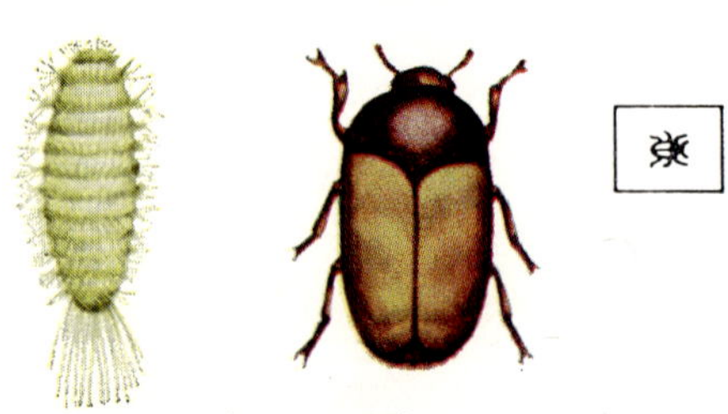

KHAPRA BEETLE
Trogoderma granarium Everts

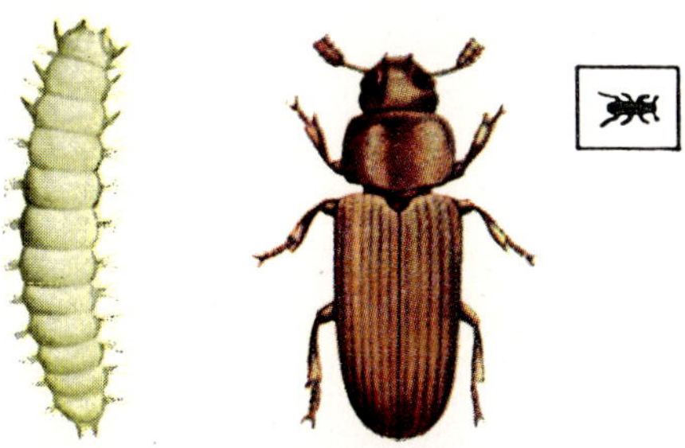

RED FLOUR BEETLE
Tribolium castaneum Hbst.

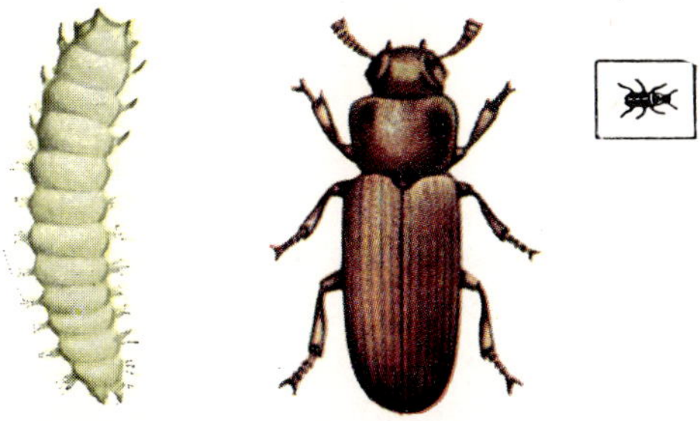

CONFUSED FLOUR BEETLE
Tribolium confusum J. du Val

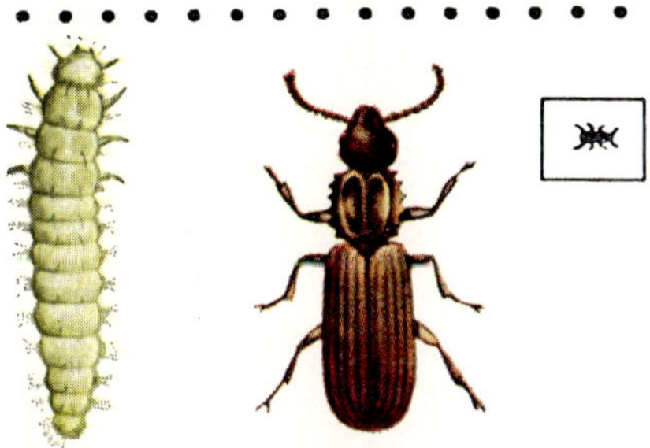

SAW-TOOTHED GRAIN BEETLE
Oryzaephilus surinamensis L.

LESSER GRAIN BORER
Rhizopertha dominica F.

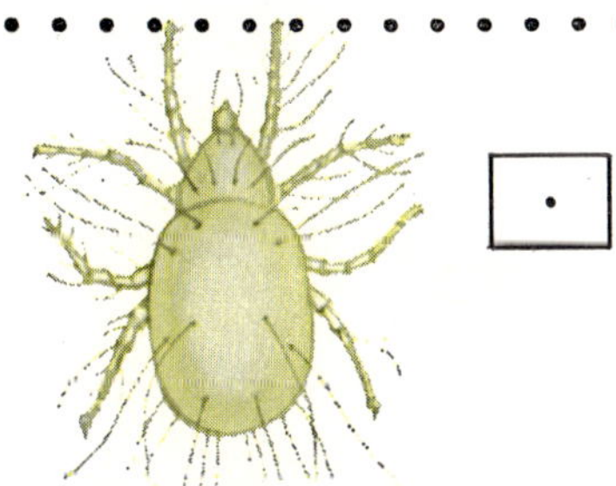

FLOUR OR GRAIN MITE
Acarus siro L.

ANGOUMOIS GRAIN MOTH
Sitotroga cerealella Olivier

RUSTY GRAIN BEETLE
Cryptolestes ferrugineus Steph.

PLATE A (opposite page). Stored product insect species.

PLATE B. Stored product insect and mite species.

Cockroaches are also a pest; by carrying microorganisms they contaminate foodstuffs, cartons, boxes, crates, etc., containing produce with which they come in contact, particularly in dwellings, hotels and canteens. Ants and termites are also troublesome in some circumstances.

Surveys of the insect species present as pests in stored food products have been made in a number of tropical countries, particularly in Africa: Sierra Leone, with particular reference to paddy and rice (Prevett, 1959); east Africa (Le Pelley, 1959); Uganda (Davies, 1960a); Ghana (Forsyth, 1966); and Nigeria (Cornes, 1964) and also in Jamaica (McFarlane, 1963). The major insect pests of food grains in the tropics are summarized in Table 14.

As a result of the insects' feeding activities, the quality of the remaining grain is lowered, germination is reduced or abnormalities occur during germination. The effect of insect attack on germination of dicotyledonous seeds such as pulses is greater than on the germination of monocotyledonous seeds such as maize. Pingale (1953) has recorded that green gram when holed by bruchid beetles failed to germinate, while wheat damaged by weevils germinated. Howe (1952b) found that about one quarter of holed wheat grains germinated; the larvae fed on the endosperm and the adult only occasionally caused holing of the germ.

Among the insects which attack food grains after harvest, i.e., during storage, a few begin their attack several weeks before harvest. Of these, the weevil *Sitophilus zeamais* Motsch. is the most important. There is evidence from a number of countries that attack by this species begins at least one month before harvest. There are other species which are unable to start their attack until the crop is almost dry or during the postharvest field drying period. As drying advances certain of the insect species are eliminated, e.g., *Mussidia* sp., a moth sometimes found on cob maize at harvest in west Africa, dies out during storage; *Bruchidius atrolineatus* Pic. which attacks cowpea pods in the field in west and east Africa dies out in store while *Callosobruchus* spp., which do not attack pods in the field until they are almost dry, become the major storage pest (Caswell, 1961; Prevett, 1961).

Insects do not breed successfully in an environment where the relative humidity is maintained at less than 40 percent (i.e., for cereals less than an equilibrium moisture content of 8 percent), and

TABLE 14. – SELECTED MAJOR INSECT PESTS OF FOOD GRAINS IN THE TROPICS

Insect species		Products infested
Common name	Scientific name	
Weevils	*Sitophilus* spp.	Maize, sorghum, wheat, rice, paddy
Lesser grain borer	*Rhizopertha dominica* F.	Paddy, rice, wheat, maize, cassava
Khapra beetle	*Trogoderma granarium* Everts	Maize, wheat, sorghum, rice, pulses, oilseeds and oilseed cake
Saw-toothed grain beetles	*Oryzaephilus* spp.	Maize, wheat, rice, oilseeds, dried fruit
Flour beetles	*Tribolium* spp.	Maize, wheat, flour, groundnuts, milled cereal products, dried fruit, cocoa, animal feed cakes and meals
Pulse beetles	*Callosobruchus* spp.	Cowpeas, grams
	Acanthoscelides obtectus Say	Beans
	Zabrotes subfasciatus Boh.	Beans
	Caryedon serratus Ol.	Groundnuts
Hide beetles	*Dermestes* spp.	Dried fish
Tobacco beetle	*Lasioderma serricorne* F.	Cocoa, cassava
Flat grain beetles	*Cryptolestes* spp. *Laemophloeus pusillus* Schönherr	Maize, rice, groundnuts, cocoa, flour
Angoumois grain moth	*Sitotroga cerealella* Ol.	Maize, wheat, paddy, sorghum
Tropical warehouse moth	*Ephestia cautella* Walk.	Groundnuts, rice, maize, wheat, cocoa, sorghum
Indian meal moth	*Plodia interpunctella* Hubn.	Maize, groundnuts, dried fruit
Rice moth	*Corcyra cephalonica* Staint.	Maize, wheat, rice, sorghum, groundnuts

the temperature below 10°C. Each species has a characteristic range of physical conditions for optimum development (Figure 13). As the temperature and humidity conditions diverge from the optimum, the time taken to develop from egg to adult increases and the number of eggs laid become fewer. Some species tolerate high humidity conditions with which fungi are associated principally

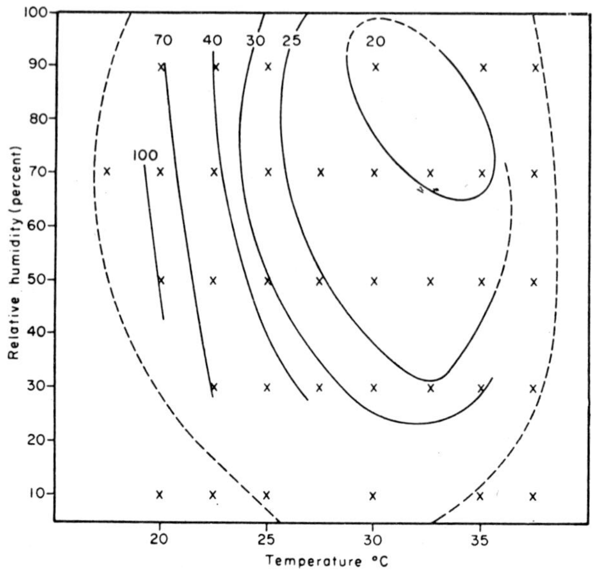

FIGURE 13. Example of interaction of temperature and relative humidity on the development of a species of insect pest. The broken lines indicate the physical limits beyond which this species cannot complete its development.

because they are mould feeders or require that the produce be decomposed by mould development in order to be suitable for them to eat. Most species do not tolerate prolonged temperatures above 42°C.

The rate of development of insects varies with the type of food they eat as well as with the physical conditions of the environment. Ashman (1963) has shown that *Necrobia rufipes* (copra beetle) completes its development (larva plus pupa) on copra alone in about 66 days compared with about 43 days on a diet of copra and fishmeal (30°C and 81 percent RH).

Notes on biology

Insects are animals with six legs; they have a hard outer skeleton or " skin " called the cuticle and the body is divided into three distinct regions, the head, the thorax and the abdomen. In the adult insects the head has mouth parts (either biting as in beetles or sucking as in moths), large compound eyes and two antennae or feelers; the thorax carries the three pairs of legs and the two pairs of wings (in the beetles the forward pair of wings, elytra, are hardened to form a protective shield for the membranous hind pair of wings with which they fly); the abdomen contains the main part of the food canal and the reproductive organs.

The adult insect lays eggs loosely in the food, cements them on to food grains, or bores with its mouth parts a small hole in which an egg is securely laid.

The egg develops and from it hatches a small grub or larva which (with beetles and moths) is quite unlike the adult. The larva feeds, but in order to grow it must cast or shed its skin (moult). This process of feeding and moulting continues until the larva has reached its maximum size (the number of moults is fairly constant for any one species of insect) when it stops feeding. At this stage it may spin (with silk from a gland inside its body) a shelter or cocoon in which it changes its shape and becomes a pupa (which may now bear some resemblance to the adult insect). The pupa remains immobile and does not feed; it develops into the fully formed adult insect which will if necessary push or bite its way out of the cocoon.

It is important to establish firmly in the minds of people handling produce that food grains or kernels do not "generate" or "germinate" insects. Insects observed in food will have come from one of the following sources: the container used; the floor, walls or roof of the building or vehicle used; infested food grains or buildings, etc.; from plants or from under the bark of trees adjacent to the storage site concerned.

It is very difficult to see the eggs or the very young larvae of insect pests and therefore the farmer or trader may often assume that grains and kernels are uninfested because he does not see insects crawling over the produce or large holes in the grain. When a hole is visible in the grain it means that for weeks before the hole appeared an insect was feeding in the grain.

The presence of a few adult insects, seen walking over or flying above stacks or bulks of produce usually indicates that there are many, many more insects inside the bags or bulk store.

Under local conditions insects breed very quickly, the life cycle or life history period from egg to adult being completed in a few weeks with each adult female insect laying a large number of eggs. For example, under ideal temperature (28°C), humidity (65 percent to 80 percent) and food conditions, a population of the flour beetle is theoretically capable of increasing by 76 million in six months.

Sitophilus oryzae L. (Rice weevil, Plate A), *Sitophilus zeamais* Motsch. (Maize weevil). These pests are between 2.5 and 5 millimetres long when adult, light to dark brown in colour, and have a characteristic " snout " which is prominent between the two antennae or feelers.

Sitophilus oryzae, the smaller of the two, is found more often on small than large grains and has a higher temperature tolerance than *S. zeamais*; both species fly and thus attack cereals in the field before harvest, but flight activity is more pronounced in *S. zeamais.*

The eggs are laid inside the grains by the female (capable of laying 300 to 400 eggs) which chews a minute hole in which to lay each egg; this is followed by sealing the egg in the hole with a secretion. It is therefore extremely difficult to detect by the human eye, although these " egg plugs " can be made evident by using staining techniques. The larva (which is legless and has a characteristic curved appearance) hatches and remains inside the grain where it feeds and is responsible for most of the damage; it develops into the nonfeeding pupal stage and then to the adult which bites its way out of the grain, leaving behind an emergence hole and a grain which has had about half its contents eaten and the remaining half reduced in quality.

Both adults and larvae feed on stored produce and are primary pests of sound, dry cereal grains. The larval stage in the life cycle is about five weeks at 30°C and 70 percent RH. Adults live for about five months.

Rhizopertha dominica F. (Lesser grain borer, Plate B). This adult insect is about 3 millimetres long, warm brown in colour and has a prominent rounded thorax with a rasp-like sculptured surface, largely concealing the head. There is a prominent constriction between the prothorax and the elytra.

Eggs are laid on the surface or in interstices between cereal grains. A female is capable of laying 300 to 500 eggs. The larva emerges and eats its way into a grain where it feeds unselectively as is shown by the characteristic damage it causes. When fully grown, the larva pupates inside the grain and the adult emerges from it.

Both adults and larvae feed on stored produce. This species is a primary pest of sound dry cereal grain and belongs to a family (Bostrychidae) the members of which are timber borers; both adults and larvae are voracious feeders. The life history period is about five weeks at 30°C and 38°C; the quickest development occurs in four weeks at 34°C.

Sitotroga cerealella Oliv. (Angoumois grain moth, Plate B). The adult is a small (8- to 10-millimetres) straw-coloured moth which rests with the wings completely folded over the back giving the insect a linear appearance. The wings are 15 millimetres across when open, and the hind wings have a long fringe.

It is found in all parts of the world, can infest produce before it is harvested, and in bulk stored grain is abundant in the surface layers (about 30 centimetres depth) only. It is a primary pest causing damage similar to that caused by weevils.

The female lays eggs on the surface of the grain (about 100 eggs per female) and the larva hatches and bores its way into the grain where it remains until fully grown. At this stage it has eaten out a considerable part of the grain; it then eats a channel to the surface, leaving a thin layer of the seed coat intact. The pupa is formed and then the adult stage appears and pushes open the thin area prepared by the larva.

Only the larvae feed on stored produce, although the adult is the only stage which is normally detected.

The life history period of the larval stage is about 5 weeks at 30°C and the adults are short lived.

Tribolium spp. (Flour beetles or bran bugs, Plate B). Adult flour beetles are rather flat, oblong chestnut brown insects about 3 to 4 millimetres long. They are widespread throughout the world and are probably the most prevalent pest on stored products. Cereal products (flour of different types), grain (broken or damaged during threshing or shelling or by the attack of weevils or moths) oilseeds and animal feeds are all attacked by these beetles.

The most important species in the tropics is *T. castaneum* Herbst., the rust red flour beetle; another species, *T. confusum* J. du V., the confused flour beetle, is also found but prefers temperate climates.

The eggs (400 to 500 per female) of *T. castaneum* are laid at random in the produce and hatch into worm-like larvae which are slender, cylindrical in shape and whitish yellow in colour giving a faint striped effect. At the posterior of the larva there are two dark upturned pointed projections.

Both adults and larvae feed on stored produce.

The larval life history period at 30°C is about 5 weeks and the adults are long lived, under some circumstances living for a year or more.

Trogoderma granarium Everts (Khapra beetle, Plate A). The adult beetle is 1.5 to 3 millimetres in length, convex with an oval body, dark brown in colour and thickly covered with short hairs (sometimes darker areas are visible on the elytra).

This species has spread in produce and on sacking from countries such as Burma and India to practically all the warm temperate regions of the world and is found in hot particularly dry countries. It has amazing powers of survival in the absence of food, is not killed readily by many of the contact insecticides and often appears suddenly after a long storage period.

The female lays eggs (40 to 70 per female) in the infested product and the larvae which hatch may develop at different rates, some taking over a year to complete development. The larvae are straw coloured and hairy so that there appear to be darkish transverse strips on each segment and a prominent tuft of long hairs at the posterior end. (The hairs are deposited, often in large quantities, in the produce.) When exposed to unfavourable conditions, these larvae collect in groups (which can be very large) in cracks and crevices in storage containers or at the seams of sacks. Only the larvae feed on stored produce. The larval stage is about 3 weeks at 30°C and the adults, which are unable to fly, live for only about 14 days.

Legislation has been introduced in a number of countries to control the movement of this insect.

Bruchidae (Pulse beetles, Figure 14). These beetles are small squat active insects with long conspicuous antennae. They are sometimes referred to as weevils but they do not have the characteristic snout of the weevil. They are serious pests of leguminous seeds in store (Table 14) in all countries; originally they infested wild leguminous seed pods. Of the 850 known species, about eight are responsible for serious damage to harvested seeds and a further 12 species cause losses by feeding on seeds in the ripening pods.

Although primarily pests of leguminous crops, *Zabrotes subfasciatus* Boh., *Acanthoscelides obtectus* and four species of the genus *Callosobruchus* have become adapted to breeding successive generations in stored seeds. Breeding on stored seed does not, however, prevent adults from migrating to the growing crop, and this tendency is greater when the density of the population in store is high. In all but *Acanthoscelides obtectus* the eggs are sealed to the surface of the pod or seed. Larval development takes place entirely within the seed and the pupa is formed in a pupal cell prepared beneath the seed coat. However, in *Caryedon serratus* Ol., the groundnut seed beetle (Davey, 1958), the mature larva pupates in a cocoon partly inside or attached to the outside of the groundnut shell.

The rate of development is affected by temperature and the species (or variety) of legume. In *Callosobruchus maculatus* F. and *A. obtectus* the life cycle is completed in about four weeks at 30°C and 70 percent RH. Adult beetles are short lived and do not feed on stored produce. Howe and Currie (1964) have summarized existing data on the biology of pulse beetles.

Oryzaephilus spp. (Saw-toothed grain beetle, Plate B). The adult beetle is dark brown in colour, about 3 millimetres long and has a flat narrow body with a serrated edge on the thorax due to six small projections or " teeth " along each side.

Oryzaephilus surinamensis L. is a worldwide pest of cereals, cereal products and dried fruit and the species *O. mercator* Fauv. is most common in oilseed, oilseed products and copra.

The eggs (about 300 per female) are laid loosely among the foodstuffs and hatch into worm-like larvae, slender and straw coloured, with two slightly darker patches on each segment. They are active and move about freely until fully grown when they construct a cocoon or silken shelter in which to pupate.

Both adults and larvae feed on stored produce. The larval stage at 30°C is 4 weeks and the adults may live up to 3 years.

Ephestia cautella Walker (Tropical warehouse moth, Figure 15). The adult moth is about 13 millimetres long and is greyish in colour

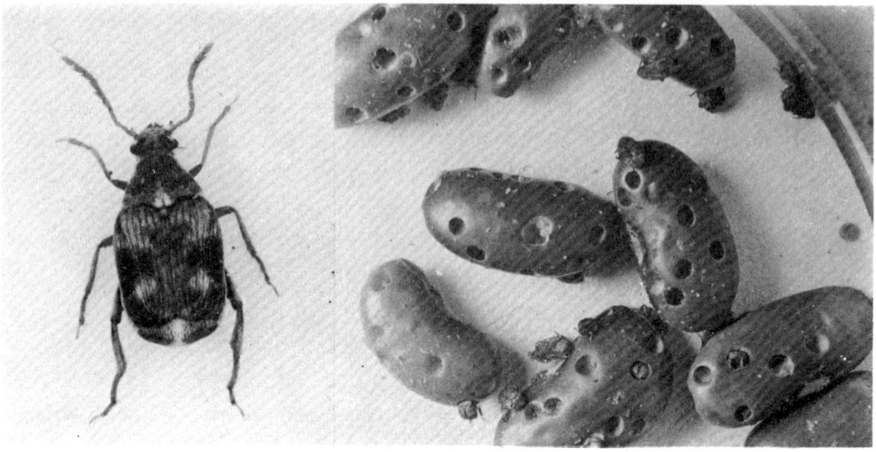

FIGURE 14. *Callosobruchus maculatus* F. - pulse beetle.

FIGURE 15. Left, *Ephestia cautella* Walker - tropical warehouse moth and its larva.

FIGURE 16. Below, *Blatella germanica* L. - German cockroach.

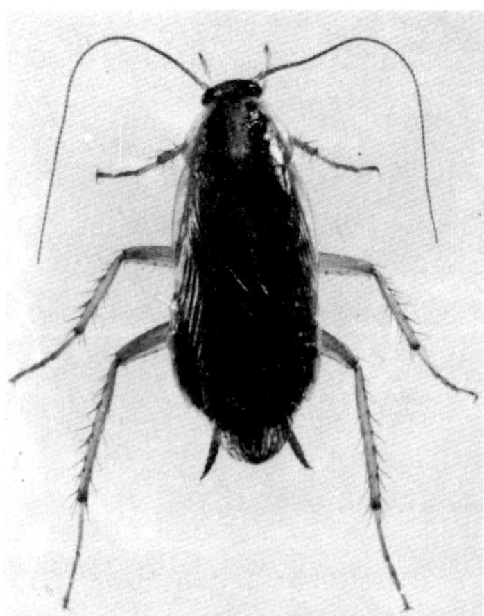

with the wings showing a rather indistinct dark band about 4 millimetres from the head. At rest the wings are held "rooflike" over the abdomen.

This moth is abundant in tropical countries on a wide range of foodstuffs. The adult avoids strong light, rests in dark places during the daytime and has a flight rhythm with periods of active flying from 5 to 7 p.m. and also at 6 a.m. when daily fluctuations in temperature and humidity occur. In warehouses in the tropics where light intensity is always low it may be found flying at any time. Infestations of this moth are sometimes reduced to a low level by the activities of a parasite, *Bracon hebetor* Say.

The eggs are laid by the female moths (about 250 per female) in the produce, often by dropping the eggs through the holes in jute bags. If fertilized at some time during the first 12 hours of emergence, the female adult will lay at least 60 percent of its eggs within the first 48 hours of its adult life. The larva which hatches is caterpillar-like in appearance, greyish white in colour with hairs rising from dark spots along the body. The head is dark brown and there are two dark areas on the first segment behind the head. The larva moves freely about the produce, feeding until mature when it enters a wandering phase, during which it trails a fine thread after it (accumulations of these threads, forming a white sheen on bags of produce, can be seen). A silken cocoon is then spun, often at the point where one bag rests against another, and from this the adult moth emerges.

Only the larvae feed on stored produce.

The life history period at 28°C to 30°C is between 3 and 6 weeks and the adult moths live for less than 14 days.

Plodia interpunctella Hbn. (Indian-meal moth, Plate A). The adult moth is about 12 millimetres in length and is characterized by the colour pattern of the front wings; along a third of their length they are pale yellow and along the rest reddish-brown with a coppery sheen and faintly visible darker transverse lines.

It is widespread on many foodstuffs throughout the world and is attacked by the parasite *Bracon hebetor* Say.

Eggs (200 to 300 per female) are laid on the produce either singly or in groups and the larvae which hatch are dirty white in colour but without the dark spots seen in *Cadra.* They feed first on the embryo or germ of the grain and while eating spin a silken thread on which the droppings of the larvae accumulate. Often these larvae feed close together and give the impression of living in colonies, with infestation first being observed due to the presence of several silken " lumps " to which granules (often of the produce) adhere. The mature larvae wander and search for a " pupation site " leaving a silken thread behind as they move. Only the larvae feed on stored produce.

The life history period at 28°C to 30°C is 3 to 6 weeks and the adult moths live for less than 14 days.

Corcyra cephalonica Staint. (Rice moth). The adult moth is about 15 millimetres long and is pale yellowish brown in colour, with faint dark lines along the length of the wings.

In the larval stage it attacks a variety of foodstuffs (Table 14) but is less common than the two preceding species and has not been studied in any great detail. Infestation is characterized by the presence of silken lumps to which grains of produce adhere. The cocoon, which is prepared by the mature larva, is white and very tough.

Cryptolestes spp. (Flat grain beetle (Plate B)). There are various species of these small beetles, which are about 1 to 2 millimetres in length. They are flat and reddish or light brown with rather long, slender antennae or feelers. The commonest species is *C. ferrugineus* Steph., the rust red grain beetle (Plate B).

They are scavengers capable of breeding only in produce which is dusty, contains broken grains and has a high moisture content or is already infested with insects, on the dead bodies of which this species can feed. Sweeney (1962) has found these beetles in the bush, feeding on seeds and in flower heads.

Eggs are laid in the produce, often in cracks or splits in the husk of the grain, and hatch into larvae which are long, slender and straw coloured with a darker twin-pointed appendage at the posterior end. The larvae feed mainly on the germ of cereals. When fully grown, the larvae spin cocoons of a sticky substance to which particles of food adhere. Pupation takes place inside the cocoons and later the adults emerge. The biology of a number of species has been dealt with by Bishop (1959).

Both adults and larvae feed on stored produce. Rilett (1949) has shown that the growth of moulds on wheat endosperm makes it a more suitable larval food for these beetles.

The larval stage at about 35°C and 75 percent RH is about 3 weeks and the adults live from 6 to 12 months.

Lasioderma serricorne F. (Cigarette beetle, Plate A). The adult beetle is 2 to 2.5 millimetres long, oval, light brown in colour and with the head deflexed beneath the thorax so that it is not visible from above.

This species is a major pest of tobacco and cocoa and has also been recorded as a pest of cassava. The adult beetle lives from 2 to 4 weeks and the development period at 30°C and 70 percent RH is 3 to 4 weeks.

Blattidae (German cockroach, Figure 16). There are three main species of cockroach which are found in storage premises, transit sheds, processing rooms, etc.: the German cockroach (*Blatella germanica* L.); the Oriental cockroach (*Blatta orientalis* L.); and the American cockroach (*Periplaneta americana* L.).

These cockroaches are scavengers and bite into packages, ruining the wrappings and the container and fouling the foodstuffs with excrement. They act as intermediate hosts to a number of small parasitic worms, carry various dangerous microorganisms on their legs and transmit others in their droppings, including *Salmonella* species (Roth and Willis, 1957).

The female lays brownish capsules containing eggs varying in number with the species of cockroach concerned. The capsules are usually laid in cracks and crevices in floors, the join of floor and wall, corners of wooden crates such as those used for transportation of bottles of local beverages. The young cockroach which hatches from the capsule is a miniature replica of the adult and may take three years to reach maturity as an adult. Depending upon the species of cockroach, the larval stage of the life history period varies from 3 to 30 months.

Efficiency of inspection methods

The inspection of produce and of buildings, storage containers and vehicles is a task of major importance.

If infestation by moulds and insects is not detected, or its seriousness is not realized at the earliest possible moment, losses will become heavy because deterioration advances at an increasing pace. There are many methods for detecting the presence of moulds and insects. All of them achieve varying degrees of accuracy in providing a true assessment of the level of infestation. The one adopted usually depends upon the amount of time and/or manpower available for inspection.

Inspection can mean walking around a stack of produce or looking at a sack or the surface of a bulk of stored produce. The degree of infestation is assessed on the basis of the areas of damp or mouldy grains observed and the number of insects seen. These methods of assessment can be very misleading. The number of insects seen can depend upon the stage reached in the life history of the insect pests present; the time of day in relation to light intensity, local temperature and humidity conditions; and where one looks in relation to insect harbourages, etc. As a rule, more insects are observed on top of a stack (by pulling a few top bags to one side) than on the vertical sides, and a general inspection should include examination of spillage, accumulation of sweepings, old sacks and utensils of various sorts lying in corners of stores.

Traps can be used as an aid to determining when insect infestation in stored produce has reached a particularly high level. Soap dishes, long sticky strands (consisting of fibres from local palm leaves dipped in a mixture of palm oil, beer and molasses as used in west Africa), lengths of corrugated paper pinned to the sides of bagged produce, or light traps (an electric bulb surrounded by four pieces of glass, each surface of which is smeared with a sticky substance) or suction traps, are used in different countries. These do not effect the control of insects in a building but can serve as a guide to the seriousness of the level of the insect population and to the need for control measures.

Hidden areas of dampness and developing mould are usually detected by observing darkened discoloured areas; by obtaining a sample from the consignment and measuring the moisture content; or by recording the number of discoloured grains (kernels).

SAMPLING

Spears

The most common method of inspection is by use of a sampling spear which is normally 30 centimetres long. This is the traditional method introduced by trading companies to obtain a sample of a commodity for grading purposes by assessing the quality of the grains or kernels in the sample. For this purpose it is accepted by the different trades in which this system is used that a sample obtained by spiking a number of bags of a consignment with a spear is a representative sample of the contents of the whole consignment.

The standard spear, 3 millimetres in diameter (Figure 17 a) if pushed into a sack with the open face of the spear uppermost, collects grains only from the outside layer. A slightly more representative sample is obtained with this type of spear by pushing it into the sack with the open face down and, when inserted, turning it upward. If a spear with an open end is used, when it is inserted in the sack grains should be allowed to continue to run out of the spear into a container thus ensuring that grains from more than the outside layer of the sack are obtained. In some trades, particularly the rice trade, a long spear with compartments (Figure 17b) is used, by means of which small quantities of grains are obtained from different parts of the bag along the line of entry of the spear.

Spear sampling methods to assess the presence of insects and/or moulds in a sack are unlikely to provide an accurate record. With such methods the problem is to know the minimum size of sample which must be taken for given quantities of the produce to be examined. Perhaps the best method to adopt is that of sequential sampling.

Sequential sampling. The following is an outline of what is meant by sequential sampling and the figures given (referring to insects, although comparable data could be suggested for the presence of discoloured grains in relation to hazards from mycotoxins) should not be taken as appropriate to the condition or levels of infestation in any particular country. Each country would have to determine the levels appropriate to its own conditions.

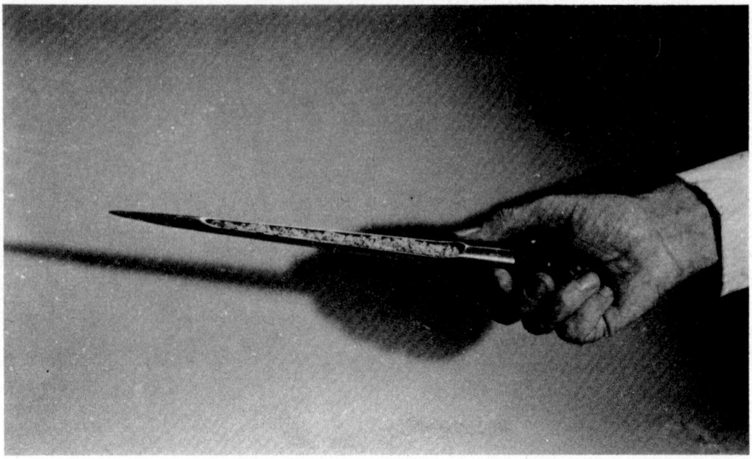

FIGURE 17. Sampling spears.
(*a*) Above, standard 33 millimetre spear.
(*b*) Below, compartmentalized spear.

1. Take a number of spear samples from several bags or parts of a bulk until a 1-kilogramme sample is obtained.

   Sieve (or examine carefully); count insects present.

   More than 15 insects: produce is *very heavily* infested
   10 to 15 insects: produce is *heavily* infested
   Less than 10 insects: resample

2. Take spear samples from a number of bags until a 3-kilogramme sample is obtained.

   Sieve; count insects present.

   More than 9 insects: produce *heavily* infested
   Less than 9 insects: resample

3. Take spear samples as above until a 9-kilogramme sample is obtained.

   Sieve; count insects present.

   More than 5 insects: produce *moderately heavily* infested
   Less than 5 insects: produce is *lightly* infested but resample

4. Take spear samples as above until a 22-kilogramme sample is obtained.

   Sieve; count insects present.

   Less than 5 insects: produce *very lightly* infested

The above figures are based on the following general assessment of infestations:

Number of insects outside grains in 90 kilogrammes:

Up to 20 insects: very light
21 to 50 insects: light
51 to 300 insects: moderate
301 to 1 500 insects: heavy
More than 1 500 insects: very heavy.

Countries have varying tolerance levels for produce termed fit for export.

Sieving

More detailed examination for the presence of insect infestation at intake and immediately prior to discharge is possible only by opening bags and " snaking " or sieving the contents.

In west Africa snaking (Figure 18) is carried out by picking up a sack of produce by the closed end, keeping the open mouth of the sack in contact with the concrete floor of the warehouse or a tarpaulin spread on the ground or floor, and moving backward in a zigzag manner so as to allow the contents of the sack to come out on to the floor at an even shallow depth. This has a sifting effect along the lower edge of the sack; the bulk of the dust and free living insects are retained along this edge and are therefore only deposited on the floor at the end of the " snake ", so that only this portion need be examined for dust and insects.

A less laborious, quicker and more accurate method for making the same type of examination consists of using a simple type sieve (Figure 18). The first to be tried, called the Donhall, was used in Ghana (Cranham, 1960); a drum type sieve has been adopted for this purpose in South Africa.

During 1967 the Tropical Stored Products Centre, Slough, United Kingdom developed a method enabling produce from a bag (or a conveyor) to be poured through a mechanism (called a sampler divider) which automatically separates a representative sample from the main stream of produce. The sample is then available for examination in the laboratory (i.e., for chemical and physical testing). This system is invaluable for carrying out routine checks on the presence of mould-infected kernels (grains) and on the chemical composition of produce.

The detection of moulds and insects in certain grains or beans necessitates the cutting open of individual beans of a representative sample (e.g., cocoa beans); a new type of inspection cutter to speed up this operation has been developed by the Tropical Stored Products Centre, as has a hidden infestation detector.

The detection of insect infestation within the produce and in buildings, etc., necessitates two types of assessment and a standardized procedure is recommended, along the lines given in Appendix C.

Since the significance of the presence of mycotoxins in foodstuffs has been realized, emphasis must now be placed on the detec-

FIGURE 18. Simple types of sampling methods. Above, snaking, below, sieving.

tion of kernels or grains on which mould has developed and in which aflatoxin and similar poisons may be present. A number of countries have set up testing procedures designed to ensure that consignments of produce are free from poison (in the case of products for human consumption) or contain less than a limited amount of it (in the case of produce for animal feed or for certain processing techniques). These tests are based on taking a sample from a consignment and carrying out a chemical test on it. Appendix D outlines the important aspects of inspection which should be considered in attempts to minimize the incidence of toxin contaminated produce, particularly groundnuts.

For information on bulk sampling, see Appendix J.

Rodents

Rodents cause extensive damage to both standing crops and stored produce in many countries. Losses to standing crops from this cause are generally regarded as being of greater importance than losses in store; nevertheless the latter are significant in certain areas. Cereals are particularly vulnerable to rodent attack, and damage to stored grain is probably greatest while it is still on the farm; in large central storage depots the rodent population seldom becomes dense enough to cause severe losses, although in some tropical countries this still happens.

Rodent damage to stored food is of a threefold nature. First, rodents consume a certain quantity of the product; secondly, they foul a much larger quantity with their excretions; and thirdly, they gnaw holes in the containers. Jute bags are particularly susceptible to this form of attack, frequently being damaged beyond repair. In some countries plastic sacking or sheeting may also be gnawed. Damage to grain stored in bulk is very much less than damage to bagged grain, because rodents cannot burrow into bulk grain and can therefore feed only at the surface. Bulk storage methods also provide fewer harbourages for rats and the types of containers used are frequently ratproof.

The harmful activities of rodents extend beyond direct damage to stored products since rodents also carry diseases which are transmissible to man. It is possible for stored produce to become contaminated with rodent faeces, urine or ectoparasites and so become a potential source of danger to persons handling or eating it. Rodent control methods are given in Chapter 9.

Notes on biology

Many rodent species, including animals such as squirrels and porcupines, attack the growing crop but rats and mice are almost always the most important pests of stored food. There are numerous indigenous rat species in Africa some of which are very important pests of standing crops, but only a few species enter buildings and damage stored produce. Three species live almost entirely in and around buildings and are pests only of stored produce.

Indigenous rats and mice. The multimammate rat, *Rattus* (*Mastomys*) *natalensis* Smith (Figure 19) is the most important indigenous rodent pest of food storage in Africa; this and other species are also of importance in India and elsewhere. It lives as well in grain fields as in buildings and sometimes invades farm stores in large numbers shortly after crops have been harvested. The species can be recognized by its soft fur, brownish on the dorsal side and greyish underneath; the tail is usually about the same length as the head and body. An adult may weigh 70 to 100 grammes with head and body measuring about 145 millimetres. Adult females are unmistakable because they possess up to 24 nipples where other rat species seldom possess more than 10. This rat is generally nocturnal.

A female *R. natalensis* is able to produce up to 20 young in a litter but the average litter size is about 11; under optimum conditions litters are produced every 3 to 4 weeks and the young mature between 2 and 3 months. This breeding potential is the highest known for a mammal although, of course, does not begin to approach the rate at which insects multiply.

The Nile rat, *Arvicanthis niloticus* Desmarest, and other *Arvicanthis* species have a wide distribution in grassland areas. *Arvicanthis* can be distinguished from *R. natalensis* by its proportionately shorter tail and its harsh, speckled fur. It is generally slightly larger than *R. natalensis*, weighing 100 to 170 grammes and is diurnal in habit. *Arvicanthis* rarely lives inside buildings and therefore causes damage only in the more primitive farm stores where

FIGURE 19. *Rattus (Mastomys) natalensis* Smith. Note the sleek fur and slender tail.

FIGURE 20. *Cricetomys gambianus* Waterhouse with oil palm fruit. Note the white distal third of the tail which distinguishes this species from all other rats.

access is free. However, damage can be serious shortly after the harvest when rats which have been feeding on the standing crop travel considerable distances in search of food.

Another indigenous species which occasionally causes damage to stored crops is the giant rat, *Cricetomys gambianus* Waterhouse (Figure 20) which is readily recognizable by its large size, its characteristic appearance and an adult weight of perhaps 1 200 grammes. Compare this with the pygmy mouse Leggada Gray, which weighs less than 10 grammes. Striped rats of the genera *Rhabdomys* Thomas and *Lemniscomys* Trouessart also enter farm stores occasionally.

Introduced species. Three rodent species now have practically worldwide distribution and two of them, *Rattus rattus* L. (Figure 21) and *Mus musculus* L. (Figure 22) are found in towns and villages throughout the greater part of Africa. The third, *Rattus norvegicus* Birkenhout (Figure 23) has, for some reason, been less widespread and is found only in the ports and in a few of the larger inland towns. These introduced species enter buildings and houses and eat the same food as man, and are usually responsible for a large part of all rodent damage to stored produce in the tropics and subtropics.

These rodents can be distinguished from each other by means of the characters described in Table 15. Both the rats are generally somewhat larger than either *R. natalensis* or *Arvicanthis* whereas the house mouse, *Mus musculus*, is very considerably smaller. The roof rat, *Rattus rattus*, is most widely distributed and is the most important pest species. It is an exceedingly agile animal, often making its entry into buildings under the eaves. The exact distribution of the house mouse is uncertain but it appears to be found in most towns. The damage caused by this species is far less than that caused by the commensal rats.

Climate

The climatic conditions of a country have an important influence on the rate of deterioration of produce in store; less marked in cool dry areas; more important in hot dry ones, even more so in cool and damp conditions; and worst of all in hot damp climates.

The importance of temperature and moisture has been stressed as a factor in promoting (or preventing) deterioration of produce

FIGURE 23. *Rattus norvegicus* Birkenhout. Note hairs on ears.

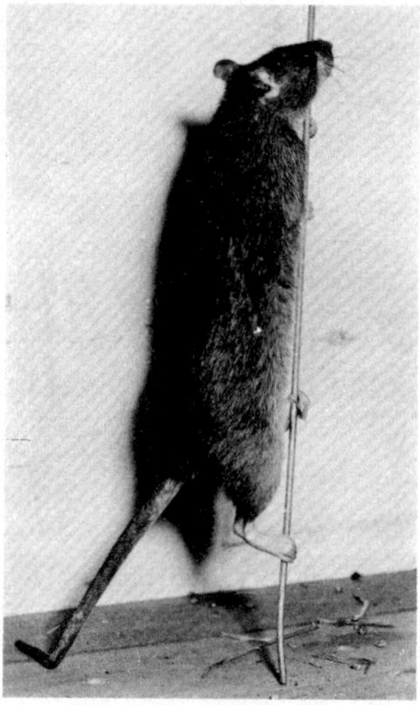

FIGURE 21. *Rattus rattus* L. Note long tail, more slender than in *R. norvegicus*, and hairless ears.

FIGURE 22. *Mus musculus* L.

TABLE 15. – CHARACTERISTICS OF SELECTED RATS AND MICE

	Rattus norvegicus	*Rattus rattus*	*Mus musculus*
Average adult weight	330 grammes	250 grammes	16 grammes
Tail length	Shorter than head and body	Usually longer than head and body	Usually longer than head and body
Ears	Thick, opaque, short with fine hairs	Thin, translucent, large, hairless	Large, some hairs
Snout	Blunt	Pointed	Pointed
Colour	Brownish grey but may be black, grey belly	Grey, black, brown or tawny, may have white belly	Variable brownish grey
Droppings	In groups but sometimes scattered, spindle-shaped or ellipsoidal	Scattered, sausage or banana-shaped	Scattered, thin spingle-shaped
Habits	Burrowing, can climb, swims well, shows new object reaction, can live in sewers, fairly conservative habits	Rarely burrows, agile climber, shows new object reaction, somewhat erratic habits	Sometimes burrows, climbs well, only slight new object reaction, erratic habits
Distribution	Only found in ports and in some of the larger inland towns	Found in towns and villages throughout Africa	Found in most towns in which recent development has taken place
English names	Sewer rat Norway rat Common rat Brown rat	Roof rat Ship rat Black rat Alexandrine rat	Mouse

NOTE: The English words "rat" and "mouse" were probably originally used to distinguish between the two common domestic rodents that were subsequently placed in the genera *Rattus* and *Mus*. But these words are now applied in an arbitrary manner to all rodents of similar appearance — and to some other mammals as well — depending upon the size of the animal concerned. There is no scientific definition for these terms as they are used today. For the present purpose, all rodents of the subfamily Marinae will be termed rats except those of the genus *Mus* which will be termed mice.

by enabling (or hindering) the development of insects, mites, fungi, bacteria and the seed grain itself. Thus the climatic conditions during and after harvest affect the ease with which effective natural drying may be carried out; dictate the need for artificial drying; and have a bearing on the incidence of reabsorption of moisture and of the temperature to which the produce is subjected. Equally, exposure to climatic conditions of an insecticidally treated surface of grain or of a building may affect the toxicity of the pesticide.

If it is possible to harvest at the end of the rainy season and dry by natural means, the quality of the produce will depend upon that of the seed and continuity of drying. During the drying period when the produce is spread out in the sun, showers of rain may occur and it is not always easy for the farmer to have the produce protected. Exposure to periods of drying and wetting, during which the grains are subjected to stresses and strains of expansion and contraction, results in cracked surfaces through which insects and fungi readily penetrate. In addition, discoloration due to biochemical and chemical deterioration takes place during the rewetting process before redrying commences.

Stored product insect pests can breed throughout a temperature range of about 20°C. Species with a maximum temperature tolerance below 30°C find the tropics too hot, but all species with a range from approximately 20°C to 40°C are likely to be pests, especially when the life history is completed at the optimum temperature in 3 to 6 weeks. As far as relative humidity is concerned, pests can be divided into dry and wet area species, although the former are usually able to live in wet areas. Dry area species can develop at a relative humidity as low as about 10 percent and the wet range species may need humidities as high as 80 percent. The lowest relative humidity can be withstood at the optimum temperature and on both sides of this temperature the humidity tolerance is less (Figure 13).

Buildings made of metals such as black corrugated iron and aluminium or of concrete will provide different temperature and humidity conditions, while storage in pits in the ground will protect stored produce from diurnal and seasonal variations. The condition of the produce at time of storage is important in terms of temperature and moisture; in the tropics products are usually stored with contained heat and, in the presence of lower temperatures outside, transfer of moisture occurs. Parts of the fabric of a building can be uninhabitable for insects at certain times, for example immediately under a metal roof during sun heat.

In considering the influence of climate, it must be borne in mind that three main types, hot dry, hot damp and cool areas present different problems in terms of buildings (Ransom, 1960).

HOT DRY AREAS

These are characterized by high daytime temperature and very low annual rainfall. During the hot season, maximum shade temperature regularly exceeds 38°C and may exceed 44°C; rarely do temperatures drop some 3 to 6°C lower. Sunlight is strong, generally from a cloudless sky; at night re-radiation from the ground is considerable. The temperature range over 24 hours is often 17 to 23°C. Rainfall seldom exceeds 250 millimetres a year although its intensity may be high during occasional storms. The rate of evaporation from free water surfaces is high. Humidities are low by day and the dewpoint is seldom reached at night. Convectional winds, which create dust storms, are common.

HOT DAMP AREAS

These have considerable rainfall and fairly high shade temperatures usually in the range of 21°C to 35°C. Seasonal and diurnal temperature variations are slight. Skies are frequently overcast but the intensity of diffuse radiation is considerable. Annual rainfall often exceeds 2 000 and sometimes 3 800 millimetres; 50 millimetres of rain per hour is not uncommon. The rate of evaporation from free water surfaces is lower than in hot dry regions. Humidities are fairly high by day, and by night large amounts of dew may be deposited. Wind speeds are generally low, especially at night when the outdoor wind speed is usually less than 5 centimetres per second (i.e., imperceptible). In these regions biological activity is at its greatest.

COOL AREAS

In the tropics and subtropics these are usually in upland regions and radiation received from the sun by day and lost from the ground at night is considerable. The diurnal temperature variation is high and increases with altitude; at 1 800 metres the variation may be 17°C. Seasonal temperature variations, however, are not so marked. Summer daytime temperatures seldom exceed 29°C, and winter daytime temperatures seldom fall below 21°C. Rainfall amounts are highly variable, depending largely upon the topography.

The intensity of fall is high in showers accompanying storms. The rate of evaporation from free water surfaces is high even in the wetter seasons. Relative humidity is low throughout the year and the dewpoint is seldom reached.

Rigid classification of an area into one of these main climatic regions is not always possible. Coastal towns, for example, may have the main characteristics of hot dry regions but high relative humidities at night. In many places, too (for example, in monsoon areas) the climate is markedly seasonal with hot dry conditions alternating with warm wet ones during the year.

5. DESIGN OF STORES

Designs of storage containers in use are dealt with in Chapter 7. It will be noted that in their construction a range of sizes, shapes and materials are utilized by local populations. Before considering these various types, major factors affecting the choice of materials and design must be mentioned. Buildings for the storage of bag produce, for example, must be discussed separately from silos for the storage of produce in bulk. This subject has been studied by Ransom (1960).

Buildings for bag storage

Until the early 1960s it was unusual to find a building in the tropics and subtropics which was specially designed for the storage of products in bags. Most, if not all, of them in use had been erected as general purpose buildings made of corrugated iron, concrete, or mud blocks or bricks and incorporating such design features as permanent gaps at the eaves, and an earth, wood or concrete floor which was not waterproof. In such buildings safe storage of produce is very difficult to maintain.

First of all a building for the storage of produce in bags must be watertight: the roof, walls, doors, windows and floor must be leakproof: the floor must not transmit water vapour from the soil with which it is in contact; and windows, etc., should be sealable in order to permit control of ventilation. Secondly, the building must be proof against the entry of rats and mice: gaps between roof and walls should be sealed (e.g., with local mud, sheet metal, close netting); pipes, shafts, ducts, etc., should be fitted with wide metal guards outside and netting inside (see Appendix E). Thirdly, it must be designed in such a way as to assist rather than hamper the control of insect pests: walls should have a smooth, uncracked finish with the floor to wall angle curved to eliminate areas from which spillage is difficult to remove; the floor should be finished in such a way that spillage can readily be swept up, and it should be free of roof-supporting pillars. The whole construction should be capable of being sealed so as to allow fumigation of the entire contents and should be built in such a way that areas of high temperature are eliminated.

In some countries, buildings consisting of little more than a floor and roof are used; in such cases the walls are nonexistent or consist of hessian; it is not uncommon for the roof to be given a considerable overhang to provide some protection from water damage. In other countries the walls and roof are built of corrugated sheets of metal bolted together in such a way as to provide permanent ventilation, usually at the eaves and also often at the ridge. Walls built of masonry such as brick or concrete blocks and with a corrugated sheeting roof are not uncommon; usually gaps are provided in the walls as sources of light and ventilation. In other cases, both walls and roof are built of masonry. In all of these, openings in the walls and roof — doors, windows, eaves and ridge gaps — should be kept to a minimum and, if ventilation points are necessary, they should be constructed in such a way as to permit a gastight closure. The aim should be to provide even temperature conditions as low as practicable in the area concerned. Provision below the roof of a ceiling continuous with the walls not only makes for a cooler store, but also helps to achieve gastightness and successful fumigation. It is of particular advantage when the roof is made of a noncontinuous material such as sheeting or tiles, although not when the roof is solid and continuous (e.g., built of shell concrete). The space between ceiling and roof should permit continuous air movement and facilitate the control of any vermin which may inhabit it.

There is an urgent need for new storage building designs providing the essential criteria for safe storage of products. Structure built according to these criteria should be:

1. entirely weatherproof;
2. gastight to enable fumigation of entire contents;
3. fitted with controllable ventilation;

4. proofed against entry of rodents and birds;
5. free of ledges and corners where dust and produce residues may lodge;
6. free from light-transmitting areas in the roof in order to avoid high temperature areas on top of stored produce;
7. designed to permit incorporation of a few fans in the walls and ducting on the floor for special bulk storage requirements.

IMPORTANCE OF MOISTURE

The presence of moisture in a building is normally associated with the products at the time of intake and with air circulating in the building. This is true of "dry" methods of construction using precast concrete, metal, asbestos and timber. However, moisture can be introduced during construction by the use of brickwork or concrete, e.g., 1 cubic metre of freshly placed brickwork or of concrete cast in situ may contain about 100 litres of water. In warm damp regions drying out the water will be slow; the use of sandwich membranes (water vapour barriers) in concrete floors and dense renderings will retard drying still further. This type of moisture may be significant only for a limited period, since it does not normally recur once it has been dried out.

However, rain penetrates a masonry wall through capillary paths between the mortar and masonry.

Where rainfall is high and evaporation rates low, saturation of the masonry or of the mortar can also occur and rain may then penetrate directly through the body of the wall. Ransom (1960) states that cavity construction, rendering, or external cladding will reduce the risk of rain penetration and can even prevent it altogether. So may the use of blocks designed to break the continuity of the bed joint and, by suitable perforation, to lengthen the capillary path from face to face. Plinths and string courses should not be used unnecessarily because there is a risk of water collecting on the projecting ledges and then entering the wall. Where they are used, all horizontal ledges formed should have a flashing. The use of parapets should be avoided because they are exposed to the weather on three faces and so become wetter than other parts of the wall; if used, they should be provided with a coping with a damp-proof course (dpc) directly underneath and a second dpc near the junction with the main wall to prevent rainwater from draining down into the building.

The ground is a natural reservoir of moisture. Except on dry, well-drained sites, floors and walls in direct contact wih the ground become damp. The risk of moisture rising through a concrete floor may be reduced by constructing it over an underlayer of hardcore or concrete with only a small proportion of fine material, but vapour barriers are essential to prevent the rise of water vapour through floor and walls. Where the water-table is high or underground storage is contemplated, special measures have to be taken.

Rain may also penetrate through the roof. This is particularly likely with shallow-pitch roofs in areas of high winds and heavy rain. With sheeted roofs, entry may occur at overlaps between sheets, through the bolt holes, and at the intersection of roof sheet and ridge. These risks can be reduced by insistence on proper overlaps, the use of durable washers, and by using curved ridge sheets which extend a considerable distance down the slope of the roof on either side of the ridge. Where a high degree of sealing is required, corrugated sheets can be sealed at the lap joints with hot bitumen or special tapes. (This will also help to prevent any accumulation of dirt or wind-borne sea spray which can promote corrosion of bare sheets in contact.) Special roofing sheets are now available which require no external fastenings and no external bolt holes. The use of this type of sheets will reduce the risk of rain penetration. Flat roofs on stores are usually of concrete; if unprotected they are seldom leak-free since thermal, moisture, and foundation movement all tend to promote cracking. They are generally covered with bitumen felt, bitumen emulsion systems, mastic asphalt, or metal. Whatever the covering, it is advisable that rainwater be shed quickly; for this reason a minimum fall ratio of 1 in 30 is recommended. Movement should be allowed for by well-designed and properly spaced joints. Joints at 9- to 12-metre intervals would be appropriate in hot, dry regions where movements are large.

At night in the humid tropics the slight drop in temperature that occurs is often sufficient to cause water vapour in the air to condense on surfaces such as concrete floors, walls, and ceilings, and also on ducts carrying cooled air in a refrigerated store where these ducts are made of materials which cool rapidly at night such as sheet metal. With absorbent materials the condensed moisture may not be obvious but continued condensation will eventually cause saturation and deterioration.

Controlled openings in a storage building can be opened to provide ventilation when temperature and moisture conditions will reduce moisture in the building, or closed when the humidity of the outside air is excessive. They permit sealing the store for fumigation. In certain instances the removal of moisture by the use of refrigerant air-conditioning can be considered; this not only reduces temperature but also removes the moisture that condenses as a result of temperature reduction, thereby improving storage conditions. Moisture can also be removed by the use of chemical dehumidifiers. The most common are silica gel, calcium chloride, active alumina and lithium chloride used in powder or in granular form. Only a certain amount of water can be absorbed by a given quantity of any one of these chemicals. The spent dehumidifier can be regenerated by heating. Some types of dehumidifying equipment contain their own regeneration unit.

Importance of temperature

Finally, the design of a building should take into consideration temperature conditions under the prevailing climate. Where stores are to be used primarily as handling buildings, i.e., where products are being handled in and out almost continuously, thermal comfort must be sufficient to enable men to work in them for considerable periods. The temperature inside a building is affected by its shape, orientation, the materials of which it is constructed, and shading. Radiation in warm wet regions is often diffuse and methods of direct shading are only partly effective; external surfaces exposed to the sun should therefore be light in colour or reflective and kept free from contamination by dirt, algae, and corrosion which reduce their capacity to reflect radiation (freshly whitewashed galvanized steel reflects eight times as much solar radiation as dirty galvanized steel; copper is twice as effective when polished as it is when tarnished).

In low latitudes more radiation falls on the east and west walls than on the north and south, and therefore buildings that are rectangular in plan should lie with the longer axis running east to west so that these walls will have the smallest areas. The greater the surface area of the store, the greater is the amount of solar radiation absorbed; for a given volume, a cube has a smaller surface area than a building which is rectangular in plan. It is better, in general, to design a cube-shaped store rather than one which is an elongated rectangle.

Sunshading can reduce the absorption of heat still further. In low latitudes small overhangs will shade north and south walls for most of the day; east and west walls, however, need shading by both vertical and horizontal projections. Roofs and walls can be more completely shaded by false roofs or walls separated from the main structure by a well-ventilated cavity wide enough to allow access for cleaning. Cavities are disliked in warm climates, however, because of the risk of infestation by birds, rodents and other vermin; if they are narrow, it is better to seal them completely since the insect proofing of ventilating apertures is difficult. A ceiling of high thermal resistance helps to reduce the heat entering from above. Ceiling sheets should be effectively sealed to one another and to the walls to reduce air transfer from the storage area to the attic space. This attic space between the ceiling and the roof must be well ventilated, otherwise moisture vapour which has migrated from the stored product to the attic space during the day may condense on the roofing material if this is cooled sufficiently. The moisture may then drip on to the ceiling, reducing its insulating value and also causing deterioration of the ceiling material. Ventilation also assists in the removal of heat stored in the structure during the day.

A store can gain a great deal of heat through windows or skylights. Skylights should not be used and other glazing should be kept to a minimum; windows should be shaded by canopies, projections, or louvered shutters. The choice of shading devices depends upon the position of the window in relation to the sun's path. Shades should be placed outside the glazing rather than inside.

In hot dry regions it is an advantage if stores are of high thermal capacity and are ventilated thoroughly at night when the outside air is cool. Controllable louvers and fans, which can provide natural or enforced ventilation whenever required, will be desirable. Lightweight buildings, even if of high thermal resistance, need considerable free air movement by day to prevent the inside temperature from rising above the shade air temperature.

CONSTRUCTIONAL DETAILS

The details which require consideration in the selection of a site and material for building have been given by Ransom (1960). The more important points are recorded here.

Site and foundation

A good site should be selected and stores built of such length that differential soil movement will not be excessive. A well-drained site should be chosen where the ground slopes away from the store and prevents water from accumulating around it. This can be of great benefit where sudden storms occur with rainfall of high intensity. Low-lying areas where water is close to the surface should be avoided. Termite-infested sites should be avoided or should be thoroughly treated with insecticide.

Stores built on unstable clay alter the natural ground moisture equilibrium, causing moisture to migrate to the clay under the building; the clay swells and the pressure exerted may be sufficient to force up the centre of the building so that it appears as though the corners had dropped; severe cracking can result. Such sites should be avoided wherever possible; otherwise special foundation techniques will be necessary. Such techniques are expensive and may entail the complete removal of unstable soil or the use of piles founded on stable soil. Made-up ground or filling is not a good base for foundations. Little control is exercised in filling waste ground and very long periods can elapse before a fill has settled under its own weight to a stage where it can support buildings with normal foundations.

Damp-proof materials

The use of damp-proof courses and vapour barriers to prevent the entry of water and water vapour is essential. The type of damp-proof course material used is important since many only resist liquid water under certain conditions.

Materials used as damp-proof courses include lead, copper, bitumen felt and mastic asphalt. In areas where conditions are conducive to rotting, as in warm damp regions, felt with a base of asbestos fibres is preferred to those based on organic fibres. In very hot regions, jointless mastic asphalt is liable to extrusion under heavy pressure; bitumen or coaltar pitch, poured hot to form a continuous layer not less than 2 centimetres thick (25 litres per 9 square metres), can serve as efficient water and water-vapour barriers. Cold solutions of these materials are not as effective because in practice they are applied in much thinner coats. If applied thinly they are permeable to water liquid and even if a number of coats are used the passage of water vapour will not be entirely prevented.

Some plastics, notably polythene and polyisobutylene, are used as damp-proof materials. Polythene used as a damp-proof course on concrete floors must be thick enough to be laid without being punctured either by rough projections in the concrete or by rough handling. Sheets of 0.12 millimetre minimum thickness are suggested for floors. Joints are difficult to seal; in practice the technique used consists of having a wide overlap, about 30 centimetres, and double-folding the polythene at the joint. It is not stuck to the concrete floor but is held down by the floor finish. A thicker sheet of 0.5 millimetre has been suggested for proofing walls. Polyisobutylene is normally used 3 millimetres thick and there should be no risk of puncturing. Sheets are joined together by softening the material at the overlap with a special solvent and then applying pressure. This causes the sheets to weld together. In hot regions evaporation of the solvent is rapid and only short lengths can be softened and joined at a time.

Floors

The floor of storage buildings will, in general, consist of a concrete screed laid over a concrete base. Concrete must be well cured. Premature drying, resulting in a lack of hydration of the cement, is a common cause of much poor concrete seen in the tropics. The concrete floor should be kept damp for at least seven days by regular daily spraying with water; by the application of a concrete curing compound; or by covering with polythene or building paper to reduce evaporation. Aggregates used should be clean and graded where possible; those containing iron pyrites or mica may be unsound in themselves while some containing minerals such as opal or chalcedony may react with the cement to cause unsoundness. Where the floor has continuous contact with damp soil, hardcore, or groundwater containing alkali sulphates, sulphate-resisting cement should be used instead of normal Portland cement. Joints in floors should be wider than those normally used in the building trade in order to facilitate complete filling with a suitable mastic to discourage infestation.

Concrete surfaces produce dust through wear of the neat cement which rises to the surface during finishing. Under normal traffic a strong, well-laid finish will not dust unduly. The high standards of hygiene necessary in stores, however, make treatment of the concrete surface with a hardener worthwhile. Sodium silicate is recommended. Grades can be bought especially for this purpose. Two or three applications will be effective on a good concrete surface; no treatment will be of much value on poor quality concrete.

Walls

Store walls are commonly of asbestos cement, galvanized steel or aluminium. In the thicknesses normally used, all three have low thermal capacities, and in a store which is to be fumigated gases will readily pass through fixing holes, at the overlaps between sheets, and through any other gaps.

Asbestos cement sheets are brittle and susceptible to impact damage (as from hailstorms and rough handling when used); in warm regions, in association with supporting timber which has high drying shrinkage, flaws are created and rain may pass through what would otherwise be a water-resistant covering. It is not uncommon in the tropics to see asbestos cement sheets patched with bitumen and hessian to prevent this penetration. It is most important, therefore, to ensure that sheets are not fixed too tightly to supports. Mould growth is rapid on asbestos cement in warm wet regions and sheets darken and then absorb heat. A 1 percent solution of copper sulphate applied by brush or spray to the sheets before erection will do much to prevent these growths. Further applications at intervals of 3 or 4 years are recommended. Asbestos cement is highly resistant to atmospheric pollution and, within the limits already described, is durable.

The resistance of galvanized steel to corrosion increases as the thickness of the zinc coating is increased. Corrosion is in proportion to atmospheric pollution, and is therefore slow in the tropics except near the coast. Close to surf beaches, corrosion can be very rapid and the more heavily coated sheets should be used there. Several types of corrugated steel sheets have protective coatings applied to them during manufacture (Table 16). Bitumen asbestos felt is usually used, bonded on to the steel core under pressure; the core may or may not be galvanized. Such sheets are very resistant to corrosion but the surface is black and absorbs heat. When galvanized steel sheets are cut (to take bolts, for example) the cut edges so exposed have less durable ungalvanized surfaces. These should be protected by a coating of bituminous paint.

Aluminium is a light and strong metal. Exposure tests in the tropics have shown it to offer considerable resistance to corrosion, even when used near the coast; a manganese-aluminium alloy is suitable and is used for most corrugated roofing sheets. Contact under damp conditions with other materials should be avoided because it can lead to severe corrosion. Copper and lead are particularly detrimental as are damp concrete, lime, and some types of wood, due to electrolytic action; this will be rare in hot dry regions but probable in warm wet regions. If the above conditions are likely to occur, electrically insulated materials should be used at all joints. New aluminium sheets have a bright reflective finish; glare decreases in intensity as the sheets weather but this is often slow. Sheets which have been surface-treated either mechanically or chemically and do not cause glare discomfort can be used.

Walls of masonry or of in situ concrete have much greater thermal capacity than those built with sheet materials.

Clay bricks and blocks, if properly burnt, are very durable in warm climates; their thermal and moisture movements are small. Deterioration is usually associated with the presence of soluble salts (sulphates) formed during manufacture or derived from rising groundwater; the presence of significant amounts of magnesium sulphate causes disintegration of the brick surfaces and of applied renderings. The more commonly found salt, calcium sulphate, is

TABLE 16. – ANTICORROSION TREATMENTS APPLICABLE TO STORAGE BUILDINGS IN TROPICAL AND SUBTROPICAL AREAS ACCORDING TO PROXIMITY TO SEA AND SOURCES OF CHEMICAL CONSTITUENTS IN THE AREA

Type of conditions / Surface	Severe (Areas in salt spray from surf shore, e.g., up to 3 kilometres or to engine sheds and "chemical environments")	Moderate (Areas near sheltered water, town or industrial sites where corrosion is noticeable but not drastic)	Mild (Inland areas where there are no cases of corrosion)
Heavy structural steel (stanchions, girders, frames, etc.)	Aluminium sprayed + moderate etch primer, + micaceous iron oxide or aluminium paint. Heavy duty bitumen or coal tar or coal tar pitch/epoxy, and wrapping.	Aluminium sprayed, with or without paint. Zinc sprayed, with paint suitable for zinc. Heavy duty bitumen, coal tar or coal tar/epoxy (less thickness needed). Zinc rich paint.	Red lead or metallic lead primer plus micaceous iron oxide or aluminium or gloss paint. Zinc rich paint.
Light structural steel (trusses, purlins, brades, etc.)	As above.	As above. Galvanized and painted with paint suitable for zinc. Wrapper with anti-corrosive paste and tape.	As above. Galvanized with or without painting with paint suitable for zinc.
Sheet steel (cladding roofs, machinery covers, etc.)	Replace by plastic sheet or asbestos, cement or aluminium. PVC coatings, bitumen coatings (factory applied).	PVC coatings. Galvanized and painted, with paint suitable for zinc. Bitumen coated.	PVC coated. Galvanized with or without paint suitable for zinc. Red lead or metallic lead primer, plus u/ct plus gloss. Zinc chromate primer (2 coats + u/ct + gloss.

Degree of corrosivity based on general corrosion per annum

Steel	Over 5 mm or 8.3 g/m²	2.0 - 5.0 mm or 2.8 - 8.3 g/m²	Less than 2 mm or 2.8 g/m²
Zinc	Over 0.5 mm or over 0.8 g/m²	0.2 - 0.5 mm or 0.3 - 0.8 g/m²	Less than 0.2 mm or less than 0.3 g/m²

SOURCE: Building Research Station, Garston, Watford, Hertfordshire, England.

seldom harmful to the brick itself but can cause applied cement renderings and mortars to spall under persistently damp conditions. Attack by soluble salts is also the main cause of deterioration of natural soft limestones exposed to sea spray.

Well-cured reinforced concrete walls of good quality are as durable in the tropics as in temperate regions. Reinforcement must, of course, be well covered or rusting and spalling will occur. This is particularly true close to surf beaches.

Natural soil is used for building in the tropics. The disadvantages of using it as a building material are that the bulk density changes excessively with changes in moisture content and it is easily eroded by rain. Its properties and behaviour can be improved by admixture with Portland cement. Stabilized soil, as it is then called, is stronger, has a lower moisture movement, and is generally more durable. It has properties similar to a weak concrete. It is used mainly in block form which needs protection from damage by splash back from the ground and from rain at corners and gable ends. It is advisable to build the lowest two courses in more durable material, for example, concrete block, or to protect the wall at the bottom by a concrete plinth or rendering.

Mortars and plasters

The denser the cement mortar and the more impervious the masonry unit, the greater is the likelihood of cracking and rain penetration. A good mortar is sufficiently plastic and water-retentive during application to permit a close bond. Mortars of volume composition 1 : 1 : 6 and 1 : 2 : 9 (cement : lime : sand), fulfil these requirements. Very similar mortars are produced when mortar plasticizers (which are alternatives to lime) are added to cement-sand mixes of volume proportions 1 : 6 and 1 : 8. These plasticizers let small, stable air bubbles in the mix and improve both plasticity and cohesion.

With external rendered finishes for walls, volume proportions of 1 : 1 : 6 and 1 : 2 : 9 (cement : lime : sand) are now recommended. Sufficient protection to a wall may sometimes be provided by a slurry of cement paint and sand mix of 1 : 2 (by weight) scrubbed into the wall with a brush and followed a day later by a single coat of ordinary cement paint. In areas of high rainfall and where poor drying conditions prevail, absorbent renderings may become completely saturated and it will be better to first apply a spatter dash of 1 : 2 or 1 : 3 (by volume) cement : sand, thrown on to the wall by trowel and scoop, followed later by an undercoat and finishing coat of 1 : 1 : 6 (cement : lime: sand). Spatter dash treatments are also useful in giving a surface of even suction and good adhesion for subsequent coats. They should not be applied to weak backgrounds, such as stabilized soil. Colourless waterproofers, i.e., sodium hydrosilicate, can improve the rain resistance of sound, crack-free walls, by lining the surface pores with a water-repellent film but these surfaces remain permeable to water vapour. This can be an advantage, since moisture which may have already found its way behind the treated surface can later evaporate. Walls which have become contaminated with salts derived from sea spray or from rising groundwater should not be treated with colourless waterproofers because the salts can then crystallize behind, instead of on, the surface and serious spalling may occur. It should be noted that colourless waterproofers do not make a wall impervious to water under pressure and therefore cannot be expected to waterproof a store subjected to hydrostatic pressure (e.g., underground pit) through a high water table level, or through rain driven by very high winds.

The degree of hygiene needed in a store demands that internal plastering should be as smooth and as free from cracks as possible. The minimum risk of cracking is obtained by using gypsum plasters of the retarded semihydrate type. Cement-based plasters similar in composition to those for external rendering may also be used.

Roofs

The pitched roofs of stores are usually covered with sheets of asbestos cement, galvanized steel, or aluminium. Flat roofs to stores are generally of concrete treated with bituminous covering; the main problem is to prevent the deterioration of the covering. Mastic asphalt, roofing felts, and bitumen emulsions applied over glass fibre or hessian reinforcements, have all been used as waterproofers. They are susceptible to damage by underlying roof movement, to blistering when applied to screeds which contain free moisture, to standing puddles, and to sunlight and heat. A concrete roof of good quality, incorporating adequately designed and spaced expansion joints, will do much to minimize the effect of movement. Mastic asphalt and many bituminous felts are laid loosely, that is, they are not bonded firmly to the roof structure, and this too reduces the effect of roof movement on them. Insulating screeds, particularly those incorporating vermiculite as the aggregate, often contain a large quantity of water which can be slow to evaporate particularly in the humid tropics. A bituminous waterproofing system should not be applied over such damp insulation. Where the roof must be finished quickly it is better to use a dry insulating material instead. Standing puddles cause marked deterioration of bituminous roof coverings in the tropics; adequate falls (1 in 30 minimum), should be provided. The effect of tropical sunlight and heat is severe but can be reduced by reflective or white paint treatments, e.g., aluminium-bitumen paint and mineral granules washed in mixed lime-tallow and embedded in or loosely laid over the bitumen, metallic foil, and tile or slab coverings. The latter two may be in contact with, or raised above, the waterproofing covering.

It is worth noting that the problem of adequately waterproofing concrete roofs can be overcome by using superimposed pitched roofs of asbestos cement, galvanized steel and aluminium, with a clear space between the two "roofs."

Ceilings and insulated materials

Ideally the ceiling material should be a good thermal insulator and should be unaffected by condensation which may drip on to it from the roof slab. It should be immune from attack by vermin, insects and microorganisms and should not provide a harbour for infestation; stability to thermal and moisture changes, reasonable strength, cheapness and ease of erection are also desirable. Many types of materials are now available.

Plain aluminium foil, free from pinholes and in thicknesses of 0.025 millimetre or more, fulfils many of these requirements. It will deteriorate, however, under damp conditions in contact with copper, lead, concrete, lime and timber and in such circumstances should be given local protection. It is fragile and a laminate is preferred in which the foil is stuck to one or both sides of a reinforced building paper. While still clean, the double-sided insulation is thermally more efficient than the single-sided. It will also give the building paper greater protection from fungal and insect attack. Sheets must be supported but are not difficult to seal to one another and to the walls. Rolls 45 metres long and 1.2 metres wide can be obtained.

Wood-wool and lightweight concrete slabs are not water- or vapourproof, have fairly high moisture movements, and will harbour insects if left unplastered. Most wood-wool slabs use wood shavings that have been chemically treated against termite attack. Those in which the binder is Portland cement or magnesium oxy-sulphate are durable in damp conditions. Wood-wool slabs can be easily handled and those incorporating metal channel edges may be safely supported by purlins spaced as widely as 2 metres apart.

Both corkboard and fibreboard can deteriorate in damp tropical areas. Special types of fibreboard can be obtained which have been treated against termite attack, but even so cases are known where attack has occurred. Insulating water-repellent plasterboard with a water-repellent core and an aluminium foil covering on one or both sides has not been used widely, and its behaviour in damp tropical areas is not yet established. Asbestos insulating boards are resistant to biological attack, do not deteriorate under damp conditions (although mould may grow upon them), have fairly low thermal and moisture movements, and are light but strong. They are not waterproof or vapourproof. All the boards mentioned can be easily handled and fixed to metal or timber supports.

Several types of plastic insulating materials suitable for ceilings can be mentioned, e.g., foamed polystyrene. These are light, flexible, have high resistance to biological attack, and are either of a continuous or noncontinuous cell structure; permeability to water vapour is extremely low. Although the thermal movement is rather high, slabs can safely be butt-joined for the material is easily compressed and so can take up this movement. A number of foamed plastics are not suitable for use where the temperature may rise above 71°C, as might occur in direct contact with a sheet metal roof.

Buildings for bulk storage

Storage of produce in bulk is carried out in a variety of types of containers and buildings, the design of which affects the storability of the produce. A number of types in use in the tropics and subtropics are given in Chapter 7. Ideally buildings should be designed specifically for bulk storage.

It is possible to adapt buildings which were originally designed for bag storage to bulk storage. Where walls are not robust enough to withstand the pressure of the produce, bulkheads either of bagged grain or of wooden " shields " constructed in the form of an inverted T may be used. Also, detrimental moisture and temperature conditions at the wall surface will be avoided.

The storage of produce in bulk in large heaps on extensive floor areas is not popular because it is generally recognized that control of insects by fumigation or other chemical measures is extremely difficult.

Bulk storage commonly takes the form of storage in baskets or bins, specially constructed for the purpose. These vary in size and may be constructed above or in the ground. Metal, wood, brick and concrete are the usual materials used.

When storage bins are constructed above ground level the design may include either a flat bottom to the container, in which case complete emptying and cleaning is often not carried out, or a conical or sloped bottom (about 32°) which makes the container self emptying. The latter type is commonly adopted only in the construction of large silos, each bin being self emptying on to conveyor bands. Such an arrangement facilitates the treatment of the grain with chemicals and, when adopted on a smaller scale, the silos may be constructed on pillars. A popular height to which a plinth, i.e., foundation and floor, is built is the height of a standard jute sack when full of produce, i.e., 1 to 2 metres. Alternatively, the height of the plinth may be kept to a minimum and emptying of the contents of the silo into sacks is effected by having a hole in the ground sufficiently large to enable a sack to stand upright beneath the outlet spout. In many instances, deterioration of grain in such silos is due to water being absorbed by the grain via the plinth. It is essential, therefore, to consider carefully the measures adopted in the construction of the plinth in order to prevent water from moving into the silo.

Plinth construction

The stability of a building is dependent on properly designed foundations. For large silos a detailed soil investigation and subsequent design based on the findings is essential. No structure should be constructed on loose earth fill unless the load of the structure is transferred to undisturbed soil which has been checked to determine that it will carry the load. Pilings may be necessary to develop the load carrying capacity needed for some structures. The area for a minimum of 3 metres around the plinth on which the silo is erected must be sloped with a fall of 5 centimetres/metre away from the centre in all directions, to facilitate drainage of rain from the base of the silo.

The plinth should be capable of supporting the load of produce which will be placed on it. If no more than the equivalent of a 1.2 metre depth of 14 percent moisture wheat is to be placed on the plinth it should support a weight of 1 000 kilogrammes per square metre. This can be achieved in a number of ways.

1. Remove all organic topsoil to a minimum depth of 10 centimetres and level without filling.
2. Prepare a base of large stones cemented together with concrete and mortar, and top with a layer (5 to 8 centimetres) of concrete.
3. Prepare a base 10 to 12 centimetres deep by using a strong concrete mix (1 : 2.5 : 3.5, cement, sand, gravel) with the minimum quantity of water to make it workable, and moist cure in situ by keeping wet for 3 to 7 days; cover the base with polythene sheet or with hessian which is kept damp, or cover with a layer of sand which is kept wet by watering.

Base structures having a diameter of more than 1.5 metres need to be reinforced with steel rods or welded wire mesh. Plinths for silos should be constructed with a vapour barrier by means of which liquid water and water vapour are prevented from entering the silos and being absorbed by the produce in contact with the plinth. Where a water barrier is placed about 7 centimetres below the untreated surface of the plinth (Figure 24), rain falling on the surface of this concrete plinth is absorbed by the concrete (above the level of the water barrier) and travels by capillary action through the concrete under any mastic water barrier round the base of the silo and hence is soaked up by the produce in contact with the concrete inside the silo.

The method of waterproofing a plinth shown in Figure 25 would obviate this problem.

CONSTRUCTIONAL DETAILS FOR SMALL SILOS AND PITS

Aboveground bins can be constructed of wicker work and mud, metal (aluminium being popular), local brick or concrete. The efficiency of these bins depends upon the effectiveness with which insect infestation and water damage can be controlled in them, and the ease with which they can be erected under local conditions. A properly constructed bin is automatically rodent and weatherproof and insect pests are readily controlled.

Of the materials mentioned above, metal is the best conductor of heat; therefore, in areas with extremes of temperature, condensation problems would be expected (and have been found) to be more troublesome in metal bins than in bins constructed from other materials. In the latter, condensation may occur on metal manholes and the grain surface below these areas becomes damp and may even germinate. Where local brick and concrete blocks are used, effective means are required to seal the joins between the building units and render the wall structure proof against moisture movement through the concrete or brick. With metal sheets, a suitable mastic must be used along all joints and bolt holes in an attempt to provide watertightness and, particularly, gastightness to enable fumigation to be carried out; expansion and contraction of metal sheets can be considerable, making it difficult to achieve effective seals.

In the construction of metal bins, care should be taken to see that the structure is weatherproof at the roof-wall joint. New designs have been and are being developed by commercial firms to ensure that these joints are also gastight.

During recent years, weldmesh silos (Figure 26) incorporating a hessian bag or lining or a continuous film type liner (e.g., butyl rubber, polythene or polyvinylchloride either as films or as coatings to a woven material) have been developed. The majority of these are less than 100 tons in capacity but a few have been designed to hold up to some 800 tons of grain. These are very easily erected and if equipped with a film type liner can provide sufficient gastightness to achieve hermetic storage conditions (avoiding the need for applying toxic-to-man chemicals) by using appropriate closure systems at the filling and outlet spouts. Designs of these silos, which incorporate a gastight door in the wall (facilitating erection of the silo and final removal of the produce) and a rodent barrier, are

FIGURE 24. Example of a plinth construction.

DIAGRAM I

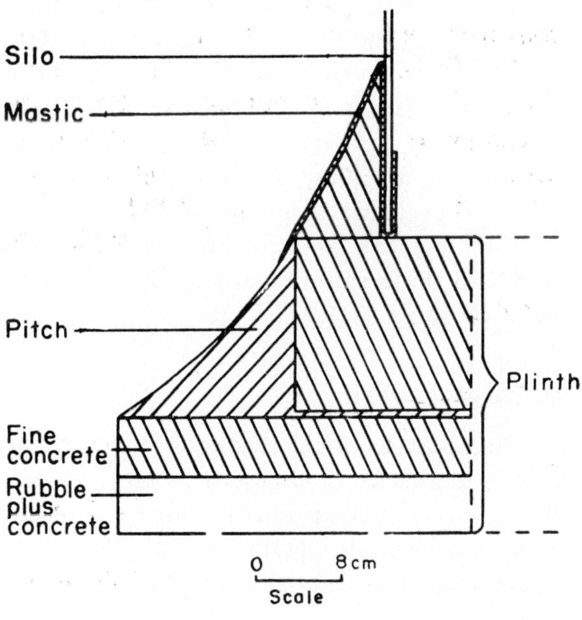

FIGURE 25. Diagram of plinth construction, showing a satisfactory method of waterproofing.

superior to those which consist merely of a gastight bag within a mesh metal wall.

Using this mesh metal framework principle, a more permanent form of silo construction has been developed, known as the Waller bin. The mesh metal is placed on a water vapour proofed plinth, hessian is hung on the inside of the silo and the bin is filled with grain to put the structure under tension.

The hessian/metal matrix is plastered on the outside (Figure 26) with 19 millimetre rendering of cement mortar which when dry can be treated with bitumen. The roof structure is formed using timber ribs over which a tailored hessian (300 grammes per square metre in weight) cover is stretched and secured in position and a coat of cement mortar rendering is applied to join up with the walls. Light reinforcing steel rods are placed in position and covered with a second coat of rendering about 2 centimetres thick which when dry is treated with bitumen. A central opening for filling and emptying is left at the top of the bin which can be closed by a wooden manhole and then sealed completely over with bitumen.

These bins if properly constructed may be sufficiently airtight to eliminate the need for applying chemical control measures to the dry grain which is stored. Various sizes may be constructed.

Filling may be effected either by a pneumatic system, by screw conveyor, or by buckets. Emptying may be either by the pneumatic system or by buckets through the top opening or, alternatively, an exit spout can be inserted at the bottom of the silo to discharge by gravity. (In order for the hermetic principle to operate the openings at the top and bottom have to be specially designed to achieve airtightness.)

For tropical conditions it is essential to ensure that the produce placed in these containers is sufficiently dry to prevent the development of fungi.

Damp grain storage

Since about 1960 storage of undried grain for animal feed has been undertaken in temperate countries in bolted metal silos (steel plates either galvanized or vitreous-enamelled); in welded metal silos; and in mesh metal silos with plastic bags. In the bolted silos which are less airtight than the welded type, there are special

FIGURE 26. Weldmesh type silos. Above, completed silos; right, the hessian/metal matrix onto which cement mortar rendering is being applied.

"seal-type" washers to effect a degree of airtightness which will ensure oxygen-free atmosphere; grain with a moisture content usually above 16 percent undergoes partial fermentation but at the end of the storage period it is acceptable to animals and appears to have no harmful effect. In one system for damp grain storage carbon dioxide from cylinders is introduced into the silo (welded type).

In the tropics and subtropics there are likely to be more serious problems of deterioration than in the temperate areas due to more rapid development of moulds after removal of grain from the silo. During emptying operations, air enters the bin and since microorganisms such as thermophilic actinomycetes and fungi capable of producing toxins can develop on low levels of oxygen, the addition of inert gas may be necessary. The use of "damp grain" storage in regions of the tropics where drying is extremely difficult may have to be considered for animal feed, and experimental work should be undertaken for this purpose. The present state of knowledge suggests that:

1. Damp grain can be stored for animal feed but in the tropics the rate of decomposition after removal from the silo is likely to be very rapid.
2. In metal bins the addition of carbon dioxide may be necessary especially during emptying.
3. Bolted metal bins are unlikely to be sufficiently airtight for use in the tropics with damp grain.
4. Mesh metal silos with flexible airtight plastic bag may be the most practical and economic form of airtight storage for use with damp grain.

Pits

Bulk storage in pits in the ground is an attractive "concealed" form of storage. Originally used to minimize pilferage, it provides evenness of temperature and utilizes the supporting strength of the earth to contain the produce. In stores of this type (see Figure 40, page 166) produce may deteriorate due to dampness from the surrounding soil (i.e., development of moulds) or from attack by insect pests. It is therefore essential that: the walls of the pit are lined in such a way as to ensure that water (both in the form of liquid and vapour) will not move into the pit from the soil; the roof of the pit will not allow water (as liquid or vapour) to pass into the pit; that the construction and lining of the pit will provide sufficient airtightness to prevent oxygen from passing into the pit; and the produce put into the pit is sufficiently dry to prevent the development of moulds.

Neither ordinary reinforced concrete nor bolted metal provide a sufficiently effective vapour barrier for airtight storage on which principle these pits operate. If metal is used, the construction must be a welded structure. Concrete is normally used in pit construction and the following points are essential:

1. The walls of underground stores must be designed to resist both the pressure of the surrounding earth when the store is empty and the pressure of the crop when it is full or partly full.
2. Vapour barriers must be incorporated to prevent entry of air and moisture and the escape of carbon dioxide; they should be protected from mechanical damage during loading and unloading. (Where groundwater may be anticipated above the level of the bottom of the pit the barrier should be continuous between the floor and wall and be sandwiched between two thicknesses of concrete.)
3. The roof may be flexible (a temporary roof of bitumen felt laid directly on the heaped grain, bonded with bitumen to the walls of the pit) or solid (a permanent roof of reinforced concrete or metal in which there are gaps for loading sealed with bitumen felting during the storage period).
4. Stores of great length should be avoided; otherwise cracking may occur. Movement joints should be provided, placed at less than 15-metre intervals (joint filling materials should be resistant to groundwater and to termite attack).

Hygiene and organization

Irrespective of the type of storage building or container used, unless storage hygiene is practised losses of stored produce will occur. It is essential that at each point where food grains are handled and stored there should be an organized approach to the problem.

FIGURE 27. Hygiene in small stores. Above, lack of hygiene and organization; below presence of hygiene and organization.

Figure 27 shows a comparison between a trader's store in which there is no attention to hygiene and organization, thus providing an ideal set of circumstances for the rapid development of pests and deterioration of produce. Next to it is a trader's store in which attention has been given to these aspects, and therefore one in which losses can be kept to a minimum.

Teaching storage hygiene and organization to the farmer, trader and warehouse foreman is the first important step in raising storage standards and reducing losses.

The following procedures summarize the techniques to be considered in a routine approach to storage.

1. Ensure that storage container is of sound construction:

(*a*) The roof is sound and free from leaks.

(*b*) The walls are free from cracks (e.g., by re-treating with mud or concrete).

(*c*) The floor is free from cracks (and, where appropriate, that it will not allow the passage of moisture into the produce).

2. Ensure that storage container is clean.

(*a*) Brush out old crop residue and clean walls, roof and floor.

(*b*) If a building, treat the walls with whitewash (lime-wash is not recommended because of its alkalinity which reduces the toxicity of insecticides applied to a surface treated in that way).

(*c*) Treat the empty container with insecticidal dust, spray (wettable powder or paste) or smoke.

3. In the chain between farmer and consumer, at each point where produce changes hands a thorough examination should be carried out so that only produce which is dry, clean and free from discoloured and low quality grains, is accepted for storage. Where necessary and appropriate, dry (off the ground on matting or plastic sheet); clean (by sieving) and hand-pick (to remove discoloured grains) small quantities of produce before intake, or install an artificial drier through which all produce is automatically passed; receiving cleaning in the process; hand-pick as above.

4. At intake, record the moisture content and other quality characteristics and weigh every bag of produce (either singly or in multiples) and record quantity taken into storage.

(*a*) Record day's intake in a stock book.

(*b*) Prepare an account of description of goods, marks, condition, shortages (if any) and remarks on damage.

(*c*) In the cases where produce is being held in store for another party, a certificate or warrant should be prepared for the owner of the produce giving description of goods, situation of warehouse, etc.

(*d*) Issue a delivery order to record: goods to be delivered; name and address of firm receiving goods; warehouse address; special identity marks; name of ship (if any); dates required.

(*e*) Check test the weighing machines in use (platform scales).

5. Where appropriate, treat the produce during intake or loading of the container with an insecticide (in one of the following ways).

(*a*) Admix an insecticidal dust with the produce.

(*b*) Inject an insecticidal dust into bags of produce and attempt even distribution by tumbling bags.

(*c*) Spread the produce in a thin layer on a tarpaulin and spray with a liquid contact insecticide; mix the produce thoroughly by shovelling before bagging.

(*d*) Spray the grain stream with a liquid contact insecticide.

(*e*) Spray the grain stream with a liquid fumigant.

(*f*) Add granules of fumigant to the produce during the filling of the container (e.g., railway truck or silo).

6. If bag storage, build the produce into a stack on a waterproof floor or on wooden dunnage (pallet form) which keeps it entirely off the floor. Where appropriate, treat the produce by one of the following methods.

(*a*) Dust each layer of bags as a stack is being built.

(*b*) Spray the outside of a complete stack with a water-dispersible powder.

(*c*) Fumigate the stack under gasproof sheets; (This control method can be carried out without the use of gasproof sheets if the stack to be treated is small and is contained in a gastight chamber.) If the sheets cannot be left in position to prevent reinfestation the exposed surface of the stack should have been treated as in (*a*) or (*b*) before fumigation.

(*d*) Effectively seal the entire building (if necessary by covering the entire building with gas-proof sheets) and fumigate.

(*e*) Completely enclose the stack in an airtight envelope.

(When second-hand bags have to be used, clean thoroughly by turning inside out and brushing, and disinfect by boiling or fumigation.)

7. If silo storage, disinfestation measures which can be adopted, other than those given in paragraph 5 above, vary with the circumstances.

(*a*) Small bulks can be fumigated by laying sacks on the surface of the produce and sprinkling with a liquid fumigant; very small bulks up to about 1 ton can be fumigated in a gastight container by exposing the fumigant in a wide mouthed vessel on the surface of the grain.

(*b*) Large bulks of grain can be fumigated.

8. With both bag and silo storage, ensure that the first parcel of grain to be put into store is the first parcel to be taken out of store and that each parcel of produce which has been treated with an insecticide should be clearly labelled with a "treatment card" on which every treatment is recorded.

Chemical treatments

To date, there is no safe, effective fungicide available for the control of fungi. Control of moisture is the most effective fungus control.

With insect pests it is usually necessary to supplement scrupulous warehouse hygiene, rotation of stocks, etc., with chemical control methods. Three types of chemicals or pesticides are available: stomach poisons, contact poisons and respiratory poisons; only the two latter types are commonly used in the control of insect pests of stored products.

Pesticides suitable for use on stored products are limited in number (see Table 20), owing to problems of taint or toxic residues which may arise. Since most pesticides used are toxic to man as well as to insects and rodents, it is essential that their use be supervised in all countries. Legislation to control the use of pesticides is almost nonexistent in tropical and subtropical countries (Appendix B).

The following problems have to be considered in connexion with the use of insecticides on stored food:

(*a*) danger to personnel handling the chemicals and carrying out the treatment;

(*b*) danger to men and animals from toxic residues in the food grains when eaten;

(*c*) specificity of toxicity of insecticides to insect species;

(*d*) onset of resistance to the insecticide in insect species;

(*e*) development of taint or damage to germination in certain produce.

Contact insecticides have more specific effects and have a greater tendency to produce resistance than the respiratory or gaseous chemicals (fumigants); the former can confer long-term protection while the latter provide no residual effect at the end of the fumigation period. Also, the contact insecticides are much less toxic to man than fumigants. However, contact insecticides do not have the penetrating power of fumigants which, being able to permeate through stacks and bulks of produce and become absorbed into individual grains or kernels, kill all stages of insect life within (Page and Lubatti, 1963).

The greatest dangers to personnel handling contact insecticides come from the sale of these products in containers not intended to contain chemicals (e.g., beer bottles) and not clearly labelled as toxic chemicals. Insecticides should always be sold in special containers labelled with detailed instructions as to the toxicity of the chemical;and the precautions necessary in diluting or applying it should be stated in a manner understandable to the local people. There may also be danger from contact between the pesticide and the skin for prolonged periods before the affected parts are washed.

In the case of fumigants, carelessness during application combined with lack of attention to keeping people away from buildings or vehicles under treatment are the main dangers.

Strict disciplining of staff in the safe and effective use of pesticides is essential. The need for checks to be carried out on the insecticide residues in produce cannot be overemphasized. The major points to be considered in the use of chemicals for the safe storage of produce are given in Chapter 8.

6. DRYING METHODS

The importance of drying food grains quickly and effectively — that is to say, efficiently in terms of speed and form of drying — after harvest and before storage, followed by the need to keep grains dry if losses are to be kept within reasonable limits has already been emphasized in Chapter 4. This may present difficulties for the local farmer and trader, particularly in areas of heavy rainfall and high humidity; not surprisingly the most ingenious methods are therefore to be found in countries where drying is particularly difficult.

Natural methods of drying make use of exposure to the sun and/or the desiccating effect of air currents in fields, farms or villages. Artificial methods include the use of fires to heat the grain directly or indirectly, with or without ventilation; and also the use of commercially available driers by which the air is heated by furnaces using oil or electricity; or by utilizing the waste heat of an internal combustion engine.

Natural drying

In countries where maturity of the crop coincides with the beginning of a dry season, the most popular method of drying is by exposure to the sun. Drying may commence before the crop is harvested, e.g., maize cobs are left on the standing plant for 3 to 4 weeks after maturing before they are harvested.

In many countries after harvest the heads of grain or the plant with the fruit attached [1] are exposed to the sun in a variety of ways for a further period of drying before being stored. Groundnuts, for example, are dried (Blatchford and Hall, 1963a, b) by placing

[1] Where the grain is left attached to the plant for part or all of the drying period, the latter is sometimes referred to as the "curing" or "wilting" period.

the freshly lifted plants (with pods attached) foliage downward on the earth and left exposed to the sun for upward of two weeks. In some countries scaffolds are constructed in the field and bunches of panicles of paddy are hung on these for between 1 and 4 weeks; stacks of panicles 1.2 metres in height and diameter may be built and left for 6 to 8 weeks. In other areas paddy, maize, cobs, etc., are laid out to dry on heaps of stubble and covered with stubble, a method utilizing ventilation rather than direct exposure to the sun. Stacking groundnut plants in the field and maize on the stalk as carried out in a number of countries achieves drying largely by the same process.

At village level, several simple methods which avoid the need for building a storage container are used for drying maize. Perhaps the most common practice is to spread the harvested, threshed or shelled crop on the ground or on a specially prepared area (e.g., matting, sacking, mud/cowdung mixture, or concrete), and expose it to the sun and wind — although also, unintentionally, to rain. Panicles of paddy are brought from the fields to the villages where they are laid out on prepared areas to dry in the sun for a number of days. Unshucked maize cobs, groundnuts removed from the plant

FIGURE 28. Simple type of natural drier: inverted lattice-work cones.

after curing, beans and peas, etc., are spread out to dry on timber and grass platforms, hut roofs, or in specially constructed inverted latticework cones (Figure 28). Because of their open structure these cones are well ventilated and allow quick drying.

In countries where the humidity is high, grain may be subjected to an initial period of drying in a manner similar to methods described above, but further drying is facilitated during storage in certain types of stores, e.g., cribs for maize and yam storage are so constructed as to provide ventilation at all times.

Methods to be encouraged

Produce left on the plant to dry loses moisture at a rate determined by the drying potential of the air and the reservoir of moisture in the immediate environment of the parent plant. It might therefore be anticipated that on the plant there is a limitation on the rate of drying and the degree of drying which can be achieved. Under certain climatic conditions the rate of drying can be reasonably fast and, provided the grains are undamaged, loss of moisture will continue without much deterioration in quality. Where, however, the rate of drying is slow after maturity of the crop and especially where the grains or kernels are damaged by pests, it is preferable to remove the produce from the plant and speed up the rate of drying. Probably the most efficient natural drying methods involve an optimum period of drying on the haulms (which has to be determined for local conditions) followed by further drying of the crop in the threshed state.

From the following summary of methods in use it can be seen that two natural aspects must be taken into consideration:

1. drying in a shallow layer by exposure to the sun on a material which prevents dampness from the ground from reaching the produce;
2. drying in a container which has open sides to permit air movement through the bulk.

Care is required to minimize excessive movement of the grains which damages the seed coat. Too rapid or overlong drying also has to be avoided. Some seed may become bleached, wrinkled and scorched, or discoloured, and with some types of produce " case-hardening" occurs whereby the surface of the grains dries out quickly sealing the moisture within the inner layers. Equally the grains should not be exposed to rain and rewetting during or after the drying period.

Shallow layer natural drying

This form of drying can be achieved by spreading the produce on suitable material on the ground, or on wire bottom trays which are supported clear of the ground. The drying rate is increased if air movement over the surface of the grain is restricted by placing the drier behind a wind break. In addition, by creating a downward flow of air through the exposed produce, drying is more effective than open sun drying (Bailey and Williamson, 1965). Considerable attention is necessary: the produce should be moved while it is drying in order to assist even drying and should be covered and carried indoors in the evening or before rain. It is at this stage that the produce can become infested and also cracked or broken due to excessive and careless handling. Breakage of the grains is minimized by the use of trays, mats or plastic sheeting, one form of which is the Allgate plastic sun drier (Figure 29).

Compared with trays and mats, the Allgate drier provides a combination of facilities including ease of spreading, collecting, and respreading; protection from rain above and moisture from the ground; protection from thieves, since the drier plus contents are easily lifted into the house at night; protection from insects and facility of fumigation to kill pests already present at harvest; and a means of measuring moisture loss each day by placing the drier plus contents on a scale before and after each drying period. Such a procedure may be particularly useful to agricultural stations where yields from trial or seed plots have to be kept separate and in such circumstances one drier per plot yield can be used as the storage container. The plastic-coated material of the container is shaped to enable produce spread over its surface to be quickly collected by pulling a cord and then covered by a flap which is part of the drier. It costs between $9 and $23 according to the size, the larger model having a capacity of about 150 kilogrammes. Large sheets of plastic could be used on drying areas to improve existing methods of natural drying.

FIGURE 29. The Allgate drier, showing the method of closing in order to give protection against rain and insects.

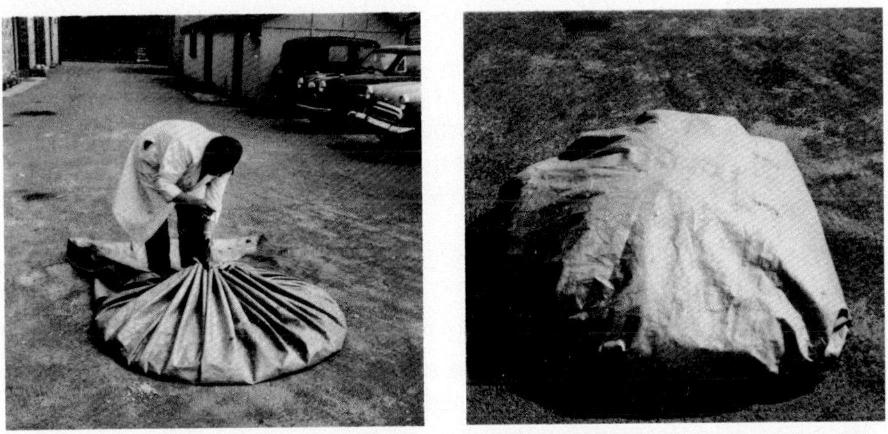

Open-side container for natural drying

This type of drying is useful for maize on the cob or unthreshed legumes and cereals. It should be remembered that more efficient drying is achieved by removing the sheath from cob maize or the pods from pulses. Where cribs of this type are used it is important to obtain the optimum drying effect by limiting the width of the crib in relation to its depth to a maximum of 2 metres and orienting it to ensure that the long axis is facing the prevail-

FIGURE 30. A natural drying and storage method: the European-type maize crib, designed for maximum ventilation.

ing winds. Cribs should be designed and constructed to prevent or minimize rain from falling on the sides; this may be achieved by a roof with wide overhangs (Figure 30).

Artificial drying

If the humidity is too high to allow grain to be dried adequately by natural means and storage methods do not facilitate further drying, it is necessary to dry the produce by using heat. Various local methods using available materials have been developed. In some areas storage has to be restricted to the amount which can be dried on a heat supply similar to that available from a kitchen fire. Thus panicles of paddy and maize stored on horizontal grids are kept dry by heat from a fire which is lit occasionally underneath the grid, and the heap of panicles is turned at regular intervals to prevent the development of mould. There are raised granaries beneath which fires are lit to complete drying. The produce receives a characteristic odour and flavour when exposed directly to smoke from the fire as well as to the hot dry air. This problem is overcome by using driers designed with a hot air chamber or heat exchange unit and smoke stack or chimney.

The most popular forms of artificial drying may be characterized by the depth of grain being dried. There are:

(*a*) deep layer driers;

(*b*) in-sack driers;

(*c*) shallow layer driers.

Drying with heated air covers the entire range from low temperature and low air volume drying, to high temperature and high air volume drying. In the former, the air temperature is raised above ambient by about 5°C to 10°C and drying should be completed in 3 to 14 days to avoid deterioration; but the depth of grain and volume of air used are important criteria and, in a system based on such criteria, the air temperature is raised above ambient by 15°C to 60°C and drying should be completed in several minutes, although with certain products multipass systems may have to be adopted.

Drier fans may be driven by internal combustion engines or by electric motors. Automatic controls are easier to install on electric motors. The fan may be located in the system so that air is moved through the grain to the intake side of the fan or forced through the grain by the discharge side of the fan. Fan efficiency is equivalent in each case but the forced discharge is chosen in almost every instance.

Deep layer driers

These consist of silo bins or rectangular warehouses fitted with ducting or false floors through which air is distributed and blown through the grain; with this method heaps of grain may be up to 3.5 metres in depth.

Deep layer driers utilizing unheated atmospheric air which is forced through the grain by a mechanical fan (or air which has been heated slightly, particularly when cold temperature or high relative humidity conditions exist) does not dry the mass of grain uniformly. The grain dries first at the point where the air enters, a drying front passes through the mass in the direction of air movement, and the grain at the air discharge location dries last. An insufficient airflow will lengthen the drying time possibly causing spoilage at the point of air discharge. Suggested operating conditions are given in Table 17.

TABLE 17. – DEEP LAYER DRIER OPERATING CONDITIONS FOR DIFFERENT CLIMATIC CONDITIONS

Climate	Representative temperature and relative humidity		Air rate, m^3/h per m^3 of storage space	Drying conditions
	Degrees C	Percent		
Hot wet	35	90	135	Add 8°C to incoming air
Cool wet	21	85	120	Add 8°C to incoming air
Hot dry	35	35	105	Use unheated air
Cool dry	21	35	105	Use unheated air

SOURCE: Dr. S.M. Henderson, University of California.

The drying air should not be heated much more than indicated above or spoilage may result at the point of air discharge due to high moisture content of the drying air at this stage unless air flow rates, and hence power requirements, are increased excessively. A period of from 7 to 30 days may be required for drying.

In-sack driers

In-sack driers consist of a platform constructed with a number of openings of the same shape but slightly smaller in size than the standard type of jute sack, with an enclosed area (plenum chamber) underneath into which heated air is blown from a heater/blower unit. The platform may be made of local material. Each hole is covered with a sack of produce. The amount of produce in the sack should be slightly less than that required to completely fill it, in order to ensure that when the sack is placed over the hole in the platform it completely covers or fills the hole. In this way the heated air must pass through the produce in the sack and cannot "escape" along the edges of the opening.

A typical oil-fired unit has a fan which delivers 9 700 cubic metres per hour heated to 14°C above atmospheric temperature and uses 4.5 litres of fuel oil/hour. This unit can deal with 2, 3 or even 4 or 5 tons of grain at a time according to platform size. With a 2-ton loading, the moisture removal rate would be approximately 1 percent per hour; with 4 tons more than half this rate.

Using electric heating, a 45 kilowatt bank will remove approximately 1 percent moisture per hour from a 2-ton batch (United Kingdom, 1966).

With these driers it is essential to turn the sack of grain after several hours of drying to assist even drying of the contents.

Shallow layer driers

These driers consist of trays, cascades or columns in which a thin layer of grain (less than about 20 centimetres) is exposed to heated air; with most driers of this type the grain moves at a continuous rate along the length of the drier.

In these driers the grain is subjected to a stream of air at the highest safe temperature and the amount of drying is regulated by the time the grain is allowed to remain in the drier, either as a stationary batch or as a slow moving stream.

Shallow layer driers are factory manufactured units and require adjustment for crop and moisture content range when installed. The air rate per unit of mass is many times that of the deep layer drier and no significant moisture gradient develops during drying. Consequently, the drying temperature is limited only by the possibility of heat damage to the grains. (Observe the safe temperatures listed in Table 12.)

EFFECT OF BAROMETRIC PRESSURE ON DRYING

Reference has already been made to the effect of altitude in relation to moisture content criteria. It is therefore relevant to draw attention to certain points concerning drying which have been summarized in a personal communication from W.F. Williamson of the National Institute of Agricultural Engineering of the United Kingdom.

Pressure changes due to weather are usually of little importance but where a drying machine designed for use at or near sea level is used at a considerable altitude the resultant low working pressure has two effects; the difference between the vapour pressure in the grain and the air is increased and allows drying to take place more readily; and the density of the air is decreased so that at a given temperature a fan delivering a constant volume will deliver a smaller weight of air at the lower pressure with consequent loss of drying performance. These effects largely cancel each other out. However, to compensate for the effect of low density on the fan, its speed can be increased up to the limit of the available power. If the power unit is an electric motor its output will, of course, be unaffected, but the power of an internal combustion engine drops off with reduced air density so that with engine driven units the compensating increase in fan speed may not be practicable. For corrections for density, the following formula can be used:

$$\text{Pressure} \times \text{Volume} = R \times \text{Temperature } (^{\circ}A)$$
$$(\text{for air } R = 53.34)$$

The precise effect of drying in farm type driers with low density air is not yet known but there is some experimental evidence indicating that when drying is done at an altitude of 1 800 metres there is a useful saving of fuel as compared with similar drying near sea level.

Methods to be encouraged

Artificial drying of produce may be effected by three methods which vary in temperature to which the air is heated and the speed with which it is moved through the grain. A simple and effective type of artificial drier is a locally built platform drier in which the products of combustion of local fuel are not allowed to pass through the produce, but heat the air which passes through the produce by means of natural air movement or convection currents. An example of this type of drier is that built for experimental purposes at Mokwa, Nigeria (A'Brook, 1963). Basically it consists of a rectangular pit. The laterite spoil from the pit is used to build the walls which bound the pit and support the drying floor. The enclosed space forms the plenum chamber in which the gastight flue made of oil drums is placed, the firebox being located outside the plenum chamber. Air heated in the plenum chamber rises through the drying floor forming a heat exchange type of drier. These driers have been built in two sizes, one to take a maximum charge of 700 kilogrammes and the other of 1 150 kilogrammes. Each cost about $1 000 to build. Other forms of platform driers, including those for bagged produce, have been referred to previously. They generally utilize the principle of high temperature and low volume air.

An alternative form of drying utilizes large volumes of air raised to a temperature a few degrees above ambient air and produced by either a static or a mobile internal combustion engine plus a large fan. This system of drying has much to recommend it, and recent work indicates that the quality of produce dried in this way is maintained at a high level, and the breakage of paddy or rice grains is low. The introduction of mesh metal silos plus a liner, fitted with a fan/heater unit, might usefully be considered for areas having high humidity. There is a very wide range of artificial driers, each producing varying volumes of air at controlled temperatures adjusted for the grain being dried, its eventual use and the relative humidity of the drying air. Although many of the machines required for this type of drying are elaborate, a number of them have worked effectively in the tropics. Where a large throughput of grain is required, these driers have to be considered and a decision reached on the particular type which, of the many available commercially, meets all local needs.

In-storage or deep layer drying

By this method the grain is not moved out of the drier after having been dried. Depths of grain to be dried are between 3 to 4 metres. If drying is being carried out with unheated air, flow rates of 300 to 400 litres per minute per quintal (2.4 to 3.2 cubic metres/minute per cubic metre) are required. When relative humidities are 78 to 80 percent, heated air is required, and air volumes can be reduced from 90 to 100 litres per minute per quintal of produce. If the storage is constructed with a false floor of perforated steel supported above the storage bin floor so that it forms a plenum chamber, the heated air which dries the grain begins to dry the bottom layers first and gradually dries the grain at the top of the bin. It is essential not to overdry the grain at the bottom of the bin by controlling the heating unit with a humidistat so that the amount of heat added is only as much as is required to drop the absolute humidity of the drying air slightly below the equilibrium moisture content which the grain would have at a relative humidity of 70 percent for the mean storage temperature for the area or 28°C, whichever is lower. Drying is completed when grain near the surface has been dried to approximately the safe moisture content and maximum use has been made of the heat supplied. This type of drier has the advantage that, once grain has been placed in storage, it does not need to be moved. If more than one bin is to be dried, the heater-blower unit must be moved to the other storage unit. This system is similar to the farm drying unit using only heated air except that, rather than depending only on convection currents to move the drying air through the grain, the unit is equipped with a fan.

Nonmixing driers

These are driers in the simplest form. They may be either columnar or horizontal.

Columnar drier. This is the type most commonly used because it takes advantage of the gravity flow of grain through the drier to reduce the amount of machinery in the drier itself and utilizes standard elevating and grain handling equipment. The grain flows downward between screens which will vary with make and design. In all cases, the driers utilize double screens which are approximately parallel. Heated air is blown into the plenum chamber which is formed between two sets of screens. It then passes out horizontally through the screens. The grain is moved gradually through the drier by removing a small amount with bottom unloading augers. Normally the plenum chamber is divided into two compartments with a horizontal separation or partition. Ambient air is blown into the lower portion of the plenum chamber to cool the grain before it is placed in storage. For some grains, e.g., rice, a number of driers are grouped together and the supply chamber then acts as the cooling and conditioning chamber for the preceding drier section. The spacing between screens varies from a low of 12 centimetres to highs of 15 to 16 centimetres. Height of unit may be about 4 metres plus the depth of the cooling bin.

Horizontal driers. These have a number of chambers. Each chamber is divided by horizontal equidistant screen-bottomed trays placed on horizontal pivots. A control lever on the outside swivels the trays into a horizontal position for receiving and drying grain and to permit turning to the vertical to discharge the grain to the tray beneath. The damp grain is placed on the top tray in a layer 16 to 18 centimetres deep. After an initial drying period, which will be the estimated total drying time divided by the number of trays, the grain is tipped to the next set of trays. Once the initial trayload is delivered, the holding time can be adjusted as necessary. For rice drying some chambers in the drier are used for cooling and conditioning. This type of drier is normally operated as a batch drier. It is therefore an advantage for the unit to have two cooling chambers so that while one batch is being removed from the machine another batch can be loaded into the drier. A typical drier of this type would comprise a drier unit with a double drying chamber, a cleaning unit, and augers or elevating units for filling the drier and for elevating the grain to storage.

Mixing, shallow-layer driers

The mixing type of air drier provides slightly more uniformity in the drying of grain. Mixing can be incorporated in the columnar type drier by incorporating baffles which deflect and stir the grain as it passes through the drier.

In another style of mixing-drier the air plenum chamber is at one end of the machine and introduces air through horizontal air ducts located in the main body of the drier. These air ducts are inverted U-troughs placed in staggered rows vertically so that the grain is mixed as it passes through the unit. The discharge system at the base of the drier regulates the fall of grain through the unit and can be adjusted to provide an adequate holding time to assure drying the grain to a safe moisture content for storages. This type of drier unit is normally quite large and incorporates a cooling fan or fans as well as the fan for forcing the heated air through the drier. It is also possible to obtain these driers as very small units for use at farm level. The air is heated in a fuel oil, coal or electric furnace. The heated air then circulates naturally through the air channels or is forced in by a blower. One such drier has a capacity of 600 kilogrammes, stands 1.4 to 1.8 metres high and is fed by hand. Moisture removal rate is approximately 3 percent in 3 to 6 hours with a blower and at least 10 hours without. The grain may be passed through the drier several times if desired.

Moving-bed shallow-layer driers

A number of driers are available which have perforated bottoms on the drier through which air is forced to dry the grain. The latter is placed on the drier in a shallow layer and is moved along by either a conveyor or by vibration of the drier bed. With units of this type speed of movement is controlled by the rate at which grain is removed from the drier. Drying is normally carried out with air at 50°C and air volumes of 350 litres per minute per quintal of produce.

Cost of drying

The cost of drying varies according to the method used, the type of artificial drier and the type and quantity of produce to be dried.

Costs can be gauged in terms of capital expenditure, labour and running costs.

With natural drying, where produce is spread on the ground or on tin roofs, only labour costs have to be considered and of course these are negligible or nonexistent where the farmer and his family perform the operations of spreading, collecting and respreading as part of their daily routine. Where, however, the produce is spread on trays or plastic sheets, there is a capital cost involved which, although very small by some standards, may be a major expenditure to the local farmer. Under such circumstances, government departments may consider subsidizing the sale of these simple devices to assist in improved drying.

With artificial drying, capital expenditure may vary considerably. The cheapest driers are in-sack driers and simple types of tray driers, utilizing locally available material. More expensive in capital cost but with slightly lower labour costs are the deep-layer driers, the ventilated bins. Most expensive in capital and labour costs are the continuous-flow driers which require skilled engineers to maintain them. Where large quantities of grain have to be dried, the shallow-layer drier is the most practical (with a throughput capacity of 34 kilogrammes per minute and a reduction of the moisture content of 100 tons and 400 tons of grain by 6 percent, the total cost per ton will be about $7 and $3 respectively).

Certain types of low temperature/high volume drying systems are said to be capable of drying produce at a cost of about $3 per ton.

7. STORAGE METHODS

Grain storage is carried out for three purposes: to retain a supply of food; to service a trading system; and to retain seed for planting the following season. Storage is therefore carried out by the producer, the trader, the processor, and the exporter, and at all these levels the methods adopted affect the problem of deterioration of foodstuffs. Since many of the methods of storage used at these different levels are somewhat similar, it is possible to survey this subject on the basis of traditional and modern storage methods.

Two methods of storage are used: in sacks, or loose in bulk in a variety of containers. The choice between these depends upon the following local factors:

(*a*) type of produce
(*b*) duration of storage
(*c*) value of produce
(*d*) climate
(*e*) transport system
(*f*) cost and availability of labour
(*g*) cost and availability of sacks
(*h*) incidence of rodents and certain types of insect (e.g., *Sitotroga cerealella*) infestation.

In general terms the advantages and disadvantages of sack and bulk storage respectively are:

Sacks	*Bulk*
Flexibility of storage	Inflexible storage
Partly mechanizable	Mechanizable
Slow handling	Rapid handling

Sacks	*Bulk*
Considerable spillage	Little spillage
Low capital cost	High capital cost
High operating costs	Low operating costs
High rodent loss potential	Low rodent loss potential
Reinfestation occurs	Little protection against reinfestation

With both methods it is essential to ensure that the container (sack, warehouse or silo) is kept free from dust, spillage and old grain residues, and that the food grains put in the container are of good quality, and that the grain is dry and free of dust and other unwholesome particles. The aim should be to put dry, clean, uninfested produce in a sound, clean, uninfested storage container.

Traditional storage

Storage of food grains by the indigenous peoples of the tropics and subtropics is mostly traditional: the methods employed today have been used for many years with little or no modification. These methods achieve varying degrees of success in applying the basic principles involved in the safe storage of food grains; the variations observed are often related to climate, but local natural resources and customs also influence the choice of storage methods. A typical range of storage methods encountered in these regions is given in Table 18.

Types in use

The storage of food grains begins immediately after the crop has been harvested. In the normal sequence of events the crop is gathered together in heaps on the ground to facilitate removal from the field. Usually such heaps are left for only a few hours or a day or two at the most. However, in some countries where the harvesting of a crop coincides with the beginning of a long dry season or more than one crop must be harvested at the same time, the heaps may be left undisturbed for quite a long time. This is a deliberate act by the producer and may therefore be regarded as a method of temporary storage.

TABLE 18. – TRADITIONAL (OR PRODUCER) STORAGE METHODS

Storage method	Special measures	Product
WITHOUT COVER		
No structure	Heaped on ground	Paddy Groundnuts
Vertical pole	Tied to poles	Maize
Horizontal cords or creepers	Hung on these strands which are tied between poles or trees	Maize
Vertical racks	Hung on horizontal poles fixed to vertical poles	Paddy
Platform (timber and grass)	Heaped on platform	Maize Pulses Groundnuts
Open baskets (grass)	Raised 1 metre or more above ground	Paddy Maize Groundnuts
Sacks (woven plant material)	Placed on platform 1 metre high	Paddy
WITH COVER		
Horizontal grid	Hung on horizontal poles; covered with loose thatch roof	Paddy
Platform	Heaped on platform; covered with 'straw hat' which rests on platform	Paddy Maize
Granary		
(*a*) Simple type (usually cylindrical)	Constructed of plant material raised above ground, with thatch roof	All types
(*b*) Structure incorporating clay	As (*a*) but with mud or clay worked into floor and walls	All types

TABLE 18. – TRADITIONAL (OR PRODUCER) STORAGE METHODS (*concluded*)

Storage method	Special measures	Product
(*c*) Wall of clay mixed with plant material supported by timber frame	Cylindrical or elliptical, raised above ground	Cereals Paddy Millet Sorghum
(*d*) As (*c*) but not supported by timber frame	Jar-shaped, raised on " foot " of clay or log. Sometimes divided into compartments.	Maize Sorghum Millet
(*e*) Wall of clay only	Various shapes, " straw hat "	Cereals and groundnuts
Clay jar (usually kept in living hut)	Sealed with damp earth; sealed with flat stone and clay; partially baked before storage; produce mixed with ash, jar sealed with clay; produce mixed with ash.	Maize seed All types of grain Maize meal Maize Sorghum
Gourds	Sealed with clay Plugged with stems of plant	All types Maize Grain
Baskets	Usually placed in kitchen	Groundnuts Paddy (seed) Beans
Commodity wrapped in matting	Kept in living hut	All types
Stored under roof of living hut	Small bundles hung from roof above fire	Cereals
Stored on floor of living hut	Temporary storage	Paddy
Underground storage	Sometimes lined with cowdung and fired. Opening sealed with clay or grass thatch and thorns	Cereals
Communal store	Large crib of millet stalks or bamboo (12-ton capacity)	Paddy
" Improved traditional "	Square sided crib with timber frame and walls of wire netting	Maize

Unshucked maize cobs are hung in bundles on cords or on creepers from trees (see Figure 31) or sometimes tied to poles stuck vertically in the ground in the field or near the village. This method is also adopted during the dry season, but the cobs may remain on the pole until they are used up.

Unshucked maize, panicles of paddy, and millet may be permanently stored on vertical racks from 2 to 3 metres high and 5 to 20 metres long, the length depending upon the abundance of the harvest. Similarly various food grains are kept on timber and grass platforms (Figure 32) between 1 and 3 metres square and raised 1 to 2 metres above ground level during the dry season.

Removable thatch roofs are sometimes used to cover panicles of paddy stored on horizontal timber grids 2 metres square and 1 to 2 metres above ground level; the edge of the roof rests directly on the grid. Occasionally a fire is lit under the grid in order to complete drying and prevent insect and fungal attack. The roof is lifted from time to time and the panicles are turned to facilitate airing.

There is a type of store intermediate between that described above and the more familiar granary (see below). The produce is placed on a platform 2 to 3 metres square and raised 0.5 to 1 metre above ground level, covered by a large thatched roof which is permanently fixed in position with its edge resting on the platform (Figure 33). Access to the grain is provided by a small hole in one side of the roof at its base. Another type consists of a raised floor supported by forked tree branches around which is built a frame of slender branches or sticks stuck into the ground and kept together by several horizontal rings of sticks bundled together from floor level upward. The whole structure tapers off until it forms a beehive or helmet shaped frame. The outside is then covered with grass bundles tied to the horizontal rings starting at floor level. A rectangular door is provided which, in some localities, is permanently closed halfway from floor level and is also fitted with a protruding half circular shelter above; otherwise the doorway is open at floor level and does not have a shelter. The door opening is usually closed by horizontal logs or branches placed in a frame on the outside, but sometimes only with grass. A peak made of grass or sometimes of gourd shells makes a roof for the granary.

Conical baskets constructed of woven grass made in varying sizes up to a capacity of 500 kilogrammes of grain (Figure 34)

FIGURE 31. Unshucked maize cobs hung in a bunch from a tree.

FIGURE 32. Food grains dried on a timber and grass platform over a fire, and covered by a thatched roof.

FIGURE 33. Produce on a platform covered by a permanent thatched roof.

FIGURE 34. Nonportable baskets of woven grass.

FIGURE 35. Storage bins made of plant material only.

FIGURE 36. A method of storing cob maize on a platform.

are used in several areas. A wide variety of other baskets are used. The materials of construction vary with local fibres and level of skills developed.

The most frequently used method of storage is the container constructed entirely of plant materials with clearly defined walls in addition to a floor and roof (Figure 35). It may be circular or rectangular in plan and is usually elevated above ground level. The dimensions of this type of container vary considerably, even in the same locality, and are determined mainly by the quantity of grain to be stored. Thus the diameter may be 0.5 to 3 metres; the walls 1 to 2.5 metres high; and the floor 0.1 to 2.0 metres above ground level. The floor is generally raised highest above ground level in areas where there is danger from floods or domestic animals.

One method employed for storing maize in humid areas is shown in Figure 36. The unshucked cobs are carefully laid in layers on a low-lying circular platform to form a cylindrical stack 1.4 to 3 metres in diameter and 1 to 2 metres high. The stack is protected from rain by a conical thatch roof which may either be left open at the sides or completely covered by the thatch.

The types of store described so far are made of plant materials only. The use of clay or mud in the construction of storage containers may be regarded as a refinement and the amount of clay or mud used in building a particular container varies; thus, the floor alone may be sealed with mud (Figure 37), or the floor and both sides of the wall, up to a level above which the roof overhang provides protection from driving rain, are plastered with mud (Figure 38). In certain regions it is more common for the walls and floor of the container to be completely encased in clay or mud. In some areas the exposed surfaces of containers plastered with mud are protected from erosion by thatched " skirts. "

In certain countries the most popular type of container is the raised compartmented bin (Figure 39). It is usually square in plan, with walls about 3 metres long and 1.5 to 2 metres high, and is divided into four or more compartments. Each compartment is provided with an entrance (generally round) 0.6 metre in diameter toward the top of a side wall. The whole structure is supported on a platform resting at least 0.5 metre above ground level on rocks or timber supports. Both external and internal dividing walls (when built of timber) and the platform are plastered with mud

FIGURE 37. Storage container having the floor only lined with mud.

FIGURE 38. Storage container with floor and walls of mud and an overhanging roof.

FIGURE 39. Storage bin made of mud, and compartmentalized.

usually derived from termitaria (mounds of termites or white ants). Sometimes the walls are constructed of mud bricks in which case the mud plastered on the platform is first allowed to set hard. After the bin has been filled with grain the top is covered with sticks and plastered with mud. The entrance hole is fitted with a lid and is sealed by smearing around the sides with mud or cow dung. A thatched roof on separate supports is then placed over the bin.

One type of container is constructed by plastering a timber frame with clay mixed with fragmented plant materials, such as twigs and grass; this is alleged to give added strength to the clay, which is otherwise liable to crack and crumble. Containers of this type are raised on blocks of laterite stone or granite and may be completely sealed with clay when full, open at the top (i.e., closed only by the thatched roof) or have an opening in the side which is sealed with a thatch or wooden door. Containers of this type may be elliptical in shape and raised 0.4 metre above ground level on pedestals of unbaked clay or timber with floors of timber which may or may not be sealed with clay.

Containers made of clay, but without timber frames, are constructed in many countries. Most examples consist only of clay (without plant fragments) and are usually of small capacity, although some may be divided into several compartments.

Food grains may also be stored in underground pits, but this method of storage is traditional in only a few countries, e.g., India. Various types of pit could be described from India, north Africa and Latin America, in all of which it is claimed that grain may be left for many years. Flask shaped pits up to some 6 metres deep have been reported; normally such pits are sealed with a dried earth cap or a large stone embedded in soft mud. Some are lined with a cylinder of grass matting, the gap between the matting and the earth being filled with millet chaff and the opening covered with grass thatch and thorns (Figure 40). Pits can be located in enclosed areas where cattle are kept because these sites are generally free from termites and are relatively dry. In some areas the walls of the pits are dried out by burning grass, etc., in the pit and then covered with a layer of clay; in other areas the pits are lined with stones or bricks which have been covered with clay to give a smooth hard finish.

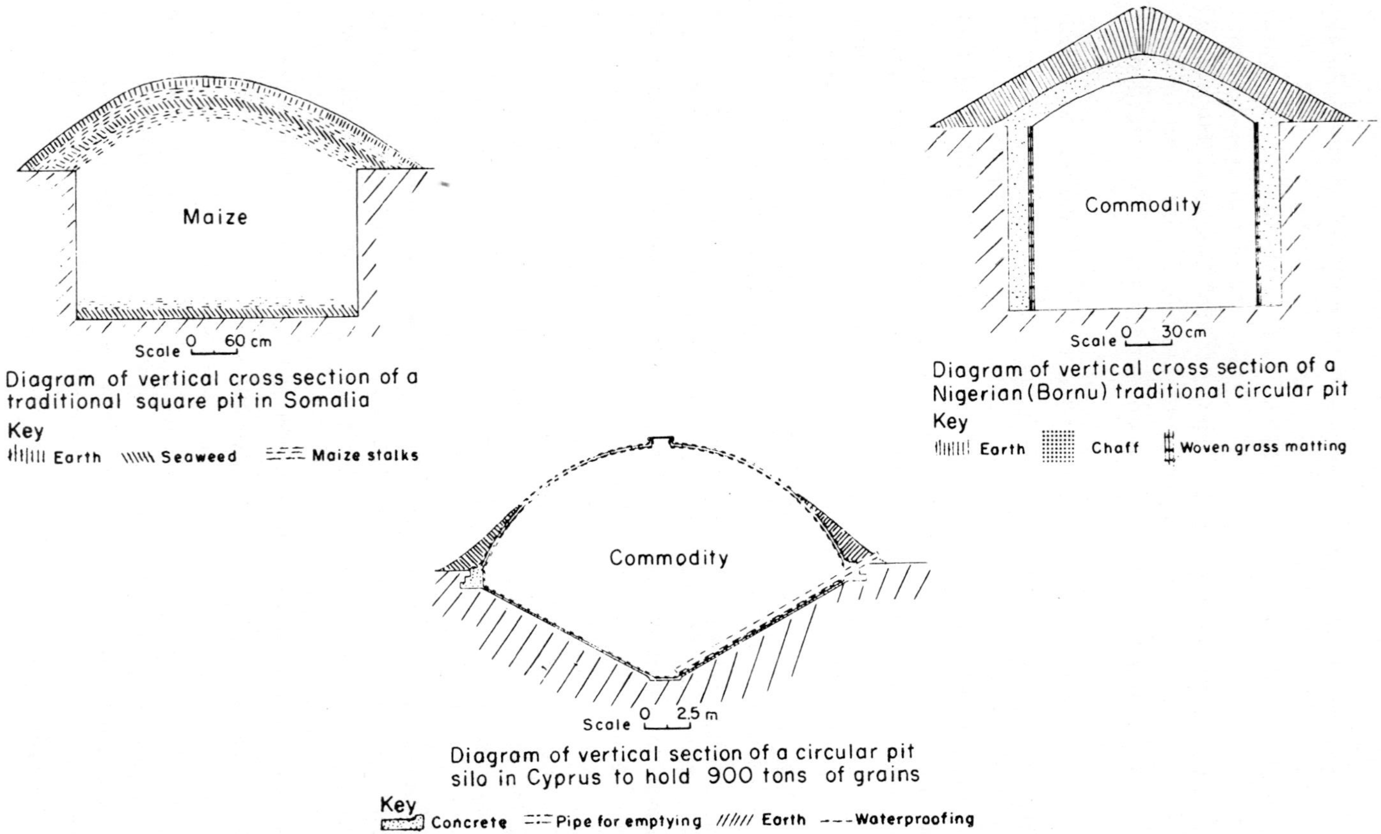

FIGURE 40. Diagrams of (above) traditional and (below) modern types of pit storage.

FIGURE 41. Portable storage bag made of plaited palm leaves with special neck closure, said to make it insect proof.

The methods of storage so far described are for relatively large quantities of unthreshed grain. Where the crop is small or grain has been removed from the granary for preparation as food, it may be stored threshed or unthreshed in smaller containers such as small baskets or jars, which can be carried easily. Small containers are also used for the storage of seed because they are more easily sealed and protected.

There is an infinite variety of sizes and designs of baskets used. It has been suggested that this feature is probably linked with barter trade in which the size of container would assume special significance as a measure. In general when baskets are used for the storage of grain they are made to serve an immediate purpose which is usually temporary. When they are used for storage over a longer period they are kept either in the dwelling hut or on top of other produce in a larger container or granary, and may be covered loosely with matting or banana leaves.

Hand knitted bags with open mouths which are made from local fibres and with fibre or leather straps for carrying are commonly used in most areas. Bags made from plaited palm leaves and paddy stalks are also used. Tapering a bag toward the top and rolling the mouth end inward (Figure 41) to protect the produce is not a new idea; such bags of very closely woven natural fibres are used in several tropical areas.

After being thoroughly dried, grain may be placed in a calabash or gourd, the mouth of which is sealed with clay, mud, cow dung or a wooden stopper. The container is then stored in the dwelling hut or on top of produce in a granary. It is used mainly for the storage of seed.

Earthenware jars are also used for the storage of grain in a number of countries. In some countries sorghum, millet, paddy, cowpeas, beans, grain and sesame seed are mixed with ash and stored in large earthenware vessels about 1 metre high; some have a narrow neck and are covered with clay (the seed is frequently taken out and exposed to the sun in layers). Earthenware jars which are cylindroconical in shape and have access holes in the sides are used in some areas.

Food grains may be stored in greater or lesser quantities on a loft in the dwelling hut. In upland regions (e.g., altitude of about 1 500 metres) the loft is built over the fireplace, while others build the loft across the whole round hut under the conical roof.

Improved simple types. Too little attention has been given to improving on the design and construction of local storage containers but it becomes clear from the data recorded that, with minor changes in design, it should be possible to effect either better drying or better control of insect and rodent pests during storage.

Two main types of traditional storage containers are in use: one with solid walls (Figure 38), and one with very porous walls (Figure 37). Each will store produce successfully under the appropriate climatic conditions, if constructed according to specific basic criteria.

The solid walled container should be used in areas where the produce is harvested dry (i.e., below the safe level of moisture content) and the humidity of the air is above 70 percent during the storage period (or a part of it). Efforts should be made to build the container in such a way that the surfaces of the walls (inside and outside) are smooth and do not develop cracks, and to completely " seal " the top entrance or loading/unloading opening using the same local mud as that employed for the walls. It may be possible to encourage farmers and villagers to incorporate cement in moulding the mud (i.e., a stabilized soil technique) and to finish with a coat of waterproof paint, or to " daub " the completed mud wall with a bituminous material (cutback or solvent in preference to an emulsion) which will impart a smooth waterproof surface inside. Alternatively, during construction of the mud container, efforts could be made to incorporate a lining of plastic sheeting in the wall in such a way as to make the container airtight. Since 1958, research workers in India have been experimenting with this idea and Pradhan, Mookherjee and Sharma (1965) have published findings which indicate that under certain conditions safe storage for very dry wheat (7.5 percent moisture content) was achieved over 16 months. They record that rectangular structures capable of holding up to 3 000 kilogrammes can be successfully constructed on the following lines. See also the illustration in Figure 42.

Size	For a 2 000 kg storage size, internal dimensions are 1.4 m × 1.0 m × 1.6 m (high).
Walls	The four walls consist of two layers (each 7.6 cm) of mud or unburnt brick with a polythene film as a sandwich. If bricks are used, 750 will be required (each 22.9 cm × 11.5 cm × 7.6 cm).
Floor and roof	These consist of two layers (each 5 cm) of mud with a polythene film as a sandwich. A wooden frame is used on top to form the mud roof.
Plastic	9 m of polythene film (180 cm wide) 700 gauge (0.18 mm).
Manhole	Placed in one corner of the top surface and measuring 60 cm × 60 cm.
Outlet	24 cm length of galvanized tin sheet pipe (9 cm diameter) with a tight-fitting lid.

The structure is built over a burned brick floor. If a burned brick floor is not available, it should be made on a suitable site.

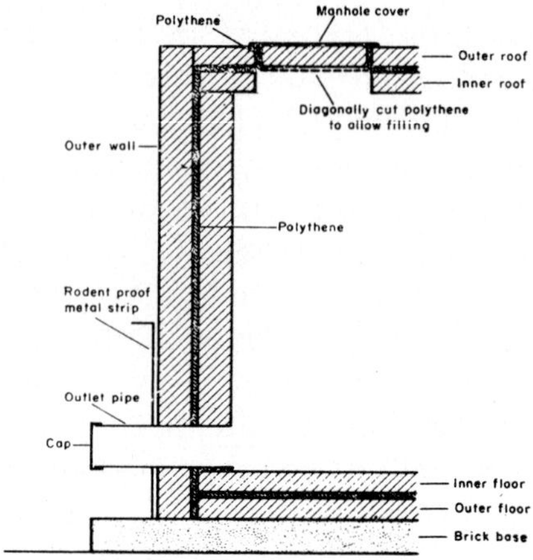

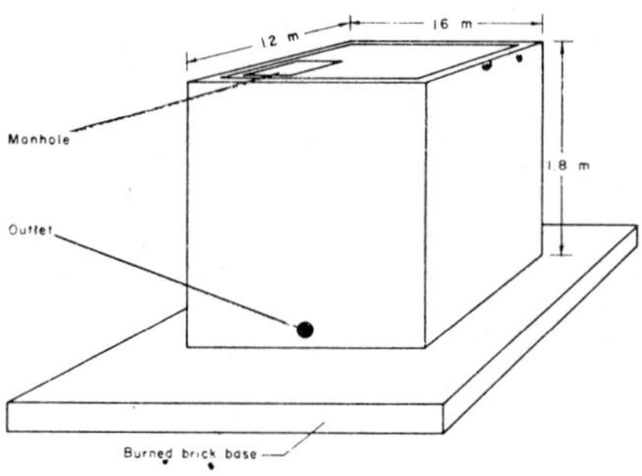

FIGURE 42. Pusa bin incorporating plastic film sheeting in mud wall construction, together with two constructional diagrams.

Next a mud platform of roughly 1.6 × 1.2 metres, 5 centimetres thick, is made and a polythene film of 1.8 × 1.4 metres is placed over it. A 5 centimetre thick layer of mud is then applied over the film covering the same size as the platform under the polythene film. The inner wall (7.6 centimetres thick) of the structure covering the four sides is then constructed. The inner layer of the mud roof of the structure is then made by using 5-centimetre thick mud slabs prepared earlier and placing them over a wooden frame. An area of 60 × 60 centimetres is, however, kept open in one corner to serve as a manhole. The entire structure is then carefully covered with the polythene film, the polythene cover having been prepared earlier by heat sealing; after this the free edges of the polythene sheet near the base are also similarly sealed. At this stage the outlet mentioned earlier is fixed by making a hole in the inner mud layer as well as the polythene film. Finally, the outer layers of the walls of 7.6 centimetres in thickness are erected all round the structure, covering the polythene film. A 5-centimetre thick mud plaster is also put over the polythene film at the top leaving the manhole. The portion of the polythene film covering the manhole is then cut diagonally to make the necessary passage. When the structure is filled with grain the manhole is finally sealed with a square piece of polythene film and plugged with mud.

This type of container may be improved by having a large thatched roof with plenty of overhang to keep the surface of the container as cool as possible.

In areas where solid-walled containers with only one opening for filling and emptying are used, efforts should be made to have a simple form of outlet spout incorporated near the bottom of one of the walls. The top half of a tin with a press-on lid can be used for this purpose. The introduction of such an outlet spout eliminates the need for a man to enter the top of the container to withdraw produce, thereby permitting the use of a fumigant in the container if necessary. This also makes for a better rotational use of the produce in store.

With new developments in plastics it is probable that various forms of flexible and solid-walled containers may in the future be successfully introduced at certain levels of farming. (Wright & Southgate, 1962) The use of metal drums (e.g., of 5 to 40 gallons) capable of being hermetically sealed has been recommended for use at farmer and trader levels.

The porous-walled container consisting of sticks, bamboo, or wire netting should be used in areas where the produce is harvested damp, and it is essential that drying out take place during the first few weeks of storage. To ensure maximum drying the size of the container should be limited and the container, which is longer than it is broad, should be orientated in the direction of the wind. The roof construction, whether of thatching material or metal, must provide protection from driving rain, e.g., by having a generous overhang which protects the sides of the container. The floor should be clear of the ground and constructed to prevent rats and other animals from getting into the container, e.g., by fitting rodentproof barriers of sheet metal protruding at least 20 centimetres at right angles to the surface of poles or base up which the rat must climb to enter the container.

Modern storage

Basically, modern methods of grain storage are elaborations of traditional methods, but constructed with the use of modern materials. There are two main types: storage in bags (e.g., sisal, kenaf and jute) in warehouses; and bulk storage in various types of silo bins. Such methods are most commonly used by traders, cooperatives, etc., and at large-scale central storage depots, but they are also being adopted by farmers in a number of countries.

Trader storage

When produce is moved from the farm it is purchased and stored by traders. It may be stored and handled by several traders before it is eventually consumed locally or exported. Thus trader storage includes methods in use by the small trader, by cooperatives and at local markets. Similar methods are in use on government farms, etc., which are therefore included under this heading.

Types in use

A variety of types of storage is used by traders. The most common method used in many countries is bag storage in a variety of types of buildings, e. g., stone, local brick, corrugated iron, and mud and wattle, with or without plastered walls and with an earth, stone or cement floor and corrugated iron or thatched roof. Such stores may often be part of the dwelling house, and storage facilities may be such that the application of insect control measures is difficult or virtually impossible.

A system of warehouse/silo storage has been adopted by some cooperative groups; hangars with a metal framework are divided into a number of cells; the floor is concrete and a reinforced concrete wall forms the exterior of the cells which are separated by movable wooden partitions.

FIGURE 43. Types of small silos as minor collecting points.

Above, locally built store.

Centre, wooden construction.

Below, metal cylinders.

Bulk storage in small silos (Figure 43) is used by some societies in land development schemes ; they are made of locally constructed brick or concrete and have up to about 100-ton capacity ; concrete silos, prefabricated metal (including aluminium) silos with "elastic joints," and wooden (including plywood) silos are in use throughout the world. Investigations have indicated that the success of these different types of silo varies. In humid coastal regions the need for artificial drying of produce prior to silo storage has been shown on more than one occasion by the poor results obtained with metal silos. In some areas cement pipes have been successfully converted into silos 2 cubic metres in capacity.

At markets, produce in bags may be kept in small rooms (metal sheds, wattle and mud-walled huts or concrete or brick buildings) and quantities of the produce are displayed on the ground on reed mats or on tables, often in a variety of basins. In a few markets, storage of produce is not allowed; all produce on sale must be brought in daily and displayed only on concrete tables which are washed at the end of each day's bargaining.

Types to be encouraged

The type of structure to be chosen for storage will vary according to region, volume of produce being handled, variety of grains, method of handling, i.e., bulk or bag, cleaning, drying, grading, treatment, power supply, available construction materials, period of storage and financial resources.

Bag storage should be retained in areas where road and transport facilities are poorly developed; where quantities of grain delivered and handled by traders are in small lots; and where a wide variety of products is to be handled. Some bulk handling facilities would aid in cleaning, drying and grading operations to provide a uniform product for the market prior to returning to bags for the trade.

Bulk storage is well suited to handling grains where the variety handled at any one time is small; where power is available for mechanization; where roads are constructed to handle trucks throughout the year; where suitable materials are available for construction; and especially where storage of grain of one type or another extends throughout the year.

In either of the above types of structure the following conditions should be observed:

Walls, if constructed of corrugated steel, must be kept in good repair and, if made of brick, concrete, etc., must be smooth and without cracks. The building must incorporate facilities for insect and rodent control. It must be proof against the weather, heat, wind and rain. It should be as economical as possible.

Central storage

In most countries, produce is stored at main centres which are usually located at large towns and at ports. These central depots are normally operated by government or semigovernment boards which are responsible for the regulation, control and improvement of collection, storage, marketing, distribution and supply of certain essential produce (e.g., maize, wheat, cocoa, groundnuts, palm kernels); the purchase, storage, sale, import, export acquisition and disposal of these products. Despite the obvious importance of the provision of appropriate storage facilities in organizing a controlled flow of produce, matters such as reserve stocks and storage policy have been referred to as miscellaneous matters.

An official organization marketing grain on a countrywide basis must provide adequate handling and storage facilities at a considerable number of points. The problem of locating such facilities to the best advantage is an extremely complex one, depending on many factors, particularly farmers' drying and storing facilities, local transportation and the demand of local urban areas in relation to supplies of crop.

Obviously, it is desirable that the distribution system be as efficient as possible, but this does not mean simply reducing the marketing organization's costs to the lowest possible level. The interests of both producers and consumers and, probably, of other sectors of the country's economy must also be taken into account. It is usually desirable to provide handling and storage facilities in production, consumption and port areas. The location of depots in production areas only could lead to serious shortages in the consumption centres if transportation services should be disrupted at any time. In view of the distances involved in most cases, it would be impossible to ensure that urban communities were supplied strictly in accord with their requirements. Equally, central storage should not be confined to the main consumption areas because transportation systems would be unlikely to be able to move the entire crop from the production areas quickly enough; additional expense would be incurred in rerouting some of the crop back into the rural areas if required. Moreover, transportation of products to a few major points at ports would only involve considerable administrative and operational problems. It is therefore essential that countries develop integrated central storage systems with units in areas of production, consumption and at ports.

Organized marketing points should be established in the main farming areas within comparatively easy reach of most producers. With improved transport facilities, very small intake points which are uneconomic and can be sources of poor quality commodities can be kept to a minimum. Warehouses or silos of appropriate capacity should be established at centres on railway lines to facilitate rail transportation to the main urban and port depots. Storage facilities at rural depots should allow for a certain proportion of the crop to be retained in the production areas from which transportation during the off season can be effectively controlled.

A proportion of the surplus stocks should be delivered to the urban depots from the production areas during the intake season, to reduce handling and storage costs. Internal movement of grain during the intake period serves to replenish stocks held at depots in the consumption areas and to meet the immediate needs of millers and other customers.

Urban depots are located in the vicinity of the larger towns and cities where food requirement far exceeds local production and from which produce can be more readily moved to export points. Such depots receive their supplies from rural depots or from producers delivering under a direct haulage programme. In some countries stocks held at urban depots can be drawn upon by local consumers.

The urban depots must, of course, possess large storage capacities, but they need not cater for the entire local demand since part of it can be met by haulage direct to consumers from stocks held at rural depots.

Types of storage in use

Various methods are used in central storage schemes which may be classified as:

(*a*) storage in bulk in the open directly on the ground or on specially prepared areas;

(*b*) storage in bulk in above ground silos or warehouses;

(*c*) storage in bulk in containers which are either totally or partially in the ground;

(*d*) storage in bags stacked in the open (but usually protected from the weather by temporary tarpaulin-type covers);

(*e*) storage in bags stacked under permanent cover, i.e., within a building.

It is not uncommon for rural depots to employ methods (*a*), (*d*) and (*e*) and for urban depots to use methods (*b*), (*c*) and (*e*) and port depots to use methods (*c*) and (*e*). In most countries bag storage (i.e., method (*e*)) is mainly utilized, although bulk storage schemes (i.e., methods (*b*) and (*c*)) are being developed.

Bulk in the open. This is the most unsatisfactory method of storage since the produce is exposed to moisture absorption from the soil, to showers of rain, to the direct heat of the sun and to insect infestation (Figure 44). This method should not be used, in view of the serious consequences which may result from dampness and the development of moulds.

Some of the problems of deterioration can be minimized by the use of plastic-type sheeting on the earth and as covering to provide protection from unexpected showers.

Insect infestation is difficult to control in exposed heaps of produce because of the extremes of conditions to which the insecticide used is subjected, and the infestation pressure from produce stores in the immediate vicinity. Layer dusting of insecticide has been used in some countries.

Bulk in aboveground silos and warehouses. In a number of countries, central storage projects are being introduced based on the storage and handling of produce in bulk in silos or warehouses.

FIGURE 44. Open-type storage used for central collection centres.

FIGURE 45. Truck unloading grids for bulk grain intake.

Three traditional designs are utilized.

The first is the warehouse structure, having walls which may or may not be reinforced to take lateral pressure of the grain ; in the latter the grain is contained within bulkheads consisting of a " wall " of bagged produce or of inverted T-shaped wooden (or metal) supports. Filling and emptying the bins is carried out by the use of several types of conveyors, e.g., pneumatic, chain, auger or bucket. In a number of countries, specially designed bulk storage warehouses have provisions for air circulation within the bulk by a system of steel ducting on the floor. This method has been used mainly in paddy storage for blowing ambient temperature air through the bulk of grain. Systems designed to ensure the storage of bulk produce without changes in temperature and humidity are said to be extremely costly, hence they have not been fully developed. Until methods have been developed for improving the sealing of sheet clad buildings and of achieving at low cost designs of concrete and brick buildings to provide controlled conditions, the use of such systems will continue to be confined to high cost produce such as tobacco and sugar.

The control of insect infestation in large bulk stores of this type is extremely difficult In some countries fumigation has been attempted and in others spray treatment of the grain at intake has been adopted.

Various sizes of such warehouse units have been built. One such warehouse is 170×45 metres with steel roof trusses, corrugated asbestos roof sheeting, reinforced concrete retaining walls (4.8 metres high) and a waterproofed concrete floor; an overhead band conveyor enables the apex of the bulk produce to reach a height of about 24 metres. The capital outlay (excluding the cost of the delivery conveyor tunnel and conveying machinery) can be about $10 per ton.

A range of silos of conventional design constructed of bolted metal plates; concrete, or brick are in use in the tropics and subtropics. At rural depots steel, aluminium or mesh metal silos of up to about 200-ton capacity can be used; these are normally erected on a concrete base. Under local conditions, the metal silos are not always sufficiently gastight to ensure successful fumigation. Condensation, particularly during the period of high diurnal temperature change, can be responsible for the deterioration of produce, though this can be controlled by the installation and proper use of an aeration system. The silo must be sealed to the foundation which has correct water vapour proofing to prevent spoilage through mould development.

Large silo units (e.g., of 10 000- to 20 000-ton capacity) referred to as elevators, constructed of steel or concrete, are in use in many areas particularly for port facilities. Each unit of the elevator may hold up to about 700 tons of produce in a column which has greater height than width. These silos are filled mechanically or by a pneumatic system. The conveying capacity may be up to about 200 tons per hour, usually in multiple units of a 20- to 50-ton per hour conveyor capacity. A dust problem occurs with all intake conveyors. Pneumatic systems with cyclones are considered to be worse than mechanical conveyor systems with filters. Double bank elevators and conveyors reduce the delays caused by unit breakdown and provide a saving in cost, e.g., by standardizing on spare parts and allowing for a measure of standby. A works building is usually situated at one end of the silo consisting of a tower housing the elevating, weighing and cleaning plant; usually it has a block of loading-out bins situated over a large bagging-off floor, a number of loading bays sited beneath the bagging-off floor at ground level, and a small office block.

Dry produce is the key to effective operation of elevators; therefore they often have drying facilities using oil-fired driers of the column type. Insect infestation in large bulks in these silos has to be controlled and in the past the traditional method was the use of a circulatory fumigation system. Tests carried out in India have shown the possibilities of achieving successful fumigation by using tableted fumigants which avoid the need to have each silo bin fitted with special piping required in conjunction with aeration piping. In India, the experience has been (Sarid and Krishnamurthy, 1965) that steel elevators, having higher installation costs than wooden bins but lower than concrete bins, do not prevent spoilage due to seasonal fluctuations in temperature, a problem which is said not to occur with concrete silos. The initial capital cost of silos varies with the amount of handling machinery installed but is usually about $30 to $72 per ton.

Grain is usually delivered in bags to silos in the tropics and subtropics by road and by rail, although there will be an increase in deliveries in bulk. Gratings at ground level, below which there are hoppers, receive the grain from road and rail deliveries (Figure 45). These receiving pits are situated at the sides of the works building and are protected from the weather by canopies.

The bags are slit open on the hopper gratings and the grain is poured into them, then fed into a system of chain or belt conveyors installed in the basement of the works building. The conveyors deliver the grain to the intake bucket elevators from the top of which the grain descends by gravity through an automatic scale and a cleaning plant from which it is re-elevated to the driers or discharged along a conveyor belt into the appropriate bin. Moisture determinations should be made on all composite samples of grain received and the necessary steps taken at time of intake with respect to moisture and insect control.

During the period of storage, samples are drawn from top and bottom of the bin and examined for signs of active insect infestation and other factors, such as excessive moisture, likely to cause deterioration of the grain, and the necessary safeguards are taken.

Grain is drawn from the silo either in bulk or in bags, for export or delivery to local millers. A number of main bins may be fitted with external gravity chutes by means of which grain can be discharged directly into bulk transport lorries. Grain from other bins may be transferred to bulk-delivery bins using conveyors and elevators suitably positioned for this purpose. If the grain loaded out in this way does not pass through the silo weighing plant, the vehicles concerned must be weighed on a weighbridge before and after loading. Grain to be despatched in bags is drawn from the appropriate bin bottom, is elevated, and then descends by gravity (via the cleaning plant if necessary) to a holding bin or directly to an automatic scale. The latter may be situated on the first floor of the warehouse or may be mounted on a gantry so that it can be placed in a position under any of the holding bins. This scale releases the appropriate quantity of grain into a sack held beneath the discharge chute. The open end of the filled sack is then machine-stitched and the bag delivered either to a lorry or railway truck by means of either inclined chutes or gravity rollers.

In a few countries, welded steel sheet silos are being used. These provide hermetic storage which is particularly suitable in the tropics for the storage of dry grain. Hermetic storage protects against insect infestation by the replacement of oxygen by carbon dioxide

FIGURE 46. Modern method of pit storage.

through the respiration process in the grain. In at least one country in Africa this method is being used for the storage of wet grain intended for animal feed; in this case, carbon dioxide is introduced into the silo to retard deterioration of the damp grain and it has been stated that the cost of such silos (of French manufacture) may be as high as $4 500 per ton.

In all of these storage methods the condition of the produce during the storage period should be observed by taking temperature records (equipment for this is available).

Bulk in containers partially or wholly in the ground. The use of concrete containers as pits in the ground covered by either a temporary flexible form of roofing (e.g., bituminous felt) or a permanent concrete roof has gained wide acceptance in Latin America where several millions of tons of produce are stored in these hermetic underground pits (Figure 46), e.g., in Argentina some pits measure 120 × 12 × 5 metres. The floor and walls are in three layers with an impermeable membrane between two layers of concrete, one of which incorporates the necessary reinforcing steel. The roof of these pits has an impermeable cover on top of the reinforced concrete support system. This design and construction make these pits impermeable to liquid water, water vapour, oxygen and carbon dioxide, and if only dry grain is loaded into them it can be retained in good condition for many years. The installation of an aeration system permits recirculation of the atmosphere in the storage with minor air replacements. The eliptical bottom permits full mechanical removal with an auger or conveyor gradually lowered to the centre of the pit.

Another form of hermetic container storage is being used in Cyprus and Kenya. In these units the permanent concrete roof is designed in the form of a large dome to increase the aboveground storage capacity. With this partially aboveground form of hermetic storage (Figures 47) minor condensation problems immediately under the filling manhole have to be prevented by suitable cover design. If only dry grain is stored little or no deterioration will occur; insects, if present at the time the grain is placed in storage, are killed by the low levels of oxygen which rapidly develop.

Other forms of bulk storage, which combine the cheapness of on-floor warehouse storage with the more efficient handling facilities of silo storage, are being considered. Thus multiple rectangular units, consisting of above and belowground chambers, loaded and unloaded by conveyor bands in the roof apex and the hopper bottom of the floor are being constructed. In such units it is essential to be able to fumigate successfully and to have each chamber as an isolated entity as in vertical type silo design. The use of fumigants in tablet form or of spray treatments with contact insecticides at intake can be considered suitable. In one country in Africa this form of bulk storage, complete with driers, is said to cost about $15 per ton.

Bag storage in the open. The storage of produce in jute bags in the open without any form of protection is still practised in many countries although, in most, such stacks are covered with a number of tarpaulin type sheets to provide protection from direct wetting by rain. It is not uncommon to find bagged produce stacked on the ground, but it is the practice in some countries to stack produce on specially prepared plinths e.g., a 2 500-ton stack will be accommodated on a plinth 55 × 11 metres. One form of plinth consists of a 23-centimetre thick brick or concrete retaining wall about 46 centimetres high, the earth within being compacted until it reaches about 15 centimetres from the top of the wall. Finally the plinth

FIGURE 47. Modern dome-shaped storage containers.

is filled with compacted crushed stone which is topped by a 1.2- to 2.0-centimetre layer of rolled bituminous premix to give a slight camber. In other cases the plinths are covered with a layer of plastic sheeting or bituminous felting (with overlaps of not less than 15 centimetres) which is carried over the edge of the plinth about 1 metre so that the excess can be folded (into the stack at about the second or third layer stack construction).

In some countries these plinths are constructed in such a way that it is possible to cover them with standard type buildings (e.g., portal frame sheds) so that covered storage can be put into use as the importance of the area being served by these structures increases.

Various forms of open-sided steel frame buildings are used, sometimes with hessian walls often 173 × 30 metres in dimension. The cost of such buildings when erection is completed is about $4 per ton, of which some $1.6 per ton is for the floor construction.

It is clear that marketing organizations may find difficulty in deciding upon storage capacities required for different areas and that flexibility of storage is required. The development of inflatable type plastic buildings, specially designed to be gastight in order to enable successful fumigation to be carried out, portable, and readily erected on a site (complete with an integral floor) with a low capital outlay of some $3 to $6 per ton of potential storage capacity, may fill a gap in the storage techniques which may be adopted by produce boards, etc.

Bag storage within permanent buildings. A range of timber-framed and steel-framed buildings with either plastered brick walls or metal cladding are in common use at main collecting centres and port areas where they are used for the receipt of produce and its temporary storage in bags prior to distribution either within the country or externally by exporting.

Transit stores at the ports are usually wide-span buildings, often with undesirable features in the design such as considerable areas of the roof which transmit light, a permanent gap at the eaves, rough textured walls, gaps round the doors and drainage pipes adjacent to the walls. Table 19 gives unit costs and details of typical port transit sheds (Hall and Stephen, 1966).

In Central Africa and elsewhere open-sided steel frame buildings are used at up-country buying centres, while steel frame build-

TABLE 19. – UNIT COSTS OF STORAGE BUILDINGS: TRANSIT SHEDS

	Barbados (two)	Mombasa	Port Swettenham	Lagos	Lagos
	1960	[4] 1961	[6] 1963	[4] 1966	[4] 1962
Framework	All steel	R.C. frame R.C. trusses	All steel	Prestressed concrete	All steel
Walls	Concrete blocks	Concrete blocks	Corrugated steel	Concrete blocks	Concrete blocks
Roof cladding	Corrugated A.C. sheeting	A.C. Watford tiles	Corrugated steel	Corrugated A.C. sheeting	Corrugated A.C. sheeting
Cubic capacity (m^3)	31 639 26 600	51 800	31 000	48 800	95 700
Net internal floor area (m^2) [1]	7 530	9 290	4 780	25 200	10 450
Inclusive cost [2] per m^2 of internal floor area [1]	$80	[5] $40	$40	$60	$90
Cost of building per m^3 of useful storage space,[3] excluding cost of foundations and floor	$8	$6	$6	$4	$7

[1] Excludes areas covered by canopies. – [2] Area costs are the actual finished costs and include foundations, floors, framework, walls, roof, lights, natural ventilation, doors, stormwater drainage and lighting protection, but not electric lighting nor internal offices. – [3] This is to eaves level and does NOT include roof space or space under canopies. The rate is therefore NOT the "estimators cube" used by architects and surveyors. The cube rate is for the building only and excludes the costs of foundations and floors. – [4] These buildings had piled foundations. – [5] Excludes cost of floor, which was laid by direct labour. – [6] Built on wharf deck and excludes cost of foundations and floor.

ings with plastered brick walls or metal cladding are in common use by produce boards at main collecting points. These buildings are capable of holding up to about 200 000 bags of produce (e.g., 173 × 30 metres in area). These steel portal frame buildings are stated to be at least five percent cheaper per bag of storage than a brick-built shed in some countries.

The design of these buildings is usually such that there is permanent ventilation, often of such a nature that sheet cladding is fixed permanently at an angle to the vertical at the floor level and midway up the walls to increase normal ventilation. Such design features make rodent proofing virtually impossible and insect control extremely difficult; in addition, buildings of this type are not only in use in the dry areas of the world but also in the wet or humid areas where produce in store is exposed to high humidity air. The reabsorption of moisture which takes place, especially in the outer layers of bags, accelerates biological activity in the produce and results in deterioration and loss of products.

Temperature conditions inside steel clad buildings fluctuate more than those in buildings clad with a material which has insulating properties. In the hot dry areas where surface temperature is extremely high, produce stacked within one metre of the roof or close to the walls becomes hot.

Converted aircraft hangars and Nissen buildings are used in some countries. Hangars may be 120 metres long by 30 metres wide with a height of 12 metres at the apex and 8 metres at the eaves. The method of construction does not allow full use to be made of the actual volume enclosed because stanchions may project inward some 1.5 metres and about 8 percent of the floor space may be wasted; similarly, because of the roof construction the effective stack building height can be 75 percent of the total height.

From the handling point of view, the width of the building has certain disadvantages and despite the fact that stackers can be used to transfer bags horizontally, a long carry may be required to move bags between transport and stack. This applies particularly in the case of rail traffic and, even though road vehicles can enter the building, it is often impossible to position them to the best advantage owing to the fact that stacks other than the one being worked may be in the way.

Stacks should be built across the width of the shed, sufficient room being left at the sides for pest control purposes. A certain amount of headroom must, of course, be left as working space for stacking and fumigation teams, but otherwise full use should be made of available space.

The construction of concrete buildings with specially designed domed concrete roofs to provide a relatively insulated, fumigable storage unit for bagged produce has been undertaken. These units, with small "window ports" in the roof, are fitted with gastight doors, a special fan arrangement for ventilation purposes, and have an unrestricted floor area of 1 100 square metres. A storage site of such units to hold 80 000 tons of produce (cocoa beans) has been erected.

General considerations

In the tropics and subtropics where financial resources may be limited and where the pattern of supply and demand may be subject to rapid change, bag storage sheds will often constitute the most practicable means of storing grain, particularly if the sheds are of a type which allows easy dismantling and re-erection at another site. Even in cases where conditions permit the establishment of a system of permanent bulk installations for cereal grains, a certain amount of shed storage will often be needed to cater for grains which may be marketed locally or be damaged by existing bulk handling methods.

Consideration must also be given to the question of maintenance costs. Very often a brick or concrete structure will have advantages over a steel structure in this respect, particularly where the building may be subjected to corrosive influences in the atmosphere. Corrugated asbestos cladding has the advantage that it needs no painting but it is very susceptible to mechanical damage, particularly as it tends to become brittle in strong sunlight.

It has already been indicated that wide sheds may present difficulties from the handling point of view, but it must also be borne in mind that, for a given storage capacity, a long narrow shed will require greater lengths of rail track and roadway than a shorter, wider structure. Provision of doors and drainage facilities will also entail increased expenditure as the ratio of length to width increases. The optimum height for the shed will obviously depend upon stacking requirements and the type of stacking equipment available. If the shed is required to hold a variety of types of grain, the stacks will usually be comparatively small and it will not therefore be necessary to provide a great amount of headroom. On the other hand, where only one or two types of grain are stored, stacking height, and therefore the height of the shed, will probably be limited only by the handling methods employed and by the load which may be imposed upon the lower layers of bags and on the floor.

It is necessary to ensure that, during storage, the grain will not be damaged by ground moisture, and although this may be done by building the stacks on some suitable form of dunnage, this approach to the problem has several disadvantages. For example, the dunnage may impede the efficient use of stacking equipment, complicate the recovery of spilt grain, and encourage reinfestation by rodents and insects. In the long run, it is usually more economical to provide a suitably prepared floor on which the grain may be stacked directly.

In the tropics rainfall intensity may reach high values; a building covering a fairly large area should therefore be provided with storm water drains of sufficient capacity to cater for the large volumes of water shed by the roof. Such drains will usually need to be concrete lined in order to prevent water seeping beneath the floor of the sheds. This problem can also be overcome by elevating the floor above ground level, but this will often lead to difficulties on the handling side.

A stage is usually reached when the volume of produce to be handled necessitates a reconsideration of the continued use of bag storage and of the long-term economic advantages in adopting bulk storage methods.

The total storage capacity to be provided in any particular installation is, of course, related to the maximum quantity of grain which has to be stored at any one time. Where it is necessary to cater for a number of different types of grain, it is unlikely that the quantity of each type of grain received will be an exact multiple of the quantity held by an individual bin; a number of bins will be only partly filled at any particular time and it will therefore be necessary to provide storage space somewhat in excess of the amount of grain to be stored. An installation comprising a large number of small bins will obviously facilitate greater utilization of storage capacity than one consisting of a small number of large bins; the construction costs will, of course, be higher. It is therefore necessary to take into account the relation between capital charges and the percentage utilization of silo capacity provided and the need to provide some form of buffer storage in which to hold small quantities of grain which might otherwise occupy a disproportionate amount of valuable silo space.

Where silos are built for the storage of one commodity of which there are only a few grades received in any substantial quantity, bins of comparatively large capacity are the obvious choice. Thus, designs based upon rows of cylindrical bins or bins which are rectangular in horizontal section are the most economic. In other circumstances, it is preferable from the economic point of view to provide smaller bins which are square in horizontal section. Much may also depend upon the availability and cost of construction materials.

The cost of land, loading restrictions imposed by foundation conditions, and the positioning for efficient use of elevators and other handling equipment are all factors which may affect the designed height of the storage structures. Under certain conditions it may also be necessary to consider elevating the bin bottom above ground level. This might apply, for example, in cases where extensive rock formations exist at or just below the surface or where there is a high water table, conditions which might add very considerably to the cost of providing unloading facilities below ground level.

Where bins are intended to be filled and emptied at frequent intervals, it is usually an advantage if the bin bottoms are sloped toward the outlets at an angle greater than the angle of repose of the grain so that the bins will be self-emptying. Flat bin bottoms have advantages over aboveground silos with hopper bottoms (but not over belowground containers with hopper bottoms) in that construction costs are lower and maximum use is made of the space enclosed by the bin walls. The main disadvantage of flat bin bottoms is, that on emptying, residues remain which must be cleaned out manually. However, since this operation need only be performed at infrequent intervals, the labour costs will probably be insignificant in comparison with the possible savings. Cleaning operations may also be facilitated by the provision of entrance hatches set into the bin walls at a suitable height.

The handling capacity of a silo must be such that it can cater for the maximum rate at which grain is to be received or despatched. Obviously, when different types of grain have to be handled simultaneously more than one handling plant will be required. This will also apply in cases where a single type of grain has to be received and despatched at the same time. In certain circumstances, however, plant provision may be reduced to a minimum by arranging for different types of grain to be handled in separate " runs " as, for example, when deliveries by producers can be closely regulated, or when one type of grain can be stockpiled in some form of buffer storage while another is being taken in.

Silo machinery should, as far as is possible, be self-cleaning so that grain residues do not remain within the system. Such residues will often constitute a breeding ground for insects and, in cases where several types of grain are handled, will also lead to contamination of one type of grain by another.

Adequate provision must be made for the various types of transport employed to move grain to and from the silo, and it will often be necessary to cater for receipt and despatch both in the bag and in bulk. Such provision will usually entail careful planning of the layout of the road and rail facilities, particularly if these are also required to serve other forms of storage at the depot. The movement of rail trucks within the depot will usually be the responsibility of the handling organization. Depending upon the volume of such traffic, motive power can be provided by small shunting locomotives, tractors, or electrically operated winches.

Reception procedure

At rural depots, the bulk of the produce may be delivered in old sacks as a head burden, a donkey burden, an ox or donkey cart load or in lorries. The produce may be emptied into a measure (in some countries a used 18-litre paraffin tin is used, six of which approximate to 91 kilogrammes) or may be weighed on a scale. The produce is graded on purchase, bagged and either stored or transported to urban depots or processors' premises.

Prior to central storage various observations and measurements should be made on the produce to be stored : these should include moisture measurement, assessment of insect infestation, counting of bags, grading and weighing.

No food grains with a moisture content higher than the " safe acceptable level " (Table 9) must be accepted for storage. If no moisture meter is available and there is reason to think that the produce delivered has a moisture content in excess of the safe limit, the produce should not be accepted until it has been tested with a moisture meter.

Samples from produce delivered on lorries or trucks should be taken from bags which have not been exposed in transit to the sun or wind. A sample for moisture test should weigh approximately 1 kilogramme, and if it is to be sent elsewhere for testing it must be placed in a really airtight tin, which is completely filled. The tin should not be left exposed to the sun and, of course, the name of the sender must be clearly indicated. It is particularly important that the contents of each vehicle be counted bag by bag as it is unloaded, and scales should be operated at the foot of stackers. Full details of each load must be recorded clearly in a book, and depots must be so organized as to make any duplicate receipting quite impossible. At the end of each day, receipts issued should be reconciled with the book entries to make certain that there has been no overreceipting.

Each type of grain must meet certain minimum quality standards before it can be accepted. Furthermore, the price paid will depend upon the quality of the consignment; each load must therefore be carefully sampled and graded in accordance with official procedures. Such procedures define the classes into which a particular type of grain may fall, depending, for example, upon the amount of extraneous matter and percentage of defective or insect-damaged grain present. This subject is usually fully covered by grain or produce marketing regulations which contain details of the standards of quality, the means by which various defects of the various products should by assessed, and of the practical process of grading. It is the duty of every person concerned with the intake of grain to familiarize himself completely with the regulations.

Producers' grain should be graded before it is weighed. When samples of any one product taken for grading amount to one bag, the contents of the bag should then be graded according to the standards laid down in the regulations, and the bag should then be taken into stock on a depot transfer voucher showing the sending depots as samples, giving all the usual details including weight. Any consignments received which are not classified at the highest grade are liable to be the cause of dispute. For this reason samples (large enough to be suitable for grading should the need arise), should be taken by the receiving station and kept until grade information has been received and accepted. This will require the following periods of time: deliveries by road, 48 hours; deliveries by rail, 10 days.

Grain cannot be accepted if it falls short of at least one of the required standards; if the fault is one which the producer can easily remedy, such as excessive moisture or discoloured grains, the produce should be returned to him with a note of explanation advising him to resubmit the grain later after appropriate attention.

Boards of management at rural depots normally pay for the grain and the sack on delivery since sacks have to be purchased by producers and buying agents operating on behalf of the boards. The standards of sacks and the correct means of closing are laid down. It is important to note that sacks must be clean and free from stains. This means that sacks which have become dirty through being dragged over the ground or covered by road dust, or have moisture or rodent urine stains, are not acceptable.

Produce delivered in sacks which do not conform to the regulations is not accepted, and the producers must rectify the faults; under exceptional circumstances the depot should carry out this work.

The standard gross weight of a bag varies in different countries, and the full gross weight of grain received must be recorded in grain receipts, though boards do not pay for excess over standard weights. At least 10 percent of each consignment should be weighed, except that when a consignment is less than 50 bags at least 50 percent must be weighed. In the case of a dispute, the checker must weigh such larger proportion as may be agreed upon with the producer or, in the absence of agreement, the full quantity. In some cases, 100-percent weighing is carried out.

The larger depots are usually equipped with weighbridges which enable 100-percent weighing to be carried out on all consignments delivered by road. At most depots, however, platform scales (to take 5 or 10 bags) are used to weigh the grain and, since this is a time consuming operation, at some depots only a proportion of particular consignments may be weighed. The total weight of the consignment is then taken to be the average weight of the bags scaled multiplied by the number of bags in the consignment. Counting of bags and weighing over platform scales usually takes place as the consignment is being unloaded. The bags may then be put into a stack or loaded into a transport vehicle and hauled to storage. Details of the daily deliveries made by each individual are entered on a receipt, one copy of which is handed or sent to the individual concerned; another copy is retained at the depot and the top copy is sent to the appropriate head office so that payment may be made.

In certain organizations, cash purchases may be made following clearance from head office. Such grain usually is delivered free of all transport and other charges, and if brought by a public carrier with charges "to pay," special authority must be obtained from head office before payment is made. Cash purchases of less than a standard bag are made for the nearest quarter of a standard bag.

STORAGE PROCEDURE

Separate stacks are required for every variety of grain of each intake season and of each class held in a depot or agency. The base area of stacks to be built is generally decided by the anticipated intake and the size of the storage areas.

All floors must be swept clean.

Several stacks may be in the process of building at any one time during the intake season and at the rural depots concurrent shipments to export and or the consumption areas may be necessary; if these operations are to proceed smoothly and efficiently, an adequate quantity of handling and weighing equipment must be available.

In stacking there must be a good system of bonding and a very slight slope inward as a stack goes higher, to avoid the danger of slip. There must be no obstruction to fumigation, which means that a stack must not be built round roof-supporting pillars or up into roof trusses in such a way as to interfere with the laying of gasproof sheets. The interior of a stack must be in regular rows which must be accurately represented by the bags which are visible on the sides and ends of stacks. Each layer of a stack is to be physically counted before the next layer is laid and the number of bags in it marked on a corner bag.

Stacks are built layer by layer consisting of regular rows of bags laid either parallel with or at right angles to the longitudinal axis of the stack. Layers of " stretchers " alternated with layers of " headers " (Figure 48) obviate the risk of stack collapse. Particular care is taken to position the outermost bags of each layer so that the stack is square and this is the responsibility of experienced stack-masters who use a line in order to obtain straight edges.

Various types of elevating machines, e.g., 15-foot loaders and 30-foot stackers may be used; these may be driven by electric motors or petrol engines depending on local facilities, and they can be converted as required from one type of motive power to the other.

Each stack should be given a stack card which records a number and indicates the classification of the grain, the year of intake, inspection dates and data on disinfestation treatments. From the commencement of building to the completion of outturn, each stack should be regarded as a separate unit and, allowing for unavoidable shrinkage losses, the total number and weight of bags despatched from a particular stack is expected to tally with the figures recorded during intake.

The stack card should be attached to a small board which is fixed on the stack, and a copy of the stack card should be kept by the depot manager or warehousekeeper. The stack number may have three components; a letter to indicate the class; a number to indicate the year of intake; another number to indicate whether the stack is the first, second or third (as the case may be) of a particular grain of a particular intake regardless of class. In the case of silo stocks, the third part of the number will indicate the permanent number of the bin in which the grain is stored.

A consignment which is railed or shipped before being placed in a stack must also be given a stack number.

When breaking down stacks the standard method to be employed is to use stackers in reverse with scales at the foot. In this way

FIGURE 48. Handling and stacking bags for storage.

the broken face of a stack can be kept regular and the whole stack can be quickly tidied up to make an accurate count of bags possible. (The procedure of tumbling sacks down to ground level after a suitably inclined face has been formed is not recommended.)

Sacks which are damaged beyond repair should be emptied of grain, put aside and counted. The loose grain should be sieved, very carefully inspected for discoloured grains, insects and moisture content, and only sound produce should be put into sound bags; a despatch voucher should then be issued to " rebagging " to account for the reduced number of actual bags in stock, i.e., the difference between the number of damaged bags and the number of bags filled with loose grain.

Sweepings should be cleaned to restore them to a condition necessary to qualify for the class of grain in the stack from which they originated. Such cleaned sweepings should be taken into stock in the original stack with a depot voucher showing the sending depot as " sweepings," and showing the number of bags and class, but not the weight. Sweepings which are infested must be immediately disinfested by fumigation.

Issue procedure

Strict control of produce issued is essential. This is usually effected by only issuing against a covering official despatch order issued by head office.

The principle of " first in, first out " should be observed insofar as is practicable. On outturn into consumption, check gradings must be carried out to ensure that the grain is within the required classification.

The stock taken in earliest should always be issued first, except that stacks not treated with insecticide should be issued prior to those treated.

No produce should be allowed to enter trade routes from central storage if it is infested.

Grain should be graded on issue before it is weighed, and as soon as the samples taken for grading amount to a bag they should be taken into stock with a depot transfer in favour of " samples " showing the number of bags and the class according to the acceptance standards.

All issues must be weighed 100 percent, except in the case of depot-to-depot transfer, for which 10 percent is appropriate. In some countries sales of less than a certain amount have to be weighed in the presence of the buyer (or his representative). Scales must always be placed on firm level bases and should be tested at least every three months with the test weights which must be available in each district. It should be remembered that boards sell by weight, not bags; and although of no great concern as regards credit customers, it is important with cash customers that the weight of grain on the despatch order is not exceeded.

8. INSECT CONTROL METHODS

As has been shown, food grains are liable to suffer heavy losses during storage as a result of infestation by insects. The importance of ensuring that produce is thoroughly dry to prevent deterioration from fungi has been stressed, but even dry produce is not normally immune from attack by insects. If maximum benefit is to be derived from the harvest, some attempt will have to be made to control insect pests many of which, as already indicated, commence infestation prior to harvest. In some areas simple traditional methods of control are used by farmers, usually to protect that part of their crop reserved for seed purposes, while in most countries chemical methods of insect control have been introduced mainly in relation to large scale central storage.

Traditional methods

Several methods carried out by farmers and traders have been mentioned. These may be summarized as follows.

Regular sunning

At the adult stage, most storage pests are capable of flight and will be activated by exposure to strong sunlight. Consequently, if an infested commodity is spread out in the sun, any adult insects present will become active. There will, however, still be immature stages present, often enclosed within the grains, so that for any appreciable effect regular sunning over several months will be necessary.

Smoking

It is very common practice in the tropics to hang unthreshed heads of grain, cobs of maize, etc., from the rafters of dwelling huts, in which position heat and smoke from the fire will promote further drying and should reduce insect infestation. In some areas a granary of mud or plant material may be built on a raised platform over a fire which is then used for the household cooking. The value of this method has not been investigated in any detail, but the mere fact that it is used shows that farmers are aware of the danger of excessive moisture and insect infestation (see Figure 32).

Admixture of local plants

It is believed in many areas that certain local plants have a repellent effect upon insects, and that when they are admixed with food produce in granaries some control of infestation is achieved. However, there is some doubt as to whether these plants are really effective and it seems likely that the farmer who takes the trouble to admix such material also carries out basic storage hygiene, and that it may therefore be the latter which is more beneficial.

Admixture of local dusts

The admixture of wood ash or sand with food grains is carried out in many areas, although it is usually restricted to the storage of small quantities in earthenware pots for seed purposes. This method appears to rely for its effectiveness upon the fact that the materials used fill the intergranular spaces and thereby restrict insect movement and emergence. A similar method which is reported to have some success is the admixture of small cereal grains, e.g., millet (which by virtue of their size are themselves barely susceptible to insect attack) with maize or sorghum stored in pots for seed purposes.

Experiments carried out in Kenya indicated that a diatomite dust of local origin had some effect as a protectant when applied to maize stored in bags (Le Pelley and Kockum, 1954). Such mineral dusts, generally known as inert dusts, scratch the thin, waterproofing layer of wax which exists on the outside surface of the insect cuticle, allowing loss of water which leads to death as a result of desiccation.

In India the powdered, dried rhizome of the sweat flag (*Acorus clamus*) has been reported (Ghose, Ghatge and Subramanyan, 1960) to possess both killing and deterrent properties when mixed with paddy or rice at the rate of 1 to 100 pounds of grain. Treatment did not impart any unpleasant odour to the rice when cooked.

Chemical methods

There are two main types of chemical used in the control of insect pests of stored products, i.e., contact insecticides and respiratory poisons or fumigants. A contact insecticide is a poison which is able to penetrate the insect cuticle and thereby enter the body tissues. A fumigant is a gas or vapour which is taken into the body of the insect through its respiratory system.

Contact insecticides can confer long-term protection (usually referred to as the residual effect), but often tend to be somewhat specific in their effect upon insect species and to produce resistance more than the respiratory poisons. Fumigants provide no residual effect but, unlike contact insecticides, have the power to penetrate throughout stacks or bulks and to become absorbed into individual grains or kernels, killing all stages of insect life within (Page and Lubatti, 1963).

Much of the information contained in this section relates to large-scale bag storage because these methods usually require the use of equipment which is not available to the farmer or small trader. However, this situation need not be a permanent one, as cooperative and similar organizations are able to purchase and hire equipment for their members.

Contact insecticides

Contact insecticides which are suitable for use on stored products are limited in number, owing to problems of taint or toxic residues which may occur (Table 20, page 205). The insecticides in use are given in the following paragraphs.

Pyrethrum

This is the best known of the natural insecticides, the most important constituents of which are known as pyrethrins. Their toxicity to insects can be greatly increased through the addition of a synergist, such as piperonyl butoxide; they are unstable when exposed to light. Pyrethrum is virtually nontoxic to man and is therefore very safe to use on food or in situations in which food is likely to pick up some of the insecticide.

Chlorinated hydrocarbon insecticides

DDT. The outstanding feature of DDT is its long residual life and for this reason it has been used mainly for the treatment of the internal structure of storage buildings. Its toxicity to man precludes its use for admixture with food products or animal feed; nor should it be applied to the external surfaces of bags containing produce or to the internal surfaces of containers (e.g., grain bins) which will be bulk loaded with food products.

BHC-Lindane. BHC is the name given to crude benzene hexachloride and consists of mixed isomers of this chemical. Only one of these isomers, the gamma isomer, is responsible for the greater part of the effectiveness of BHC, and only the refined BHC known as lindane (which has not less than 99 percent gamma isomer) should be used in stored products insect control. The use of crude BHC can lead to taints and odours in treated foodstuffs and also increase the potential toxic hazard to man.

Lindane is basically a contact insecticide, which under tropical conditions does not persist for very long. Its vapour pressure is such that at tropical temperatures there is also some fumigant effect which may be quite important in certain treatments.

Dieldrin. This insecticide is an extremely persistent one, more so than DDT. It is also more toxic to man than DDT. Dieldrin is used for the control of termites in the soil (e.g., when preparing a site for building) or of cockroaches particularly in the ducts of certain buildings, but should not be used for any other pest control operation connected with stored food.

Organophosphorus insecticides

Although some organophosphorus insecticides (e.g., parathion) are among the most poisonous insecticides in existence, a number are relatively safe and can be used for the control of pests on stored food.

Malathion. This is a " safe " insecticide and virtually all countries allow direct admixture of malathion with foodstuffs provided certain contamination limits are not exceeded (see Table 20). In some circumstances, dilute dust formulations break down rapidly into products which are not insecticidal. This may happen before the dust is used or after it has been applied to the produce (e.g., grain) as an admixture treatment. Unsuitable (i.e., high) moisture levels of the produce (Watters, 1959), high temperature (e.g., after artificial drying without cooling), and the presence of enzymes in flour (being used as a dust base) or in the grain being treated (Rowlands, 1964) are three important factors which increase the rate of breakdown. Malathion is also unstable when applied to alkaline (e.g., cement) surfaces.

Only premium grade deodorized malathion should be used in stored products insect control.

(Two insecticides which show some promise for the control of beetles infesting stored products are *fenitrothion* and *bromophos* (Lemon, 1967), but they have not yet been cleared toxicologically for use on or near stored foods; they appear to be more stable than malathion.)

Diazinon. This material has been widely used in public health work, but very little in the field of stored products. It is very much more toxic to man than malathion (Table 20) and should only be used to treat the structure of storage buildings.

Dichlorvos. Better known by its trade name DDVP. It is much more toxic to mammals than most of the insecticides used in storage practice and is unlike any of the others referred to in Table 20 in that it acts almost equally both as a contact insecticide and as a fumigant. Because it vaporizes so easily its persistence as a contact insecticide is short. Plastic strips impregnated with dichlorvos have been shown to give off vapour over a period of about three months and this insecticide appears promising for the control of moths (Green, Kane and Gradidge, 1966).

Carbamate insecticides

This group of insecticides is not yet widely used in the storage field. Many of them have a low toxicity to mammals and it is possible that they may be more widely used in the future for the protection of stored foods.

Carbaryl. Better known by its trade name Sevin, this chemical has not been used very much for stored product insect control. It has a long residual life.

Problems relating to the use of insecticides

Danger to personnel handling insecticides

The danger depends on the degree of mammalian toxicity of the chemical ; the circumstances under which it is sold ; the concentration at which it must be used; the way it is prepared for use and is employed; and the local facilities for personnel handling the insecticide to wash immediately afterward.

Toxicity is expressed in terms of the necessary (or estimated) dosage to kill 50 percent of a large population of the species of animal under consideration (i.e., LD 50 figure). This figure quoted for laboratory animals (usually a particular strain of rat) is normally expressed in terms of acute oral toxicity (milligramme of poison per kilogramme of body weight of the animal). Mammalian toxicity may occur by absorption of the chemical through the skin, through intake of small quantities of the chemical over a period of time, or through the exposure of the human body to a single large dose of the chemical (either inhaled or ingested).

The insecticides considered above are listed in Table 20 in order of decreasing mammalian toxicity.

The greatest dangers in this category are delay in washing any parts of the body which have been in contact with an insecticide and the sale of insecticides in containers not intended to contain chemicals (e.g., beer bottles) and not clearly labelled in a manner understandable to the local population. An insecticide container should always be clearly labelled, with detailed instructions about the toxicity of the chemical and the precautions to be taken in diluting and applying it.

Pest control personnel handling contact insecticides should wear protective clothing (e.g., boiler suit, rubber or PVC gloves, long-peaked cap, goggles, lightweight face mask utilizing disposable filter

TABLE 20. – TOXICITY OF INSECTICIDES USED IN STORAGE AND INFESTATION WORK (THOSE UNDERLINED MAY ONLY BE USED TO TREAT THE STRUCTURE OF STORAGE BUILDINGS)

	Acute oral LD 50 [1] for rats, mg/kg body weight	Residue tolerances at time of consumption in ppm [2] (range based on variations permitted in some countries)
Dieldrin	46	Nil
Dichlorvos	80	Nil
Lindane	91	0; 1; 2.5; 5; 10; 12.5
Diazinon	108	Nil
DDT	118	0; 3.5; 7; 20
Carbaryl	350	Nil
Malathion	1 375	8; 10
Pyrethrins and piperonyl butoxide	Virtually nontoxic	1; 3; 25

[1] SOURCE: U.S. Dept. of Health, Education and Welfare (1963). Also Edson, Sanderson and Noakes (1966). – [2] Parts per million.

pads) in order to minimize the risk of dermal absorption (Bills, 1966) ; under tropical conditions where the temperatures are high and there is a high perspiration rate, the wearing of a face mask and gloves during treatment followed by immediate and thorough washing are recommended.

Danger from insecticide residues

This danger varies with the insecticide used (toxicity, vapour pressure); the absorptive properties of the produce; the handling and processing to which the produce is subjected after treatment and before being eaten by man or animals; and with the storage period between time of treatment and consumption of the produce.

The danger is increased by nonuniform exposure of the produce to the chemical (e.g., poor admixture of dusts resulting in high dosages at certain points), by repetition of treatments (often unwitting) or by the use of seed stocks, which might be expected to have received heavy dosages of insecticides, as food. On the other hand, the danger is lessened by loss of chemical before consumption (by volatilization or mechanical means); during storage and cleaning; by processing and cooking methods; and by treated produce making up only a small proportion of the whole diet.

In cases where the produce is not treated directly with chemicals, consideration must be given to the transference of the chemical from a treated surface such as a jute sack or wall of a silo bin to the produce. Transference of this kind increases with the dosage rate and with decrease in the particle size of the food, increase in oil content, storage period and temperature. Thus there will be increasing absorption through the following variety of products: cereals, oilseeds, cereal products, oilseed products.

In some tropical countries, residue tolerance levels for insecticides are being considered. A joint FAO/WHO committee on pesticide residues meets periodically to review scientific findings related to residues and publishes its recommendations (FAO, 1969). However it must be clearly stated that, while in some countries these residue levels are permissible on produce at time of consumption (higher levels being permissible at time of treatment if required to kill the insect pests), in other countries treatments which would exceed these residue figures must at no time be carried out. The pharmacological action of pesticides varies; in assessing the significance of residues in foodstuffs consideration should be given to the reversible or irreversible nature of the chemical interaction which takes place inside the human body (e.g., DDT compared with organophosphorus insecticides, the latter being decomposed in the human body, while the former accumulate in the fatty tissues within the body).

The need for detailed checks on insecticidal residues in produce after treatment and particularly immediately prior to consumption cannot be overstressed.

Specificity of toxicity of insecticides to insects

It is well recognized that chemicals used in the control of pests have a certain degree of specificity. The general purpose insecticide which is effective against all pests under all conditions does not exist.

Table 21 refers to chemicals in use against storage pests and indicates some of the insect species which are particularly susceptible to each; it shows that specificity must be carefully considered before

TABLE 21. – EXAMPLES OF SPECIFICITY OF TOXICITY OF INSECTICIDES

	Relatively susceptible insects	Examples of species with records of resistance	
		Resistance factor	Country
Lindane	*Sitophilus* spp. Bruchidae	*Sitophilus oryzae* (9.5) *S. zeamais*	Kenya
	Sitotroga cerealella *Cadra cautella*	*S. oryzae* (7) *Tribolium* (4)	Pakistan, East Nigeria
DDT	*Tribolium* spp. Bruchidae	*Tribolium* sp.	Nigeria Sierra Leone
Malathion	*Oryzaephilus* spp. *Sitophilus* spp.	*T. castaneum* (40)	Nigeria
Carbaryl	*Oryzaephilus* spp. *Tribolium* spp.		
Pyrethrins	All species		
Fumigants	All species		

deciding on the appropriate insecticide to be used, and therefore the most appropriate insecticide for the pest present and the commodity to be treated must be carefully selected.

In considering an insecticide's specificity of toxicity, it is necessary to remember not only that different species of insects vary in their susceptibility or resistance, but that within a species the different stages of egg, larva, pupa and adult may vary in their reactions. Thus in certain beetles the larval stage is the most resistant and therefore the dosage required to kill that stage has to be used. This applies particularly to fumigants.

The effect of physical environment on the efficiency of insecticides in killing insects has to be remembered in considering specificity. Thus data available for a particular insecticide have usually been obtained under a certain set of temperature and humidity conditions. It may be found that under a different set of conditions (e.g., higher temperature) it is either more or less effective at controlling the same pest. Extensive investigations are required under local conditions in the tropics to determine the most effective dosage rates for different insecticides against local strains of insect pests. At present, considerable reliance is placed on fundamental data obtained under quite different sets of conditions.

Development of resistance in insect species

During the past few years there have been indications that stored product insects are showing resistance to the range of insecticides in use (Table 21); this, under practical storage conditions, includes the insecticides DDT, lindane and malathion (with a number of storage beetles) and dieldrin (with cockroaches) and under laboratory breeding conditions, malathion, carbaryl, lindane and pyrethrins (Parkin, 1965).

It has been suggested that, if an insect shows a high initial susceptibility to an insecticide, a resistant strain will be selected more rapidly than if the initial susceptibility is low. This is unlikely since the rate at which resistance develops depends upon the:

(*a*) incidence of resistance in the genetic makeup of the starting population;

(*b*) dosage rate of insecticidal application;

(*c*) frequency or uniformity of the treatment;

(*d*) life history of the pest in relation to exposure to the insecticidal treatment.

Thus if insects are exposed to insecticidal treatment at all stages of their life cycle, they are likely to develop resistance more rapidly than insects exposed at one stage only of their life cycle. Equally, resistance is more likely to develop if the whole rather than only a proportion of the population is exposed to the chemical.

Since under certain local conditions in warehouses the insect population may be replenished at frequent intervals from population sources nearby which are not being exposed to similar chemical treatment, resistance development is suppressed due to the introduction of genetic material with a range of resistance and susceptibility potential.

Taint or damage to germination

The use of insecticides, in addition to the presence of chemical residues which may be toxic in produce, may result in an odour or flavour which detracts from its quality; the ability of the grain or kernel to germinate may also be impaired.

These aspects of deterioration are affected by the inherent characteristics of the produce, the conditions of storage, and the properties of the insecticide used.

An oilseed such as cocoa beans, and spices such as ginger are more susceptible to taint problems than cereals and in such instances chemical control (other than fumigation) may be confined to the use of pyrethrins. Equally, the moisture content of the produce can affect susceptibility to taint and to reduced germinative power. The latter is particularly true in the case of fumigants.

INSECTICIDE FORMULATIONS

Insecticides are used in many ways and in many forms or formulations. Examples in a number of countries are given in Table 22. It is important to use the correct formulation of insecticide, the correct equipment for applying it (Bills, 1966) for each problem. The different formulations available for use in stored products work are as follows:

Dilute dusts

These are ready for direct use and no dilution is required. They may be sold in small containers (e.g., a tin with a perforated top) which are also applicators, or they may be applied through a special dusting machine. Large power-operated dusting machines are available but for some problems a small knapsack or hand held machine may be sufficient (Figure 49). For dusting layers of bags a uniform deposit may be obtained by the use of a simple method such as "dumping" a close weave bag containing the dust over the surface to be treated (Figure 49). Alternatively, a machine which does not create a dust-filled atmosphere (Figure 49) may be used.

Most dilute dusts have a content of between 0.1 and 5 percent of the active ingredient; the remaining 95 percent or more is the base or diluent. There can be a wide variation in the bulk density of dusts; some organizations are said to prefer a light dust because it gives good bulk for mixing.

Dilute dusts must be kept dry. If they are damp, the insecticidal efficiency will deteriorate due to chemical breakdown of the insecticide, and a damp dust will of course not be applied uniformly.

FIGURE 49. Insecticidal dust treatment. Top left, dusting each layer of bags as a stack is being built; top right, dusting the outside of a completed stack of bagged produce; left, a vertical drop duster for treating layers of bagged produce with insecticidal dust.

Dilute dusts are used mainly for admixture with grain, for dusting the external surfaces of bagged produce to prevent reinfestation, for applying a band of dust around a stack of produce, for example, to prevent crawling insects attacking it, or for dusting hides and skins, fish, etc. Dusts may also be used for disinfestation of railway wagons, although they are less suitable for this type of problem than sprays because generally they do not stick well to vertical surfaces.

Dispersible powders

These are all concentrate powder formulations which are intended for dilution with water before application, i.e., wettable, sprayable, soluble and dispersible powders. These powder concentrates usually contain between 20 and 80 percent per weight of the active ingredient (ai) of the pure insecticide; the exact percentage should always be clearly marked on the outside of the containers. Also included in the formulation are stabilizers, wetters and stickers. These additives help to prevent sedimentation of the powder in the water before spraying, to stick the insecticide to the target so that it is not easily brushed off, and to spread the spray liquid over the target during spraying.

Dispersible powders are usually used for treating store fabric (walls, roof, floor), for treatment of external bag surfaces, and for disinfesting railway trucks, lorries, ship holds and barges, grain or flour bins, etc. Thorough preparation of the suspension is essential; once the required amount of powder has been weighed it is necessary to mix it into the correct volume of water. First, a little water should be added to the powder and stirred to produce a smooth paste; this is then added to the rest of the water and thoroughly stirred until an even suspension is obtained.

Dispersible powders tend to settle out after mixing and therefore only spraying machines equipped with an agitation system should be used for their application.

Emulsifiable concentrates

These are liquid concentrates which are intended for dilution in water before they are applied. As with dispersible powders, all emulsifiable concentrate insecticides should be sold in containers which are clearly labelled with the percentage concentration of

TABLE 22. – EXAMPLES OF USE OF PESTICIDES IN THE TROPICS AND SUBTROPICS

Chemical	How used	Treatment	Country and date of record
Lindane	Cob maize (in the sheath) in cribs gave 6 months protection	Dusted to give 10 ppm	Many parts of Africa (1953)
	Maize in bags	0.5% dust	British Honduras (1955)
	Groundnuts (unshelled)	0.5% dust	The Gambia (1962)
	Beans admixed with dust	0.5% dust (1.10 g/kg) (5.5 ppm gamma BHC)	Ghana (1962)
	Paddy. Layer dusting to prevent insects crawling under sheets covering stacks	0.5% dust	Guyana (1964)
	Extra protection on rice in farm storage	Smoke generators 5 g lindane per 100 m^3 storage space	Japan (1961)
	Wheat stacks dust layer by layer	0.5% dust or 1.0% at 57-85 g/90 kg bag	Kenya (1961)
	Maize on cobs dusted at end of drying period	1.0% dust at 455 g/m^3 maize cobs	Kenya (1965)
	Beans	0.1% dust at 113 g/90 kg bag	Kenya (1967)
	Gammexane insect powder as dust on rice sacks	9-14 g per bag	Malaya (1953)
	Bagged decorticated groundnuts	Spraying with wettable powder at 1.0 g/m^2	Nigeria (1947-57)

NOTE: The examples quoted were recorded by the Tropical Stored Products Centre, United Kingdom, from journals, annual reports and private communications.

TABLE 22. – EXAMPLES OF USE OF PESTICIDES IN THE TROPICS AND SUBTROPICS (*continued*)

Chemical	How used	Treatment	Country and date of record
Lindane	Unthreshed sorghum or millet stored for 6 months or more (sandwich treatment recommended)	0.5% dust 125 g per kg heads	Nigeria (1963)
	Recommended on unthreshed Guinea corn	0.5% BHC dust 5 ppm	Nigeria (1963)
	Only insecticide applied directly to bagged food grains	Gamma BHC as 1% dust or smoke generator	Pakistan, East (1965)
	Spraying of godowns for rice storage	50% wettable powder spray	
	Maize seed	Dusted with 0.5% lindane	Australia (Queensland) (1963)
	Sorghum seed	1% lindane dust	
	Maize on cob unsheathed	250 g of 0.5% gamma BHC per 100 kg cobs	Uganda (1962)
	Beans and cowpeas	250 g of 0.4% gamma BHC per 100 kg	
	Trogoderma infested godowns: cowpeas. Bags fumigated then dusted with BHC + floor and cracks. Produce may be mixed with BHC	-0.5% BHC dust -0.04% dust	Tanzania (Zanzibar)
Malathion	Grain	44 ppm	Australia (1964)
	Interior surfaces in contact with grain	2.5% malathion residual spray	Australia (1966)

TABLE 22. – EXAMPLES OF USE OF PESTICIDES IN THE TROPICS AND SUBTROPICS (*continued*)

Chemical	How used	Treatment	Country and date of record
Malathion (*coutinued*)	Warehouse disinfestation Used for maize, rice, coffee and black beans	4% dust after MeBr fumigation of coffee and fog of 60% oil-based malathion. Dust once a month, fog every week	Brazil (Port Santeo) (1963)
	Shelled groundnuts	Admixture of groundnut kernels sprayed prior to shipment	The Gambia (1965)
	On cockroach *B. germanica*	2% malathion/kerosene solution	Hong Kong (1963)
	Wheatstacks dust layer by layer	2% malathion replaced 1% lindane at Nairobi and Eldoret because of the higher temperature there	Kenya (1961)
	Food grain	125 g of 1.0% dust mixed with 100 kg; 85 g of 2% dust/sack	Kenya (1967)
	Recommended on outside of sack	85 g of 2% dust/sack	Kenya (1962)
	Wettable powder sprays of bagged storage Maize	Lindane tested as a replacement gave 6 months protection	Rhodesia (1962)
	Grain		Rhodesia (1960)
Methyl bromide	Grain	50 g/m³ by gravity 30 g/m³ with forced circulation	Argentina (1965)
	Groundnuts	40 g/m³ for 24 hours	Australia (1963)
	Rice	48 g/m³ for 7 days	Burma (1964)

TABLE 22. – EXAMPLES OF USE OF PESTCIDES IN THE TROPICS AND SUBTROPICS (*continued*)

Chemical	How used	Treatment	Country and date of record
Methyl bromide (*continued*)	Cereals Pulses	16-24 g/m³ of enclosed space for 24 hours	Burma (1966)
	Animal feed	80 g/m³ for 48 hours	
	Cocoa beans	32 g/m³ under PVC sheeting	Ghana (1961)
	Rice	10 g/m³ for 72 hours	Japan (1959)
	Yellow maize	32 g/m⁰/ft³ for 48 hours	Kenya (1967)
	Groundnuts	28 g/m³	Nigeria (1963)
	Tobacco	32 g/m³ for 72 hours	Rhodesia (1965)
	Maize	48 g/m³ for 24 hours	South Africa (1960)
	Stored produce	Vacuum fumigation at 720 mm Hg. at 80 g/m³	Tahiti (1963)
	Beans, all varieties	32 g/m³ for 24 hours	Tanzania (1965)
	Copra	32 g/m³ for 24 hours	Tanzania (1965)
	Groundnuts	32 g/m³ for 24 hours	Tanzania (1965)
	Maize	32 g/m³ for 24 hours	Tanzania (1965)
	Rice	48 g/m³ for 24 hours	Tanzania (1965)
	Wheat	48 g/m³ for 24 hours	Zanzibar (1957)
	Imported infested produce	48 g/m³ for 24 hours	Zanzibar (1957)

TABLE 22. – EXAMPLES OF USE OF PESTICIDES IN THE TROPICS AND SUBTROPICS (*continued*)

Chemical	How used	Treatment	Country and date of record
Ethylene dibromide	Grain	24 g/m³ as a surface spray. Used after phostoxin	India (1964)
Ethylene dichloride Carbontetra-chloride Mix 3 : 1	Stored seeds	350-500 cm³/m³ of space 48 hours	United Arab Republic (1958)
Carbontetra-chloride + carbon disulphide	Grain	80% w/w carbontetra-chloride (CCL_4) 20% w/w carbon disul-phide (CS_2) at 250-500 ml/ton	Argentina (1965)
Carbon Bisulphide	Stored seeds	200 cm³/m³ of space for 24 hours	United Arab Republic (1958)
Chloropicrin	Rice	1 kg/60 m³ for 72 hours	Japan (1959)
Phostoxin	Grain	5 tablets/ton	Argentina (1965)
	Grain	½ tablet/ton. After fumigation with EDBr	India (1964)
	Maize and wheat bran in bags in rail trucks and also in stores under plastic sheeting	4 tablets/ton	Kenya
	Carobs in bags under plastic sheeting	4 tablets/ton	Cyprus
	Groundnuts (shelled)	1 pellet/bag	Zambia

TABLE 22. – EXAMPLES OF USE OF PESTICIDES IN THE TROPICS AND SUBTROPICS (*concluded*)

Chemical	How used	Treatment	Country and date of record
Malathion	Where resistance to DDT and malathion 50% dieldrin and 25% BHC	WDP spray of walls and ceilings of empty stores to eradicate infestation	Sierra Leone (1965)
	On *Trogoderma* infested godowns, cowpeas removed and fumigated	Godown drenched with malathion (1 part : 100 parts water)	Zanzibar (1957)
Malathion + pyrethrins	Maize	113 g (1.0% malathion + 0.2% pyrethrins)	Kenya (1966-67)
Pyrethrins	Pyrethrum and methyl bromide only chemicals used on cocoa		Ghana (1962)
	Fog cocoa sheds each day at dusk	0.4% w/v in Shell Risella No. 17 oil. 0.7 litres/1 000 m^3	Ghana (1965)
Pyrethrum	*Cadra cautella* Tropical warehouse moth	0.4-1.0% in oil for surface spraying of bagged grain at 3.6 litres/232 m^2	Kenya (1967)
Pyrethrins	Copra	1.86 litres 1.3% pyrethrins per 1 000 m^3 nightly	Trinidad (1961)
Pyrethrum	In heavy oil for spraying large moth infestations	1.3% weekly 89.6 litres of spray per 1 000 m^3	Uganda (1962)
Pyrethrins + piperonyl butoxide	Maize	1 139 g (0.2% pyrethrins + 1.0% piperonyl butoxide) to 90 kg maize	Kenya (1966)

insecticide in the formulation; usually this will be in the same sort of range as for dispersible powders.

Emulsifiable concentrates are used in the same way as dispersible powders (i.e., for treating store fabric, external bag surfaces, disinfesting trucks, bins, ship holds, etc.); however, they may also be used for admixture treatments, particularly in relation to bulk grain storage where a flow of grain has to be treated with insecticide. Agitators are not generally required in machines used for applying emulsifiable formulations but the insecticide should be stirred just before refilling the spraying machines.

Liquid concentrates

This term is usually applied to formulations intended for direct use through aerosol or fogging machines. These formulations generally do not contain emulsifiers or other additives and so cannot be diluted with water. They often consist simply of the insecticide dissolved in a light mineral oil.

An aerosol is a spray of very small liquid droplets which remain suspended in the air for an appreciable length of time, often up to half an hour or so. The droplets are of 2 to 50 microns in diameter (1 micron = one thousandth of a millimetre) and, although capable of penetrating into cracks and crevices and the furthermost corners of a store, they do not penetrate through spillage and accumulations of dust, etc. They are dispersed by wind and air currents and so are usually only effective when used in warehouses whese there is not too much ventilation. Aerosols may be dispensed from the household type of canister which holds a mixture of "Freon" liquified gas and insecticides; the internal pressure blasts the insecticide into aerosol-sized droplets as the mixture leaves the nozzle. Alternatively, there are several types of machines which produce aerosol droplets by compressed air, by dropping the insecticide onto a very rapidly spinning disc, or by hot air or hot exhaust gases or steam to blast the insecticide into the very small droplets.

Pyrotechnic preparations

These are the smoke bombs, smoke pellets or smoke canisters.

A smoke is in effect the solid equivalent of an aerosol. The particles are about the same size as aerosol droplets but they are solid, not liquid. Smokes have the same properties as aerosols with respect to penetration, and ventilation in stores has the same effect. These preparations consist of a mixture of insecticide and a pyrotechnic powder made up into a firework-like device complete with taper fuse for lighting. The fuse is lit and a dense column of insecticidal smoke is emitted. The insecticides used in these preparations are those which are moderately heat-stable; lindane, DDT, and mixtures of the two have been widely used.

Admixture of insecticides directly with food products

Due to the potential hazards to health imposed by treatments of this type, it is very important to ensure that only those admixture treatments which are officially recommended are used. At the present time, only three insecticides may be considered for these treatments: pyrethrum, malathion and lindane. Admixture treatments can be recommended for all grains and pulses, but not for flours. Malathion is perhaps to be preferred to lindane in so far as the potential toxic hazard to man is concerned. Against this, malathion has the disadvantage of a certain amount of chemical instability and tends to break down and so become partially ineffective in certain circumstances. In some parts of the world certain insect species have become resistant to lindane; this factor also has to be taken into account.

Admixture is suitable for grain destined for long-term storage and is normally carried out at an early stage in the chain of events that occur between harvesting of a food crop and its consumption. It may be used to protect cob maize and other unthreshed cereals stored in cribs or farmers' granaries. In Kenya, for example, following experimental work by Le Pelley and Kockum (1954), the use of lindane on cob maize is officially recommended. A rate of 12.5 ppm of lindane (120 grammes of 1 percent lindane per cubic metre of cobs which is equivalent to 100 kilos of grain) is applied to the maize as it enters the crib; the level of lindane remaining on the grain after shelling has been shown to be rather less than the 1 ppm allowed on shelled maize by law in that country. Experimental work carried out in Nigeria has shown a similar treatment of unthreshed sorghum and millet to give effective protection (Giles, 1964) without the development of harmful residues.

Admixture may be carried out on the farm after drying, at the time of bagging the grain, or at the trader level before acceptance by a central store. Dilute dust formulations are normally used at a rate of 120 grammes per 100 kilogrammes of grain. It is important to mix the dust very well with the grain. This may be done by shovel mixing on a tarpaulin or in a drum with eccentric axle (Figure 50); by dusting the stream of grain entering the bag from a shelling machine; or by adding 60 grammes to a bag half full of grain, holding the bag shut while shaking and turning, then repeating with another bag half full of grain before adding the contents together to fill one bag. Machines for mixing dust with grain could be used. Failure of admixture treatment is usually due to inadequate mixing of the insecticide with the grain but it is possible that failure to note that the grain must be well dried before applying the dust has been responsible in some cases. Insecticides recommended are:

(*a*) *Malathion* (120 grammes of 1.0 percent dust per 200 kilogrammes of grain);

(*b*) *Lindane* (120 grammes of 0.1 percent dust per 200 kilogrammes of grain);

(*c*) *Pyrethrum* (120 grammes of 0.2 percent pyrethrins plus 1.0 percent piperonyl butoxide dust per 200 kilogrammes of grain).

It is also relevant here to refer to the use, particularly at trader levels, of liquid insecticides (emulsifiable concentrates) for direct application to grain. These are usually applied through a mechanized precision spraying apparatus which applies the insecticidal spray to the produce. This can be done when the produce is spread on a drying floor (care being taken not to overwet the produce) or while it is moving in a conveyor, e.g., before it enters a bulk storage container (Figure 51). The output of the machine can be calibrated to the flow of the grain, achieving even distribution of the insecticide. There is the added advantage that liquid formulations are generally more stable than dusts. The volume of water used must not be so great that the moisture content of the grain being treated is appreciably raised and should certainly not be greater than 2.5 litres per 1 000 kilogrammes of grain. The insecticides recommended are pyrethrins or malathion.

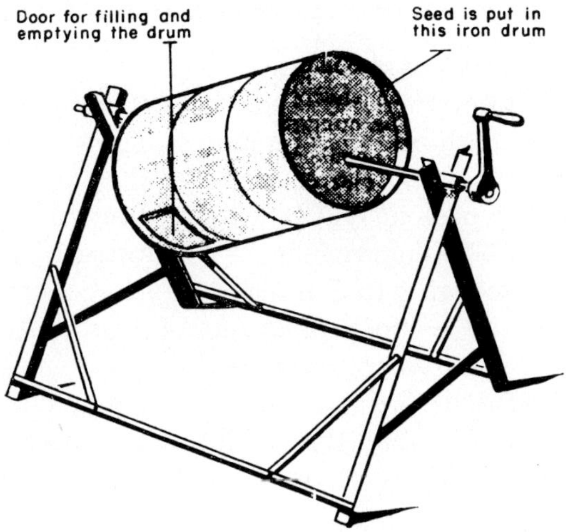

FIGURE 50. Dusting grain in a drum with an eccentric axle.

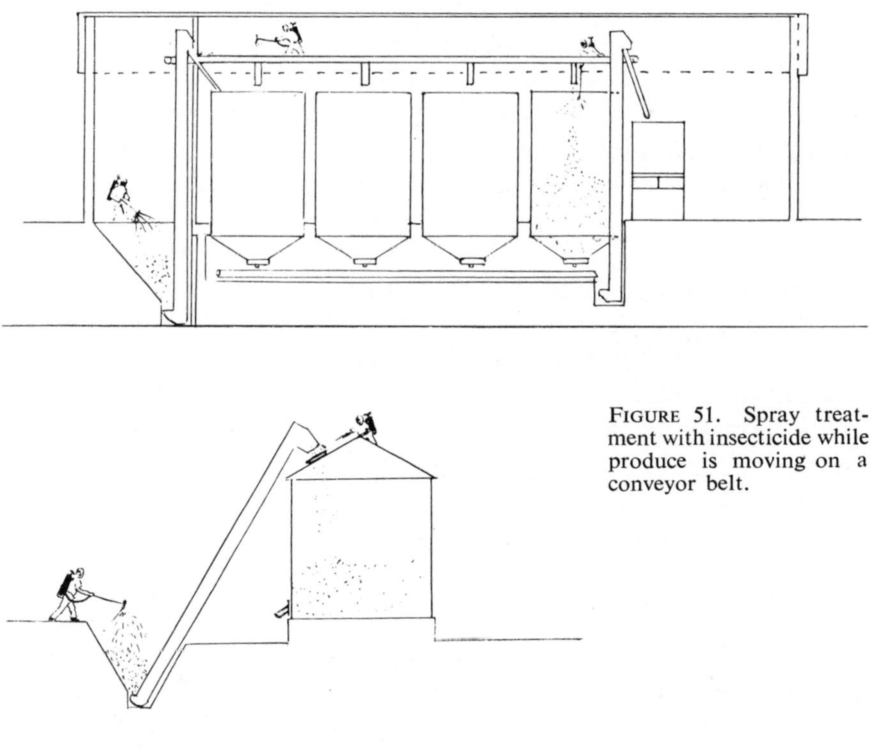

FIGURE 51. Spray treatment with insecticide while produce is moving on a conveyor belt.

Admixture of insecticides for the protection of seed

It is possible to use relatively high concentrations of insecticides for admixture with seeds to prevent insect infestation. In addition to malathion, lindane and pyrethrum, DDT can also be employed if there is no possibility of the seed being used for human consumption; 3 or 5 percent DDT dust has been used at a rate of 100 grammes per 100 kilogrammes. Malathion, lindane and pyrethrum may be used at 2 to 5 times the rate recommended for food-grain storage. It is most important that precautions should be taken to ensure that seed treated with these high rates of insecticide or with DDT will not be used for human consumption. If there is any possibility that this might occur, application rates should be the same as those recommended for food grains.

Residual spraying of storage buildings and vehicles

Before spraying the structure of stores, bins or transportation units, thorough cleaning should be carried out. Malathion or lindane should be used to spray all internal surfaces, including floor and roof. The dispersible powder formulations are preferable to emulsifiable concentrates for application to cement, brick, stone or whitewashed surfaces. This is because emulsified insecticides are largely absorbed into cement and stonework and are not present on the surface with which the insects are in contact. With dispersible powders, the particles of powder (containing the insecticide) are filtered out on the surface of the cement, the water being absorbed into the wall (this is known as the " filtration effect "); the residual life of the insecticide-impregnated solid particles left on the surface is less than that for applications of emulsifiable formulations on nonabsorbent walls (e.g., metal, painted or other nonabsorbent surfaces). Treatment should be carried out at intervals of 3 weeks. Rates of application recommended are:

(*a*) *Malathion.* 400 grammes of 25 percent dispersible powder, or 200 millilitres of 50 percent emulsifiable concentrate, in 5 litres of water per 100 square metres.

(*b*) *Lindane.* 200 grammes of 50 percent dispersible powder, or 500 millilitres of 20 percent emulsifiable concentrate in 5 litres of water per 100 square metres.

In many countries DDT has been used in sprays to treat store fabric, railway trucks, lorries, etc. This cannot be generally recommended in circumstances where foodstuffs are likely to come into direct contact with the surfaces sprayed, as would be the case with silo bins or where bulk transport of grains, etc., in lorries or railway trucks is concerned. A mixture of lindane and DDT has been used successfully in certain areas.

(*c*) *Lindane/DDT.* 100 grammes of lindane 50 percent dispersible powder plus 200 grammes of 50 percent DDT dispersible powder, or 250 cubic centimetres of lindane 20 percent emulsifiable concentrate plus 400 cubic centimetres of DDT 25 percent emulsifiable concentrate, in 5 litres of water per 100 square metres.

In some circumstances it is beneficial to incorporate some pyrethrum insecticide (malathion and piperonyl butoxide are somewhat antagonistic). This activates the insects, facilitating a more thorough treatment of certain areas than might otherwise be carried out by the operator, and increasing the pickup of the main insecticidal components in the spray.

It cannot be overemphasized that, in order to achieve maximum insect control through uniform spray deposit and avoid insecticide residue problems, pest control personnel must be properly trained in spraying techniques.

Space treatments

It may be necessary to use space spraying techniques to control infestations of flying pests entering from outside and those not controlled by residual treatments. Space treatments will need to be repeated at very frequent intervals, preferably every day, if effective control is to be achieved, and this will also depend upon how well the building is sealed. Treatments carried out less frequently than three times a week are not likely to give adequate control.

It is very important to carry out space treatments at a time of day when the pests are most active, generally at dusk. This is quite convenient because it is necessary to close doors and ventilators, etc., and keep them closed for an hour or two after treatment, which is often not possible during working hours. Also, in the tropics there is often a calm, wind-free period around dusk and this will help to increase the efficiency of the treatment by reducing the movement of air through poorly closed ventilators, etc.

The insecticide usually used is pyrethrum with or without a synergist, e.g., piperonyl butoxide at about five times the pyrethrin content, although lindane or DDT may be used (particularly in the form of smokes) and dichlorvos has been used experimentally (Green, Kane and Gradidge, 1966).

For fogging or aerosol spraying with pyrethrum, a liquid concentrate containing 0.4 percent pyrethrins plus 2.0 percent piperonyl butoxide is recommended against beetles. The rate of application for this formulation should be 50 millilitres per 100 cubic metres, repeated once daily or three times a week. Where moth pests (for example *Ephestia cautella*) are predominant, a liquid concentrate containing 0.5 percent pyrethrins alone or plus 0.5 percent piperonyl butoxide should be used at the same rate.

Lindane or DDT smokes are relatively easy to use, requiring no special aerosol or fogging machine, but these do not achieve the same level of control as pyrethrum fogging.

Dichlorvos fogging of stores has been used experimentally and this treatment may become more widely used in the future. This pesticide is toxic to man and care must be taken to ensure that personnel are not in the building when the treatment is being effected (from outside the building) and that no hazard arises in relation to the operator. A maximum safe level of 1.0 ppm in the atmosphere for continual exposure to workers has been laid down in the United States.

Regular aerosol or fogging treatments may be somewhat laborious or expensive and therefore are not generally favoured when some other treatment (e.g., fumigation or residual spraying) could be appropriate. However, there are occasions when regular space treatments are the only practical means of effectively controlling infestation. This might apply, for example, when fumigation is not possible and the dominant pests are moth species which are not well controlled with the commonly used residual sprays. In calculating the dosage for space spraying it is important to remember that this should be based upon the *free* space and not the total volume of the store.

TREATMENT OF BAG STACKS

Two treatments commonly used are referred to as layer by layer and external stack treatments; these are only capable of reducing infestation. In the layer by layer method, sprays or dusts are applied to each layer of bags during construction of a bag stack. The efficiency of such treatments is probably greater against the more mobile pests than against those that tend to remain within bags. Dilute dust formulations have been used. Insecticides recommended are 2 percent malathion dust or 0.5 percent lindane dust at a rate of 25 grammes per sack or 50 grammes per square metre.

The external stack treatment usually consists of a spray application to the four sides and the top surface of a bag stack (Figure 52). Dust treatments may be successfully used on the top surface but are most inefficient on the sides of stacks because it is not possible to get good coverage. Wettable powder formulations should be used wherever possible because of the filtration effect; emulsified insecticide tends to be absorbed into the fabric of the bags where it is not available for killing the insects. The insecticides most commonly used for this purpose are malathion and lindane (at the rates recommended above for structural spraying). Pyrethrum is generally believed to be inefficient for the surface spraying of bag stacks because of its instability to light.

Insecticidal treatments of external bag surfaces are used to prevent reinfestation. For example, stacks should be sprayed immediately following a fumigation or, preferably, immediately prior to sheeting, in order to minimize the risk of cross infestation. Alternative methods of achieving this include the use of mechanical barriers (e.g., cotton sheets or plastic fumigation sheets left *in situ*) but their use raises special problems unless humidity and moisture levels are low and temperatures are even. The weak point in a mechanical barrier is where the sheet is in contact with the floor; here it is necessary to apply a band of insecticidal dust (e.g., lindane, malathion, DDT). In the dry north of Nigeria, it was demonstrated that a 5 percent carbaryl dust was very effective (Halliday, 1962), persistence being as good as that of DDT (at least 6 months), and better control against *Tribolium castaneum* was achieved.

FIGURE 52. Spray treatment of bag stacks. Left, spraying the outside of sacks with a knapsack sprayer. Below, a spraying machine being used to treat the sides of a large stack of bagged produce.

Bag stacks will particularly require surface spraying when they are in a store containing other produce which is infested or in an area where infestation from external sources (or from the fabric of the store) is high.

FUMIGATION [1]

It has already been mentioned that the application of highly volatile chemicals able to penetrate a stack of bagged produce or bulk grain stored in a silo will kill any infestation present (including eggs and other immature stages inside the grains) but will not give lasting protection such as prevention of reinfestation or reinvasion by insects. Such protection can be provided by the use of contact insecticides.

In considering specificity of fumigant toxicity it must be remembered that different species of insects may vary in their susceptibility, and also that within a species the different stages of egg, larva, pupa and adult may vary in their reaction. Thus in certain beetles the larval stage is the most resistant and the dosage required to kill that stage has to be used. Bowden (1960) has pointed out that under practical conditions of silo storage in Uganda, the preadult stages of the weevil *S. oryzae* proved the most resistant against the fumigant phosphine. Using fumigants under tropical conditions, a comparable percentage kill of insect pests can be expected at a concentration x time product (i.e., concentration of gas maintained throughout the stack or bulk of grain being fumigated for a certain period of time) which is about half that required in temperate countries. It might have been anticipated that factors such as the absorptive properties of the commodity under high temperature conditions, the amount of gas leakage occurring under the fumigation conditions, etc., would necessitate use of a high dosage, but work carried out in India and elsewhere has indicated that low dosages can give effective kills.

Toxic and other hazards

As a result of chemical reaction between a fumigant and a food product, permanent residues may be formed. For example, fumi-

[1] See FAO (1969).

gation with methyl bromide or ethylene dibromide may result in the formation of inorganic bromide residues. It has been shown that sorghum fumigated with methyl bromide on several occasions, under circumstances which minimized airing of the stack after each fumigation, contained residues of the order of 200 ppm. A tolerance level of 50 ppm has been quoted for sorghum (FAO 1969).

The viability of seeds may be affected by fumigation; furthermore early growth from fumigated seeds may be impaired. Caswell and Clifford (1960) describe trials in Nigeria in which growth of maize was reduced when seed at a moisture content above 11 percent was fumigated with a carbon tetrachloride, ethylene dichloride mixture. High temperature may also be a factor leading to poor germination, as in the case of fumigation using methyl bromide (Strong and Lindgren, 1961). The same authors (1960) report that fumigation using phosphine should not affect the germination capacity of seed.

Most fumigants are highly toxic to man and should therefore be handled only by properly trained personnel.

FUMIGANTS USED IN STORAGE AND INFESTATION WORK

Carbon disulphide

This is not a very widely used fumigant but is of practical value in the tropics where vaporization is enhanced by high temperatures. Owing to its tendency to burn or explode it is more commonly used in a mixture with the nonflammable carbon tetrachloride for fumigation of small quantities of bulk produce in solid walled containers.

Liquid fumigants

So called because of their application in liquid form, these fumigants should be handled carefully to avoid inhalation of toxic vapours. A gas mask equipped with an appropriate canister should be used when applying fumigants. This group of fumigants includes ethylene dibromide, carbon tetrachloride, ethylene dichloride, mixtures of ethylene dichloride and carbon tetrachloride, and trichlorethylene. They give most satisfactory results when used in small-scale bulk storage. For grain in bags, empty bags and for bulk grain not more than 2.5 metres deep, a mixture composed of 3 parts ethylene dichloride and 1 part carbon tetrachloride should be used; for grain more than 2.5 metres deep a mixture of these chemicals in equal proportions is more effective.

In India a portable circulatory fumigation device has been developed for use with an ethylene dichloride/carbon tetrachloride mixture for stack fumigation (Pingale, 1963).

Phosphine

The tablet or pellet form of this fumigant (aluminium phosphide) makes simple its application to bags or to bulk grain during loading into a bin (Figure 53); fumigation results from the liberation of phosphine gas due to the interaction of the temperature and moisture in the grain with the tablet. The residual powder from the tablets, of which there is a small percentage, consists of inert aluminium hydroxide.

This fumigant is very toxic to man and, since it requires an exposure period of some three days, precautions must be taken during this period to avoid the possibility that personnel working nearby may be affected. Successful use of this type of fumigant has been reported from a number of tropical countries (Davies, 1958; Rai, Sarid and Pingale, 1963) in relation to fumigation of bulk grain in silos, bagged produce under sheeting, produce in railway trucks and single bags of produce.

Methyl bromide

This has been the most commonly used fumigant, but because it requires special equipment and specially trained personnel its use is confined to the fumigation of produce stored on a large scale, often for export purposes and for treatment of infested imported produce.

In India, the successful use of a mixture of equal parts of methyl bromide and ethylene dibromide has been reported (Perti, 1965) for the fumigation of rice. However, an experimental study of the behaviour of the components of such a mixture (Heuser, 1964) in flour has shown that almost complete separation of the two gases occurs, with resultant problems (the penetrative property of methyl bromide being considerably better than that of ethylene dibromide).

Application of liquid fumigants

For the fumigation of small silo bins or small quantities of bagged commodities, a watering can or stirrup pump may be used; in the case of bagged commodities immediate covering with a gasproof sheet is necessary. Where more than a few gallons are to be applied a mechanically driven pump is preferable (but *not* an insecticide sprayer, which gives too fine a spray, making the time of application unnecessarily long).

In terms of operator hazard these are the safest of the fumigants considered in this manual. However, it is important to remember that application should be carried out as quickly as possible; in the case of bagged commodities a gasproof sheet should be in such a position that it can be pulled over the bags immediately after the dose has been applied. An operator treating a silo bin must always remember to avoid inhaling fumigant vapours. When this is not possible, a gas mask fitted with an appropriate canister nust be used.

Application of aluminium phosphide

Bagged grain

Tablets of aluminium phosphide may be incorporated into a stack layer by layer as it is built, at the rate of one tablet per two bags, provided that the stack is of such a size that it will be completed and covered with a gasproof sheet within two hours. On completion the stack is covered with gasproof sheets which are anchored to the ground using sand snakes or a heavy chain wrapped in hessian, and the sheeted stack is left for at least three days. Bagged produce can be treated in railway trucks in a similar manner, so ensuring that the trucks are sealed against leakage.

An alternative method of sheet anchorage, which is being used in central Africa, utilizes old unserviceable gasproof sheets which are cut up to give strips 1 metre wide. Before stack building commences these strips are placed on the ground along the line of the edges of the stack. The outside bags of the first layer of the stack are then laid so that half the width of the strip is covered. The weight of the bags placed on succeeding layers ensures that the strip is firmly held in close contact with the floor. When the complete stack is prepared for fumigation, the edges of the gasproof sheets and the protruding section of the strip are rolled tightly together and clamped to form the seal.

Materials for fumigation sheets which have been found to give satisfactory service in large-scale work are polyethylene and polyvinyl chloride (4/1 000 inches thick), unsupported film or nylon or terylene fabric coated with neoprene or other plastic.

In order to fumigate an existing stack the required dose of fumigant may be distributed around the base (Figure 54) of the stack on trays (which are removed following the fumigation) containing the aluminium hydroxide residue. It is important to note that gloves should be worn whenever tablets are being dispensed from tubes by hand.

Bulk grain

Tablets or pellets may be scattered over the surface provided the bulk being treated is not excessively large. They may be inserted into the bulk grain by means of special probes (Figure 55) which are supplied by the manufacturers; as even a distribution as possible should be achieved. In the case of an initial fumigation of silo-stored grain, this can best be effected at intake through the application of tablets by hand to the moving grain stream, whether this is falling from a grain auger or on a horizontal conveyor (Figure 56).

APPLICATION OF METHYL BROMIDE

Bagged grain

Methyl bromide is normally delivered to the top of a stack by means of 1.25-centimetre bore high pressure polythene tubing, with the arrangement of tubing and delivery jets at the top of the stack depending upon its shape (Brown, 1959). It is usually necessary to rearrange the surface bags to provide " fumigation channels " to accommodate the piping, and to secure pieces of old tarpaulin or similar material across the top of the channels in order to protect the plastic sheets which will cover the stack against the solvent action of liquid methyl bromide. Very careful handling of gasproof

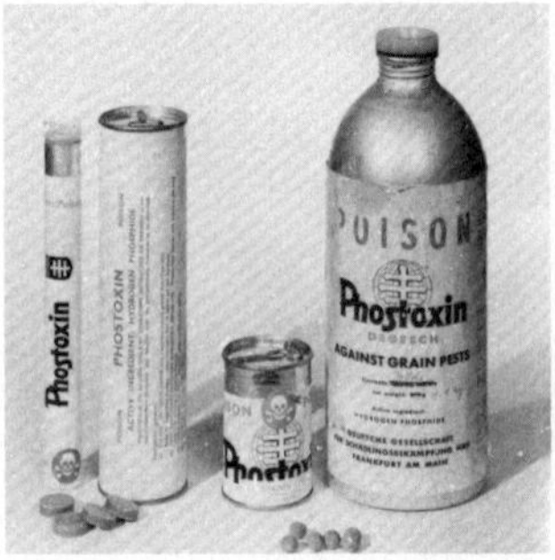

FIGURE 53. Tablet and pellet forms of phosphine.

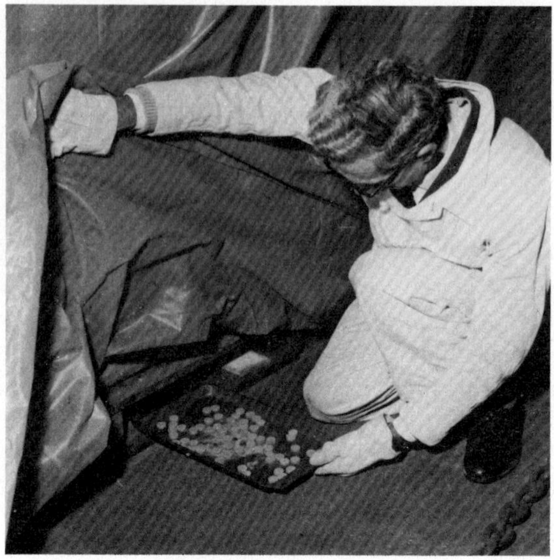

FIGURE 54. Distributing the required dose of aluminium phosphide on trays round the base of a stack.

FIGURE 55. Applying aluminium phosphide to silo-stored grain by means of a special probe.

FIGURE 56. Dropping aluminium phosphide tablets onto the moving grain stream at intake.

sheets is necessary in order to avoid damage which will result in loss of gas.

In the fumigation of large stacks (Figure 57) the use of several gasproof sheets will be necessary; the sheets are draped to overlap each other, and the overlapped joints are rolled and secured with G clamps. The method of anchorage of the sheets to the floor has already been described. In a few countries attempts have been made to enclose entire warehouses in gasproof sheeting in order to fumigate the building and the contents (Figure 58).

The dosage usually employed for stacks containing less than 5 000 bags is 1 kilogramme of methyl bromide per 30 cubic metres; for larger stacks it is 7 kilogrammes per 150 cubic metres. The standard exposure period is 48 hours.

Gas masks should be worn by all operators undertaking this type of fumigation, particularly when the gasproof sheets are removed. It is most important to ensure that there are no slack couplings in the line conveying the fumigant gas and that the sheet is properly secured to the floor.

Bulk grain

Fumigation of grain in silos with methyl bromide is carried out effectively only if the silos are fitted with a gas circulatory system (Figure 59). The gas is circulated for a sufficient time to allow four or five air changes within the bin. Following this the grain is kept under gas for at least 48 hours.

Gasproof sheet fumigation

Reference has been made to the use of certain fumigants on bagged produce under gasproof sheets.

With most fumigants there is an advantage in artificially aiding distribution of the gas under the sheets by the use of an electric fan. Such an aid is at present rarely used in stack fumigations, but is more commonly seen in specially constructed fumigation chambers. The fan may be sited under the sheets at one corner, the sheet being pulled out from the stack at this point and secured to the floor of the warehouse at some three feet from the base of the stack.

FIGURE 57. Fumigating large stacks with methyl bromide by the use of gasproof sheet. Above, sheeting the stack; centre, the fully covered stack undergoing fumigation; below, removing sheets from the fumigated stack.

At the end of the fumigation period, it is the practice to remove the sheets and allow the stack to air. They should be removed quickly since the hazard to the operators is high at this stage because of the high gas concentrations attained during a 24 to 48-hour fumigation period. When many sheets are involved, it is normally best to remove a few first (for example, at the four corners) and allow partial aeration before returning to remove the remaining sheets. Where one very large sheet is used, it is probably best to remove part of it from the stack at first and then remove all of it when the stack has been partially aired and is thus less hazardous to the operators. With methyl bromide fumigations, a halide detector lamp should be used to check that no methyl bromide remains in the vicinity of the stack.

A small building containing produce may be fumigated under sheets in the same way as a large stack. Care must be taken that gasproof sheets are not torn by protruding edges, sharp corners, etc. The sheets should be of plastic-coated nylon strong enough to withstand the rough usage that will inevitably occur in such fumigations.

The principles for fumigating small stacks of produce under gasproof sheets are the same as for large stacks. Methyl bromide is perfectly satisfactory but it is often easier to use phosphine or one of the liquid fumigants, for example, an ethylene dichloride/carbon tetrachloride combination. Should the stack be of intermediate size (of several tons of produce), however, methyl bromide or phosphine would be the most appropriate fumigant.

In-bag or in-drum fumigation

When produce is stored in sacks which are gasproof (e.g., sacks with polythene liners) it is possible to carry out in-bag fumigations using aluminium phosphide pellets. The pellets may be sealed in paper envelopes at the time of treatment and placed on top of the produce in the open sack or liner which is then promptly sealed. The stack may be heat-sealed or closed by the simple bunch-and-tie method. The sacks should not be opened until they reach the end user who should safely dispose of the paper envelopes containing the toxic residual powder left by the pellets. A great advantage of this method of fumigation is that the gasproof sacks prevent rein-

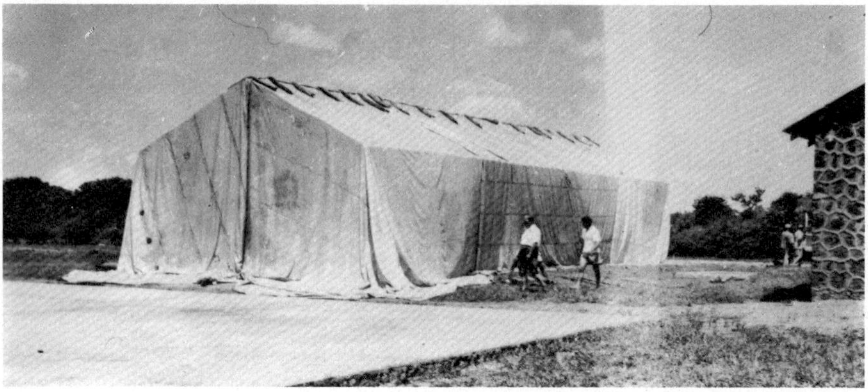

FIGURE 58. Enclosing an entire warehouse in gasproof sheets for purposes of fumigation.

FIGURE 59. Diagram of grain silos fitted with a gas circulatory system of fumigation.

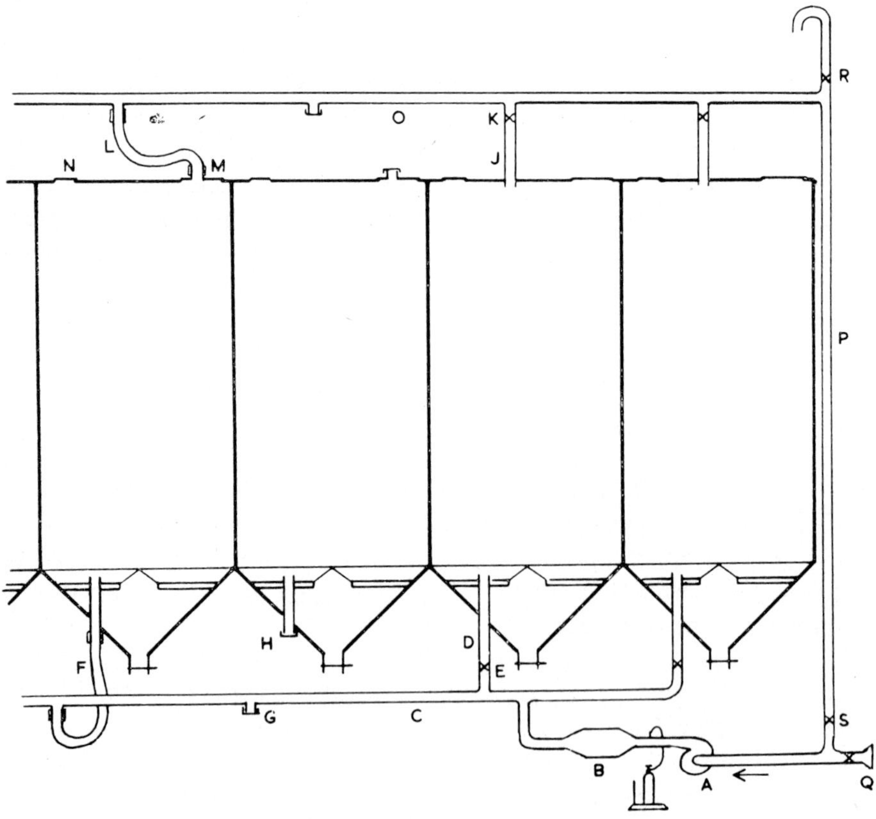

festation of the produce after fumigation and also prevent loss or gain in moisture.

When the volume of produce to be fumigated is very small it is often more practical to use an empty oil drum or similar metal container as a fumigation chamber. The drum may be sealed by a polythene sheet fixed to the top (open end) of the drum by masking tape. Alternatively a metal lid may be used to close against a gasket fitted on a collar on the outside of the drum. The liquid fumigants or phosphine are suitable for fumigations of this sort.

FUMIGATION CHAMBERS

Treatments carried out in a properly designed and constructed fumigation chamber can be undertaken with maximum efficiency and minimum hazard. The chamber itself is merely a gastight room with a gastight door, and perhaps with an inspection ventilation hatch situated opposite the door. Portable fumigation chambers of plywood or gasproof fabrics supported on a framework may be used. Permanent chambers are usually built of concrete or brick, well sealed internally. The chamber should be equipped with a fan to exhaust the gas through the doorway or ventilation hatch after fumigation. The fan should have a capacity permitting one complete air change of the empty chamber in not more than 3 minutes. Care must be taken to ensure that exhaustedg as from the chamber at the end of a fumigation will not constitute a hazard.

The fumigation chamber is loaded so that there is an air space of at least 1 foot between the top of the produce and the ceiling of the chamber; any of the fumigants listed earlier may be used, methyl bromide or phosphine being the most likely choice. In the case of the latter, the tablets should be scattered over the produce immediately before closing the door. With methyl bromide, the cylinder (or 1-pound tin) is left outside the chamber and, after closing the doors, the fumigant is introduced through piping (installed at time of building) inserted in the wall of the chamber. The dosage is calculated in the usual way, according to the cubic capacity of the chamber. For methyl bromide the fan should be operated during the first quarter to half hour of fumigation to ensure good circulation of the gas around the produce and again to exhaust the gas at the end of fumigation. The latter is particularly necessary where cross ventilation is not possible. A variety of systems can be used for ensuring that there is adequate circulation and exhausting of the air/fumigant within the chamber. Axial flow fans which deliver large volumes of air should be used. The Pest Infestation Laboratory, Slough, has recommended a 30-centimetre fan driven by a $^1/_3$-horse power motor at 2 900 revolutions per minute (rpm); this delivers about 28 cubic metres per minute through a 3-metre duct of 20-centimetre diameter, at a linear speed of 12.5 metres per second, and is suitable for a chamber of about 84 cubic metres in capacity. Alternatively a 30-centimetre impeller driven by a motor of $^1/_6$ hp at 1 400 rpm with 30-centimetre ducts will give about 28 cubic metres per minute.

Fumigation in ships, barges and railway trucks

The hold of a ship or barge (Figure 60) may form a convenient chamber for the the fumigation of produce. However, only expe-

Figure 60. Using the hold of a barge as a convenient chamber for fumigating produce.

rienced personnel should carry out such fumigations, as difficulties often arise in achieving good gas distribution or adequate ventilation at the end of fumigation. Methyl bromide is the fumigant commonly used. Normally the entire crew should be evacuated from the ship during fumigation and only allowed to return after thorough checking at the end of fumigation has shown that no gas remains in any part of the ship.

Stationary steel railway trucks of the closed type make quite reasonable fumigation chambers. The doors may be sealed with a self-adhesive plastic tape or, if no large gaps are concerned, adhesive paper may be used. The trucks should be placed on a siding where they can be left undisturbed for the duration of the fumigation. Trucks being fumigated must be well labelled to prevent accidental opening before completion of the fumigation.

Under certain circumstances it may be possible to fumigate produce in moving trucks. The movement of doors, etc., that inevitably occurs when the truck is moving requires that doors must be sealed very carefully, using materials such as plastic self-adhesive tape which is to some extent elastic and allows a certain amount of movement without breaking. More than ever it is necessary to place prominent warning labels on trucks and to ensure that they are met at destination point by a fumigation officer who will supervise the airing of the truck before unloading commences.

Inspection and reports

The close inspection of produce at intake has been emphasized; present methods are subjective in most respects both in sampling and inspection procedures. New methods are being developed to make quality inspection more efficient and quicker to operate so as to minimize delays in transport systems.

Similarly, when produce has been taken into store it is essential that an accurate assessment of its condition be obtained. Keeping stacks of produce in store without knowledge of any changes taking place within the bulk or stack is poor warehousekeeping practice. A record of temperature changes within the produce and of the appearance of insects is essential if appropriate measures are to be taken in time.

In addition, when insecticidal treatments have been carried out it is necessary to inspect all stocks within the premises at regular intervals. Records of temperature changes and special attention to possible sources of residual infestation such as bags of accumulated grading samples, sweepings or privately owned stacks should be made and the necessary steps taken. These may include fumigation.

It is an essential part of good warehousekeeping to keep accurate records of stock intake, inspections carried out, spray treatments and fumigations, together with details of the quantities of pesticides used and in stock.

Wherever applicable, the records should be checked by a person in authority.

Costs of pesticide control methods

The cost of pesticide control methods employed in the tropics is highly variable. Two main types of pesticides have been referred to — contact and respiratory chemicals — which have different characteristics. Contact chemicals rely on the insects moving into the area where they have been applied; some are reasonably persistent and have fairly specific effects and tend to result in problems of resistance. By comparison, the respiratory chemicals or fumigants act as gases which permeate the produce to the place where the insect is located. They have little residual effect once the produce has been aired, and are much more toxic to man than contact insecticides. Some chemical treatments are more expensive than others because of the quantities required and the skilled labour needed for their application.

Also, the cost of insect control treatments varies with the local conditions within a country in terms of distances to be travelled and quantities of produce to be treated at a particular time; in general, treatments carried out by commercial firms are more expensive than those undertaken by government or semigovernment bodies.

Complete pest control programmes involving dusting and spraying with contact insecticides and fumigation can range from about 16 cents to $3.30 per ton, while fumigation treatments with methyl bromide can cost from 8 cents to $1.30 per ton, and fogging treatments from about 6 to 40 cents per ton.

Physical control methods [2]

AIRTIGHT STORAGE [3]

In a completely airtight container, insect pests in dry grain will eventually die from lack of oxygen; damp grain will undergo some chemical changes due to partial fermentation but will not be subject to serious deterioration due to microorganisms such as bacteria and fungi. In practice, because of difficulties in making structures sufficiently airtight, it is more difficult to achieve successful storage under tropical conditions with damp than with dry grain. With many types of containers (including silos) and all types of buildings, it is usually more satisfactory to control insect infestation by using fumigants or contact insecticides. The buildings or containers should be sealed tightly to prevent reinfestation.

Reference has been made to the traditional use of underground storage pits in a number of countries and, although these pits are often claimed to be airtight, few scientific studies have been carried out to assess their value. The incorporation of plastic sheeting to achieve airtightness in local designs of pits is a useful improvement. Various designs of pits in use have been mentioned and the modern approach to this form of storage, using concrete, was pioneered in Latin America. It has also been used in Cyprus and Kenya.

Various designs of modern silos are constructed with a view to achieving airtightness, which is most successful in welded metal or butyl rubber (or similar plastic) bag type silos. Concrete silos have to be specially proofed and fitted with gasketed inlet and outlet spouts.

Experiments have shown that metal drums (for example, of 200-litre capacity) with tight fitting lids, specially sealed, can be used very successfully for the storage of small quantities of grains in airtight conditions.

Future experimental work is needed to evaluate the airtightness of various types of plastic bags (at least $^1/_{100}$ centimetre thick) for food storage.

---

[2] See Watters, 1965.

[3] See Hyde, 1962; Bailey, 1956, 1957.

Insect-proof containers

The use of plastic sheeting as a means of preventing reinfestation of bagged produce following fumigation has been mentioned previously. This technique has been taken one stage further in the development of the airwarehouse, a portable fumigatable and insect-proof storage building constructed of PVC-coated nylon or terylene, or neoprene-coated nylon (Wright and Southgate, 1962; Southgate, 1965). Such buildings, designed for the storage of produce in bags or bulk (particularly the former), are being evaluated in a number of countries, especially in Africa.

The suitability of flexible bulk containers 1 to 15 tons in capacity and of plastic sacks or plastic liners for natural fibre sacks is also being considered. One of the limitations in the use of plastics for the storage of food grains is that, in addition to preventing the entry of insects, they form a barrier to the escape of water. Clearly, such techniques with currently available plastic materials may only be used for produce that has been adequately dried.

Irradiation

Radiation disinfestation of grain, whereby infested grain may be subjected to ionizing radiations to inhibit insect reproduction and to kill, is a technique which is still under development. The recent literature on this subject has been reviewed by Golumbic and Davis (1966).

Work carried out in the United States (Cogburn, Tilton and Burkholder, 1966; Tilton, Burkholder and Cogburn, 1966) has shown that beetles are more susceptible to gamma radiation than moths; 25 000 rads will kill all stages of the beetles *Sitophilus oryzae* and *Tribolium confusum*, but more than 100 000 rads are probably necessary to sterilize the moths *Plodia interpunctella* and *Sitotroga cerealella*.

The Food and Drug Administration of the United States of America has approved a single treatment of wheat and wheat flour with gamma radiation at a dose range of 20 000 to 50 000 rads (Laudani, 1967).

Sound

Experimental studies in the United States have shown that the number of progeny from eggs laid during a 4-day exposure of

Plodia interpunctella to amplified sound waves from two sources was only a quarter of that from eggs of unexposed moths (Kirkpatrick and Harein (1965)). Moreover, the length of life of adults developing from the eggs of exposed moths was reduced. Further studies of this subject may merit more attention.

Percussion

Experimental work has shown that sharp impact or percussion kills insect stages which are present in foodstuffs, and even the egg stage contained within cereals. The adaptation of centrifuge type machines to provide a percussion effect on every particle of produce passing through the machine therefore affords one method of eliminating insect pests from free flowing materials such as cereals, cereal products and vegetable mixes. One such machine, the Entoleter, provides a convenient method of treating free flowing materials, particularly of powder type produce such as flour and bran. Foods that have passed through an Entoleter should be placed in insect-free containers that are properly sealed, in order to prevent infestation.

The coarser the product treated in this way, the lower may be the speed of operation of the machine (revolutions per minute, rpm) to achieve a successful kill of all stages of insects and mites present. At 1 450 rpm, satisfactory treatment of cereals and similar granular products is obtained while some 2 900 rpm is considered necessary for finely powdered products such as flour and soymeal.

A machine such as the Entoleter fitted with a scourer and aspirator may be used to improve the appaearance of certain types of produce such as parboiled rice.

It is fairly common practice to incorporate Entoleters in flour milling systems, sometimes at grain intake points to attempt to ensure that only uninfested grain enters the mill. Entoleters are also used immediately prior to bagging-off the flour to ensure that flour put into store or sent is uninfested.

It may well be that animal feed mills will give more attention to this method of disinfesting all dust removed in grain handling and milling systems. Material suitable for treatment is that which is sufficiently dry and open in texture so as not to clog or cause bridging inside the machine.

9. RODENT CONTROL METHODS

Methods used to minimize the damage caused by rodents include proofing, repelling, trapping and poisoning.

Proofing

Local granaries constructed of mud are generally rodent-proof to some degree, particularly if they are raised from the ground. In some countries granaries are mostly built upon piles and the ground around and beneath them is kept clear of vegetation in an attempt to deprive the animals of coverage. Conical ratguards and inverted metal casks are attached to the legs of raised bins. In other countries rectangular granaries constructed of local plant material and mounted on piles 1.5 metres high are protected from rodent access by fitting wooden or metal rings or just thorny creepers to the piles. Reinforced concrete stores entirely ratproofed by means of sheet metal are in use.

Many traditional storage methods can be adapted to include rodent proofing and this is being done in several countries. Where stores are already built on piles it is an easy matter to fix sheet metal baffles at the top of the piles. Certain types of African stores normally built at ground level might also be adapted for erection upon piles.

Baffles should be at least 1 metre above ground level and should project a minimum of 23 centimetres beyond the diameter of the piles. Vegetation around and beneath the store should be kept down and any branches which may overhang it removed. It should be remembered that any object such as a farm implement or even a bicycle that is allowed to rest against such a store may act as a ladder whereby rats can gain access. When erection upon piles is not practical, stores can be protected by means of a rodent-proof fence. This should be constructed of small-gauge wire netting topped by a sheet metal baffle projecting at right angles to the fence and should completely encircle the store. The bottom of the fence should be buried to a depth of at least 30 centimetres.

The proofing of large central storage depots should ideally be considered during the planning stage; proofing at very low cost can be incorporated in the construction of each building. If stores are constructed without rodent proofing, its introduction at a later stage tends to be costly. Detailed specification for the rodent proofing of all types of building (Appendix E) are available and should be given serious consideration by any organization that is concerned with the construction of grain stores. In certain cases the possibility of surrounding the storage area with a rodent-proof fence may have to be considered.

It is an elementary precaution with any proofed stores or storage areas to eliminate all rats by poisoning or trapping before the grain is brought in.

Repelling

Various types of chemicals have been considered as rodent repellents but none have proved completely satisfactory under practical conditions.

A new high frequency device for repelling rats and mice (also birds) has been mentioned which transmits sound waves through special transducers to give signal coverage of a given indoor area. An essential feature of operation is the bouncing of erratic high frequency sounds from walls within an enclosed area.

Trapping

The use of cats, snakes and traps has been reported from a number of countries. Pot trapping, consisting of a clay pot or petrol tin, partially filled with water, over which a maize cob is suspended as bait, is also used; the cob is strung horizontally on its axis so that it can revolve freely. The rat reaches for the cob which turns, causing the rat to lose its balance and fall into the pot. Trapping by this method or with spring traps, however, is generally only suitable for controlling small infestations.

In order to achieve an appreciable degree of control over large infestations, it is necessary to use a high trap density and the initial cost of the traps or the labour involved in setting them often makes this method uneconomic. In addition, the success of trapping is frequently limited by the degree to which the rat population becomes trap shy. Prolonged trapping of an infestation with one type of trap is likely to exert progressively less control over the rat population. In Hong Kong (Romer, 1965) steel breakback (snap traps) and wire cage traps of the spring door type have been used.

Poisoning

The use of poisons incorporated in a bait is generally confined to central storage but is the most popular method used in rodent control. The application of 2 percent dieldrin to the walls of warehouses and the application of DDT powder to the floor around stacks have been reported as giving control but these methods are not recommended.

When used correctly, poison baiting is one of the cheapest and most effective methods of controlling rats on a large scale. There are, however, certain precautions that should be observed when handling the more toxic poisons. In general, most rodenticides are as toxic to man and other mammals as to rats. Care should be taken to ensure that all persons who are likely to come across bait containing poison are aware of its dangers and that domestic animals likely to eat the bait in quantity or to eat dead rats be kept away from the baiting area.

Types of poison for use in baits

Two types of poison are commonly used against rodents. Chemicals of the first type are known as acute poisons; these are used at concentrations in the bait sufficient to kill at a single dose. Considerable care is needed therefore in their application, and sale to the public should be governed by regulations. Examples of acute poisons that are currently used against rodents are arsenious oxide, zinc phosphide and sodium fluoroacetate (or 1080). The mean lethal dose for Norway rats of the first two compounds is respectively about 190 and 40 milligrammes per kilogramme of body weight, whereas that for sodium fluoroacetate is only 2 milligrammes per kilogramme body weight or even less than this. The extreme toxicity of the latter poison and its marked propensity to produce secondary poisoning in man and in other animals that have eaten rats killed by it make it unsafe for most control operations in stores, and it is not recommended for use in the tropics. Similarly, fluoroacetamide, although not as toxic as 1080, rapidly penetrates the body tissues and therefore presents a high risk of secondary poisoning. A number of other acute poisons are being used in some countries in the tropics; these include thallim sulphate, yellow phosphorus, aluminium phosphide, calcium cyanide, strychnine, Norbomide, Eastrix and Antu.

The second group of rodenticides are the chronic poisons or anticoagulants which are used at such a low dosage that they usually cause death only after the animal has fed on the bait for several days. When ingested, these poisons interfere with the blood clotting mechanisms, causing haemorrhage and ultimately death. Warfarin is the best known and probably the most widely used of the anticoagulant poisons.

Choice of bait

The success of poisoning depends largely upon the choice and skilful placing of bait and this should be food that is more attractive to the rats than their normal food supply. Bait in the form of meal can be mixed directly with the poison and used dry but whole grain must have a " sticker " added to ensure that the poison adheres to the grain; technical white oil is frequently used for this purpose. Whole maize is not very suitable for use as a bait in this way because many rodents eat only the germ, discarding the integument, and consequently waste much of the adhering poison. Whole maize can be used as a bait, however, if it is soaked in a solution of a water-soluble poison such as sodium salt of warfarin.

Rats living in a store containing large amounts of grain sometimes cannot be induced to take normal baits, and in these circumstances offering them poisoned drinking water often produces results. The chances of success by using a water bait will be improved if the rats' usual water supply can be cut off. This may be done by improving drainage around the store and by cutting back grass and low vegetation in order to reduce dew formation. This is, of course, only possible in the dry season or in the drier parts of tropical countries.

Damp baits often prove more attractive to rats than dry baits but deterioration of the former due to moulds and to bacteria is very rapid in warm climates; baits that have deteriorated even slightly in this way are often totally unacceptable to rats. Mould can be prevented to a certain extent by the addition of 0.025 percent paranitrophenol, but this almost invariably lowers the palatability of the bait.

Baiting technique

Bait should always be laid in places which are readily accessible to rats and, if possible, they should be positioned between the rats' harbourage and their normal food supply. Baits should not be laid in exposed places as rats will not feed freely in the open.

After mixing with a suitable bait base, acute poisons can either be used directly or with prebaiting. Prebaiting involves laying unpoisoned bait at suitable sites for 2 to 4 days before the poison is laid. In this way rats become accustomed to feeding on the particular bait that is used and at the sites where the poison is to be laid. Greater success can be achieved with the prebaiting technique than with direct poisoning because rats are more likely to take a lethal dose of the poison if they have first been conditioned to feed on the bait. Rats normally approach a new food source with caution and sample it only. With direct poisoning therefore, there is a risk that some rats may take a sublethal dose and thereafter become bait-shy. That is, they will not eat either the poison or the bait (or both) again for perhaps up to several months and in the meantime it will be necessary to resort to another poison and bait.

Arsenious oxide should be mixed with the bait at 10 percent by weight and zinc phosphide at 2.5 to 5 percent. Thorough mixing is essential, since concentrations of poison localized within the baiting material will cause unpalatability.

Anticoagulant poisons have the advantage that they do not cause bait-shyness and therefore need no prebaiting. However, they have the disadvantage of high bait consumption since rats normally need to feed for several days before a lethal dose is ingested. Individual rats vary considerably in the amount of poison required to cause death; some may die within two days of beginning after feed on the bait, whereas others may still be alive and feeding a little after ten days. The only safe rule with anticoagulants therefore is to continue baiting until no further takes are evident.

Warfarin is normally used at 0.005 percent against *Rattus norvegicus* and at 0.025 percent against other species. In the United Arab Republic, however, it was found that *Arvicanthis* sp. responded best to the poison at 0.05 percent. Above 0.05 percent the poison tends to become unpalatable to rats. Anticoagulant poisons are not normally marketed in pure form but are mixed with an inert base and sold as a "master mix." This is to facilitate the final mixing with a bait, since the small amount of the active ingredient that is required would otherwise be extremely difficult to mix in thoroughly.

The following recommendations have been made for rodent baiting in a number of countries:

A. *Bait mix recommended*

1.	520 g maize meal	*or* 1.	90% uncooked (broken) rice
2.	28 g castor sugar	2.	5% castor sugar
3.	312 g liquid paraffin or technical white oil	3.	5% technical white oil
4.	28 g warfarin 5	4.	1% warfarin master mix to give 0.025% bait

B. *Baiting methods*

The bait should be placed on wooden trays or shallow boxes throughout the infested area. Baits should be protected as far as possible, e.g., by sacks or bales of other produce, to reduce the risk to domestic animals. Land drains only should be used outside and lean-to pieces of stone or other material could be placed at the open ends. The use of 10-centimetre land drains to protect the poison from the weather and birds or other animals should be tried. Baiting points should be at frequent intervals, i.e., not more than 2.5 metres apart.

C. *Baiting procedure*

Day

1 60 g baits should be laid at all baiting points.

3 Visit all points and, if there have been complete takes, put 120 g of poison down; if there are partial takes top up to the original 60 g.

5 Visit all points, as on day 3, doubling to 240 g. Dead rats should be evident and should be removed.

8 Visit all points again and, if there is still evidence of takes, proceed as before.

10 Remove bait except from points where reinfestation might occur.

10. SOME ECONOMIC ASPECTS

In many tropical and subtropical countries the systems of crop forecasting and of determining the needs of the consumer population are inadequate; in such circumstances it is difficult if not impossible to plan in advance against either shortages or surpluses of produce. These tragedies have different impacts on countries, affecting the health of the population in the former case, and their pocketbooks in the latter.

Nevertheless, agriculture and the marketing of produce are still too frequently considered to be of minor importance, and must compete with educational programmes, development of hydroelectric schemes, heavy industry, etc.

Profit is probably the vital spark in initiating developments and the question of cost of produce may be considered the most important single factor. The cost of staple food commodities plays a vital part in the cost of living and in the living standards of the majority of the population. It is therefore indispensible to take measures to ensure that the producer receives a fair price for his products, that they are made available to the consumer at a reasonable price, and that processing and distribution costs are not excessive. Efficient storage and marketing are key activities in safeguarding both consumer and producer interests.

Detailed economic analyses of farmer and small trader storage facilities have rarely been undertaken in developing countries, but the economics of storage by produce boards have been documented with emphasis on the price structure of controlled commodities for which the boards are responsible. These commodities generally have a high weight to value ratio with commensurate costs for transportation and storage.

Such characteristics, together with the local consumers' increasing demand and the always present export demand for higher quality produce, the fluctuations of supplies available and prices on world markets and the fluctuations in annual production, all require the operation of properly organized marketing systems. The organization operating the marketing system must have storage facilities available to meet the demands of their operation.

A strong tendency toward price instability is inherent in the marketing of agricultural products because of the seasonal nature of output, difficulties in adjusting production to demand under uncertain weather and low elasticities of demand for basic food grains. Price fluctuations are particularly severe in economically less developed countries because producers are forced to sell immediately after or even before harvest to meet living expenses and repay debts.

Where commodity markets are narrow, price fluctuations are magnified by speculative activities. Sharp price increases after the bulk of a seasonal crop has moved into wholesale channels discourage purchasing by consumers and export buyers without the producer benefiting. Farmers require not only facilities for handling and storing produce but also for marketing and foı credit if they are to be able to overcome the present pressures encouraging them to sell the crop as soon as it is ready for harvesting. At present many growers store only the grain needed for their food and seed.

If farm prices could be stabilized at the average price level which consumers have been found to be willing to pay, farmers in less developed countries would gain considerably. Several countries have been attempting to do this by means of government procurement and buffer stock operations, accompanied by regulation of imports and exports, designed to remove supplies from the market in periods when prices are low and release them when prices rise, These "measures" may include the setting up of a network of government-sponsored buying stations to which producers bring their produce for sale at a guaranted minimum price; alternatively farmers may be granted low interest loans in security for grain stored at harvest time in approved warehouses. It is essential to ensure that the farmer actually receives the benefits of price guarantees and quality differentials.

Because of lack of capital, small farmers are often forced to seek loans (usually at high interest rates) in periods of shortage and obliged to sell their products through moneylenders below market prices in order to renew their loans. Lack of capital may also mean that a farmer harvests a crop, such as coconuts, before it has fully matured in order to obtain some money, so that on the one hand quality standards are not met, and on the other a smaller financial return is obtained.

In such an environment the trader-moneylender system has come into existence. The terms of loans by intermediaries to farmers are a combination of interest payments and the obligation to market their produce through the lender on terms favourable to the latter; a low price to the farmer is an indirect part of an interest payment.

The multiplicity of intermediaries reflects basic economic problems in the tropics and subtropics. In many countries commercial production is undertaken by large numbers of small farmers (operating far from markets and ports) having little storage capacity and cash reserves and who must therefore sell in small lots at frequent intervals. Most intermediaries themselves have only limited capital so that they operate on a small scale which requires little capital or training, but means that distribution is labour intensive.

It is often suggested that the presence of large numbers of intermediaries and processors at any particular stage in the distribution chain necessarily results in paying producers disproportionately low prices; there is, however, ample evidence that keen competition could raise producer prices.

The complexities of local marketing systems in tropical and subtropical countries require detailed study. Existing systems have been developed over the years along locally traditional lines. One example of such a system indicates the difficulties of advancement from present practices.

The day's price for a commodity will be fixed by the first woman trader who arrives at the market with produce, a price which will be in line with the closing price of the previous market in that area and to which other trades align their price. Any deviation from this price by one trader is quickly followed by other traders so that most markets have many traders selling the same produce at the same price. Most foodstuffs are sold not by weight but by measure, which may be a kind of bowl or tin. Each trader's profit is very small and is usually derived from a minor adjustment made in the weight and quality of the produce. Produce may change hands several times in the course of the day according to the fluctuating prices, but it is not uncommon for a trader to sell produce at the original purchase price but because of the use of the measure as a unit still make quite a handsome profit from changes in the weight being sold.

Numerous middlemen intervene between the time of purchase from producers and sale to consumers. The principal traders are specialized in wholesale or, rather, semiwholesale buying, and have a sharp trading sense. Some traders store produce, sort, clean and resell at a favourable moment, or in regions where there is a shortage.

The principal middlemen sell wholesale to a group of agents who in turn sell to a network of subagents who dispose of the produce at semiwholesale rates. These agents and subagents will not voluntarily become disengaged from marketing.

Cooperative and produce board marketing

As soon as a farmer ceases to produce on a subsistence level and begins to produce for a market, he requires credit. The best results may be achieved by small farmers joining cooperatives.

There are three main types of cooperatives: cooperative credit societies, produce marketing societies and cooperative farming societies. The two former are perhaps the most common while the latter is of recent origin.

There have been successful combined operations by departments of agriculture and by cooperative development agencies, the former providing technical advice and the latter an organizational framework together with arrangements for financing by banks and for orderly marketing, eliminating abuses such as false weights and poor quality, and providing low cost transport, without which wide outlets for commodities are inaccessible.

Marketing societies purchase their members' production at fixed prices based on the prevailing market prices, with safety margins in the case of commodities subject to price fluctuations. They handle only produce which has been sorted and graded, and therefore more stringent quality standards may be achieved through these organizations in the future.

In making provision for the marketing, transport and storage of produce, cooperatives are generally handicapped by shortage of capital.

The existence of agricultural credit cooperatives has made a significant impact on the development of subsistence agriculture in certain countries. The establishment of produce boards for marketing produce in an organized manner has had a beneficial impact on the methods of handling commodities to meet export requirements. In addition, through successful statutory marketing, substantial surpluses of money are accumulated which make it possible to stabilize prices to the producer. (Often the policy is to fix the statutory minimum price slightly below the world market price.) In some countries the problem is to make the price offered to the producer sufficiently attractive to prevent overland export to adjacent countries when prices are higher there.

All controlled produce must be delivered by farmers to the produce board, either directly, or through a producers' cooperative or a registered buying agent. The board pays a prescribed producer price, payable on delivery to specific collection points.

In some countries producers may enter into an agreement with the board by which they contract to purchase, at the difference between the boards' selling price and the prescribed producer price, all or part of their harvest for resale in their own neighbourhood. The producer thus provides a local source of supply while saving on his own and the consumer's transport costs. Buying agents may also contract with the board to retain for resale products acquired from producers, and remit to the board the difference between the selling price and the producer price, minus certain charges. In remote areas, processors with storage facilities contract with the board to store controlled products required locally; the processor is paid a storage fee and pays the board as supplies are sold. Such marketing practices constitute a means of meeting local requirements in rural areas.

Role of storage in improved marketing

Produce should be stored at harvest when prices are low, and sold in periods of scarcity when prices are high enough to make storage economic.

The first objectives of any storage scheme should be to increase the income of the farmers without necessarily inflating the price paid by consumers. Farmers should therefore be trained in methods of storing produce safely and should be given financial assistance; greater attention to development at this level, through local demonstration of improved handling and storage practices and the financial returns from adoption of these methods, would prepare a sound basis for raising agricultural producers above the subsistence level.

Benefits accruing from the use of improved storage may be summarized as follows:

(*a*) saving in physical losses of food grains;

(*b*) saving in quality deterioration;

(*c*) increased ability to hold grain;

(*d*) ability to take advantage of seasonal rises in prices;

(*e*) improved efficiency in grain marketing channels.

Economic principles of storage

The erection of new storage buildings and the purchase of equipment, application of pest control measures, and engagement of skilled staff require an immediate input of capital. The questions which must be asked before such investment of fresh capital is undertaken are: what will be the savings or income resulting from it and will these be sufficient to cover running and maintenance costs, interest charges on the capital employed and repayment of the investment over the effective lifetime of the plant and equipment, and still offer net benefits to the investor? It might seem to be a straightforward comparison between costs and returns. In practice such a comparison is not straightforward, however; while the costs can generally be estimated fairly accurately, the returns are more difficult to evaluate. The returns from good storage facilities depend very much on how intensively storage is used, on how much benefit it brings in terms of convenience, and on the standards of public health and food hygiene required by local and overseas markets which in the past have been very tolerant of low quality produce.

STORAGE COSTS

The cost of storage varies with the quantity of grain involved and the period over which the grain must be kept. From the information already presented it is clear that the small farmer, using locally available material for the construction of a storage container, can provide himself with a satisfactory structure requiring only a few improvements in drying and insect infestation control methods.

There are many examples of the profit margin to farmers obtained through ability to store produce for several months without deterioration. Caswell (1961) showed clearly that in Nigeria, if farmers had the means to store cowpeas in good condition for some six months, the results would be:

(*a*) a saving of foodstuffs (which at present are eaten by insects and not by man) of some 10 kilogrammes per ton;

(*b*) a gross profit of $12 to $24 per ton.

He points out that this could be achieved with a capital outlay of some $360 over a 10-year period, or an annual outlay (for a 25-ton silo bin with auger) of about $1.50 per ton. If a simplified form of storage were used, the capital outlay would probably only be some $180. Caswell points out that in Ibadan the price of cowpeas on sale increased by some $24 to $48 per ton from the end of one harvest to the start of the next. Taking into consideration the price increase listed and the costs of providing storage, the net profit to the farmer would be over 8 percent. The widespread use of storage stabilizes prices in the markets because it permits an even flow of produce to the markets.

Data given in Table 23 also demonstrate that efficient storage can be profitable.

Where the State intervenes and creates stockpiles, long-term plans must be drawn up for appropriately placed central storage. In some countries where over one million bags of produce are in store each month, the average cost of storage is stated to be about 18 cents per ton per month.

Where silo installations are used, the cost per ton of storage depends upon the use of the silo mainly as a storage unit or a transit

TABLE 23. – FIGURES DEMONSTRATING THAT FOOD STORAGE CAN BE PROFITABLE IF CARRIED OUT IN THE PROPER MANNER

	Average cost per ton for bin storage		
	Maize	Sorghum	Cowpeas
	............U.S. *dollars*............		
DRYING COSTS			
Depreciation of equipment	3.60		
Labour	1.20		
Materials (electricity, etc.)	2.20		
Total drying cost	7.0		
	Storage period		
	8 months	9 months	9 months
	............U.S. *dollars*............		
STORAGE COSTS (per period)			
Depreciation of bins	1.80	1.90	[2] 3.90
Cleaning and treating bins	0.04	0.05	0.50
Fumigating grain in bins	0.36	0.36	
Electricity for conveyor			0.39
Total storage costs	2.20	2.31	4.79
Total drying and storage	9.20	2.31	4.79
Sale value [1]	71.40	58.20	144.15
Purchase price	49.50	48.00	120.23
Difference	21.90	10.20	23.92
NET MARGIN, per ton	12.65	7.69	18.25

SOURCES: Upton (1963) and Anthonio (1963).

[1] The sale value exceeds the purchase price by virtue of the fact that there is a seasonal variation in price (greatest in the case of cowpeas) and purchase and sale were in the postharvest and preharvest periods respectively. Under normal conditions of bag storage without the use of insect control measures, an overall loss would probably have been experienced as a result of weight loss. The sale values given above take into account any such loss that did occur due to moisture loss or infestation. – [2] The depreciation is greater in this instance since the full capacity of the bin was not in use.

unit. The following data indicate the costs involved for storage units of 500-ton and 2 000-ton capacities.

500-ton storage facility

	U.S. dollars
1. *Machinery*	
39 kW electric generator	4 500
2 corn-shelling machines	2 700
drier or continuous hot-air flow	4 100
caterpillar or suction elevator	1 050
	12 350
2. *Buildings*	
1 to 5 metal silos (500-ton)	6 200
hygrometer	200
protective roofing for silos	2 000
foundations	1 050
contingencies	900
	10 350
3. *Occasional expenses*	
insecticide (estimated at $0.75 per ton)	400
electrician, mechanic, watchman	1 700
drying (40 days)	250
machinery running expenses for a season	900
workmen's wages for 2 months	600
	3 850
Gross total	26 550

In arriving at the cost per ton, an allowance must be made for depreciation of machinery and buildings, and this is calculated as a 20 percent and 10 percent annual charge respectively.

Annual cost	U.S. dollars
1. *Machinery* $12\ 350 \times \frac{20}{100} =$	2 470
2. *Buildings* $10\ 350 \times \frac{10}{100} =$	1 035
3. *Occasional expenses*	3 850
Cost per 500 tons	7 355
Cost per ton (approximately)	15

If a network of storage facilities is set up with a total capacity of 40 000 tons, annual capital costs and operating costs are estimated at $500 000.

2 000-ton storage facility

1. A new concrete and/or metal storage plant capable of holding some 2 000 tons of maize might, together with drying and cleaning equipment, requires a total investment of $100 000 ($50.00 per ton capacity).

2. If this plant were depreciated over a period of 20 years (such a plant should last longer) and the money borrowed at 5 percent and repaid in instalments over 20 years, the annual operating costs would be as follows:

	U.S. dollars
Yearly repayment of $100 000 at 5 percent over 20 years (interest calculated on unpaid balance)	8 000
Labour	8 000
Upkeep and repairs	1 000
Fuel and light	2 000
Insurance and miscellaneous	1 000
	20 000

3. If the plant were filled to capacity and emptied only once a year, then the storage cost per ton would be $10.00. In regions with two harvest seasons it might be filled once, emptied, and perhaps half filled again. The average annual cost per ton might then be $7.50 or so, depending on whether in-plant handling labour was retained throughout the year.

4. The interest charged on fixed and working capital should be calculated on the basis of the prevailing local rates. The latter is important because it takes account of alternative uses for the money invested in storage improvements. Interest charges should also include repairs, salaries of superintendent and handling labour, expenses incurred in maintaining records, cost of bags (for bag storage), of fuel, light and other supplies as needed, and insurance charges.

Location, size and operation of storage facilities

The basic grains are harvested once or twice a year in fairly short seasons and are consumed in small quantities daily. Ability to store means that the rate of flow into the market can be adjusted to consumers' needs. It also facilitates bulking for economical transport and so widens the market area that can be served.

The nature of the part played by storage in marketing varies from area to area, depending on the length and direction of the marketing channels through which grain flows from producer to consumer. In pure subsistence farming societies, the grain produced may not go out of the village. Each family maintains its own stocks for seed use and consumption throughout the year, and perhaps holds over reserves from abundant seasons. Under such circumstances each family has its own storage structure. In areas where there is a tradition of communal storage, all the grain of a village might possibly be stored in one unit which would be a community responsibility. This concentration might afford opportunities for savings on bulk storage and fumigation, provided that the various owners felt their individual interests were adequately protected.

In some areas where cooperative societies have been operating, produce has been purchased from members at a low price at harvest time, shelled by machine, dried in bags by means of a platform drier, admixed with an insecticidal dust and stored in cylindrical plywood bins (Blane and Forsyth, 1957).

A marketing system common in many areas is the sale of small lots of grain by producers to nearby consumers who do not produce grain for themselves. The small producer from time to time takes one or two bags of grain or even less to the local or village market. The market days vary in different areas from once every week to once every ten days or two weeks. At these markets local consumers buy directly from producers. Standard weights or quality grades are rarely used; a price is negotiated for a particular lot as it is seen piled on the ground, or in a pan or tin. Under this system of direct contact between producer and consumer there is no wholesaler or retailer, and storage is undertaken only by the farmer. Because the farmer's approach to the market is one of disposing of his own varying surplus rather than of maintaining a regular service to consumers, from time to time supplies to the market may dry up. In local market economies of this type having no commercial link with outside sources of supply, fluctuations in prices are often very great.

The next stage in marketing is the emergence of the wholesale buyer who brings into town a few bags of grain which may be stacked in a room of his house while awaiting resale; a bag at a time or even less will be sold to the small retailers or market traders who will then retail it in smaller lots to the consumer. A storage unit providing protection from weather, insects or rodents at low cost, and facilitating the sorting of mixed purchases from small suppliers into lots adapted to particular orders, would be of great help to this type of business.

Where there are large concentrations of urban population or agricultural communities which concentrate on the production of cash crops for export, a more elaborate marketing system is needed, and with it storage sited specifically to facilitate marketing. Also forming part of the marketing system is the careful inspection of produce, and rejection of poor quality, which can be carried out on the farm and at primary collecting points. The use of specialized equipment on the farm would probably not be feasible for small producers and traders so the provision of such facilities at these primary collecting points would be a valued marketing service.

Advantage can be taken of specialized equipment at processing plants for moving grain from place to place and weighing it accurately, by means of hand trucks, conveyors, bagging scales, automatic scales, etc. The type of storage and ancillary equipment most suited to this type of marketing enterprise depends largely on the terms on which grain is sold in wholesale channels and the type of transport used. If it is to be sold to buyers applying exacting moisture content, freedom from foreign matter, and other quality standards, cleaning and sorting equipment will be necessary. If expensive hired transport vehicles are employed, then space to accumulate a load, ease of access, and speed of loading will be important considerations. In most export marketing these considerations are essential.

If the grain is milled into flour, or into polished rice in the case of paddy, before sale to the final consumer, another specialized demand for storage arises. In less developed economies the first specialized grain storage units to be installed by private initiative are generally associated with mills. For efficient operation of the mill, there must be sufficient stocks on hand for a substantial running period. In order to recover investment in milling machines the operator needs a regular clientele of retail buyers. He must also have a stock of the milled product on hand if he is to retain their custom throughout the year. Mills and associated storage warehouses in the main towns are a normal feature of the grain marketing system in many countries.

Where supplies may vary greatly from harvest to harvest as a result of climatic factors, and where there are many consumers who maintain no stocks of their own and therefore depend on what the market offers, special measures may be necessary to maintain reserves in the hands of state authorities. This is especially important in countries where purchases of basic food grains make up a large percentage of the total cost of living.

Thus, savings on physical losses and deterioration in quality, and ability to hold grain safely while awaiting higher prices, are basic objectives in all programmes to improve storage facilities. Nevertheless, the returns on these grounds alone may not justify the acquisition of specialized facilities and equipment. Their acquisition is more attractive to marketing enterprises and processors who can integrate them with other marketing operations and so use them more intensively. They are also more attractive to large public marketing organizations and governments which expect to buy, sell and store on a large scale; such organizations can finance large initial capital investments at lower cost because of the better security they offer; they may also appreciate the opportunity to simplify their operations as compared with the administrative task of supervising a large number of small storage units of the traditional type.

The choice of a location for a storage installation calls for very careful consideration. The range of possible locations for farmers and wholesale traders or millers is generally limited to the area where their business operations are already based. Availability of a site at low cost is a major consideration. Other practical points are that the site should be well drained, free from risk of flooding, easily accessible to vehicles used for movement of grain; in the case of commercial plants the site should be on a paved road (or railway track if available). There should be enough space around the building to permit free movement and possible expansion. Location within town limits is not essential; provided electricity is available, a site situated on the outskirts but convenient for entry from the producing area may be preferable and less costly. Proximity to the owner's residence or place of work may permit closer supervision and lower management and labour costs if staff can also be used on other remunerative work.

The problem of determining the most suitable locations for storage are more serious in the case of large enterprises and governments seeking to offer large-scale storage services in areas where they have not been used previously. Many plants erected under such conditions have been criticized as being unsuitably located, and as a result are used either much less than their capacity would warrant, or under continuing operational handicaps. Of all planning errors, the erection of a solidly built plant in the wrong place is the most difficult to rectify; there are known examples of concrete silos that remain empty 90 percent of the time. Some reflect situations which seemed improbable when the project was first undertaken; at some ports bulk handling facilities are only capable of exporting produce and not of also handling imports. Radical shifts in demand and in relative prices have taken place which have reversed production trends afer a plant has been built; or there has been involuntary abandonment of a development programme in which the plant would have been a key feature. Some of the large silos near capital cities were built so that the people would feel that reserve stocks were conveniently available should the need to use them arise. For this reason, interests of economy require that construction be coordinated with normal commercial requirements wherever feasible.

The risk of such errors should be reduced by insistence on preconstruction surveys by teams made up of independent economists, marketing and storage specialists working jointly with architects and engineers.

In most countries a well-chosen location plan would be one envisaging some storage in the main production areas if they include a substantial nonfarm population, as well as sites convenient for distribution to the urban population centres. There have been cases of grain being moved away from production areas into storage in the main cities and then, later in the year, transported back to meet local needs.

Another important factor is the means of transport available. If transport of surplus grain from the producing area after harvest is easy, then relatively little storage may be needed there. Storage should be located at points where transport to meet prevailing marketing movements would be most economical. Rail, water or road transport possibilities, including planned new developments, should be taken into account. To construct a grain store having a 20-year lifetime on a site bypassed by a new road constructed two years later would be wasteful indeed. Plans for the establishment of new processing facilities, such as flour mills or feed mixinig plants, should also be taken into account. Import and/or export needs must be considered as well. If substantial imports or exports of grain are envisaged, the construction of grain storage with bulk loading and unloading equipment at ports or rail terminals will usually be advantageous.

If a government programme to maintain reserve stocks or help stabilize prices is contemplated, the need for locating storage facilities where they will best serve such programmes introduces another consideration. If, for example, a government wishes to ensure that producers obtain certain minimum prices, facilities will be needed in the production areas so farmers can deliver their grain without high cost and thus obtain full advantage from the government programme.

Many economic factors influence the size and therefore the type of storage plant to be built. If the amount of grain to be stored is small, capital scarce, and labour plentiful and cheap, very simple storage built of local materials is likely to be the most economic. Often only improvements to make existing structures proof against rats and other vermin and facilitate the application of suitable insecticides are justified. The type of construction must be related to the local costs of different types of materials and the reliability of labour to build it efficiently.

In developing countries, where capital is likely to be the limiting factor in relation to labour and time, and excessive expenditure on one project may cause the cancellation of several others, there is probably more to be said initially for selecting the less expensive of the practicable alternatives. To build technically advanced and costly warehouses and mills and then find them only partially utilized because no money is available to establish complementary facilities is indeed unwise.

The amount of mechanical equipment installed in a grain storage plant should be related to the turnover of grain during the year, the cost of such equipment, and the cost of the hand labour alternative. If the plant is situated at an important terminal market where it would be filled and emptied a number of times during the year, a substantial investment in mechanical equipment for loading and unloading and for transferring grain from drier to bin and from one bin to another could be justified, because speed in handling would permit fuller use of the storage capacity and more efficient marketing. If, on the other hand, the plant is one where the grain is put in once a year and removed only once a year, or at even longer intervals, then mechanical handling equipment should be kept as simple as is practical.

The original capital cost is only one factor in deciding the type of construction to adopt. There may be a case for building a structure with greater capacity than required initially. It is important to look to the future. If it is known that storage needs in a certain place may be greater in a few years' time, it is advisable to build a plant having a capacity which can be expanded, e.g., the elevators and other equipment installed in the first place could be large enough to serve this expanded capacity without supplements.

A critical consideration of the internal design of storage units is whether or not the grain must be kept in separate lots, each easily accessible for movement in and out of the store. This applies especially to stores intended to serve a number of different grain owners and to handle several varieties or types of produce. Reports on storage enterprises in India indicate that seasonal contents of a storage structure are rarely purchased or sold in one lot.

Account may have to be taken in some areas of possible opportunities to use storage space profitably for other purposes than holding grain. This does not apply at large collecting centres where the storage facilities should be specialized to be economically viable. On the other hand, many stores built in rural areas are of the general warehouse type, in order that part of the year they may be used to hold fertilizer or other farm supplies.

The ownership of storage facilities is often an issue in developing countries where it is felt that merchants able to store essential commodities have profited from this strategic position to manipulate market releases and raise prices. Usually ownership of storage facilities is not alone responsible for apparent high margins, but rather a combination of marketing defects, including the lack of alternative storage capacity and of trading competition, and the high cost of credit and the risk of loss. However, the necessary maintenance of competition requires that ownership should not be concentrated in a few hands. If a significant proportion of the storage available for commodities such as food grains (which may have a political influence) is held in farm, state or cooperative ownership, it ensures some diversity of interest.

The question of who should own and operate storage units intended to serve communities and to permit economical access to artificial drying (especially in humid areas) is more controversial. Responsibility for adequate management must be clearly assigned and this is often most effective when it coincides with traditional authority in the community concerned. In areas where cooperatives are well established, storage may be set up and operated specifically on this basis. In many countries, governments provide credit on favourable terms for the construction of crop storage. Precautions are needed, however, against the tendency for easy access to finance which can result in the construction of facilities which are unnecessarily expensive and rarely used to capacity. Under circumstances where money is loaned, the eventual owners of the storage facilities should be required to repay its cost within its economic lifetime.

Local trading and milling enterprises are likely to build the storage needed for their business on their own initiative. Since they usually have to obtain the necessary funds on the commercial loan market, they are likely to limit their expenditure to the minimum both in terms of capacity and construction materials. Consequently they often require more storage space at certain times and try to meet this need by renting it elsewhere. Though the demands of occasional trade users can generally be met only at higher costs, municipalities and railway authorities often provide storage for public use. Since the use of space is less intensive, higher operating costs are offset by benefits in terms of increased trade in the market and town concerned and increased use of the transport service offered.

Grain storage construction may also be undertaken by governments either to hold stocks required for stabilization purposes or as a service to grain producers and traders. Usually a special department or agency is established to operate the stores. It should maintain its own accounts according to approved business procedure and employ suitably qualified staff. It is important that bidding by contractors, to provide items having detailed specifications, be competitive, and it is essential that contracts be awarded on the basis of the lowest bid.

While storage for stabilization purposes is usually financed entirely by government capital, storage and marketing set up as a public service might be operated by a mixed government and private company. Participation by grain trading enterprises which are potential users of the stores provides additional assurance that the stores will be built and operated in accord with practical marketing requirements. Participation by government should ensure that the storage facilities are not used solely in the interests of particular traders. In developing countries especially, government help may be essential to traders in the financing of storage construction, because it permits a longer and broader view regarding the return on investment, and because of the political risks which may deter private investors.

Whether a store is owned privately, cooperatively or by the government, the charge to users should be such as to cover all costs including provision for repairs and repayment of investment in the building and equipment over its expected lifetime. Where the money to build a plant has been borrowed, the charges to users should provide for a schedule of payments so that the loan will have been repaid at least by the time the plant must be replaced.

The importance of skilled storage management should be kept in mind at all stages. Storage is an economic and technical service which requires competent planning and day-to-day maintenance by trained personnel. Some governments which have undertaken extensive storage construction programmes have established special training programmes for plant managers, fumigators, advisors on farm storage and other necessary specialists. More training of local personnel is urgently required.

Since farmers and traders are only likely to use a commercial store if they know what it will cost, a schedule of charges in terms of quantities by volume or weight, per day, week or month of storage must be posted and maintained for specified periods of time. Usually fumigation and aeration, or movement of the grain to keep it in condition are included. An additional charge is made for receiving, weighing in and out, and discharging grain, varying according to whether the grain is handled in bulk or in bags, etc. Receiving and discharging may also be included in a standard storage charge per quantity unit; in this case, however, there is usually a minimum charge (for three months, for example) to cover the increased handling costs when grain is brought in and taken out at frequent intervals. Where the stores are very small and it would be impossible to keep labour on hand, users could move grain in and out themselves with the assistance and supervision of a single storekeeper. This may lead to difficulties, however, in getting the grain stacked properly, making full use of capacity, etc. Often it is best to allow the storekeeper to call in workers living nearby who would gain experience and be fully under his control.

Overhead and running costs have to be met by charges set in terms of actual use, not capacity. It is essential, therefore, to make realistic estimates. Commercial wheat storage plants studied in India in 1957 showed an average use of about 140 days per year. In Honduras it was found that 10 cents per quintal (100 kilogrammes) per month with a minimum charge of three months were sufficient to meet expenses at small country storage points provided they were used to capacity for 200 to 250 days per year. This fee covered receiving, fumigation while in store, rebagging and bringing out. A cooperative warehouse would normally charge the same amount as its competitors, either government-sponsored or private. Any surplus amount would be refunded to members in proportion to the use they made of the store. If it were the only commercial store in an area it could set charges estimated to cover costs amply, knowing that any overpayments would be refunded.

The full cost for the first year or two of operation cannot always be reflected in the charge to users. In areas where commercial storage is not a common practice, the quantities brought in initially may be small; to make them carry their full share of operating costs might mean charging rates so high as to deter potential users. It is therefore advisable to set an initial rate low enough to attract business. It can be raised later when there is competition for storage space, if the increased use of the capacity available is not in itself enough to bring in sufficient income to cover all costs, including those not met in the first years. Additional information on the economics of grain storage can be found in *The state of food and agriculture 1968* (FAO, 1968).

Appendix A

SPECIALISTS ON AFRICAN STORAGE PROBLEMS WHO CONTRIBUTED DATA TO FAO INFORMALWORKING BULLETIN No. 24

Technical information was contributed to FAO Informal Working Bulletin No. 24 by a number of specialists with particular expertise on different aspects of the subject.

Abbott, J.C.	FAO Rural Institutions Division
Ackroyd, P.	United Kingdom. London School of Hygiene and Tropical Medicine
Anthonio, Q.B.O.	Nigeria. Nigerian Stored Products Research Institute
Ayerst, G.	United Kingdom. Pest Infestation Laboratory
Batwell, B.L.	Botswana. Department of Agriculture
Bowden, J.	Uganda. Department of Agriculture
Cooper, J.E.	Liberia. Department of Agriculture and Commerce
Cornes, M.A.	Nigeria. Nigerian Stored Products Research Institute
Cyanamid International, Agricultural Department	United States. New Jersey
Davies, J.C.	Uganda. Department of Agriculture
Doughty, Mrs. J.	United Kingdom. London School of Hygiene and Tropical Medicine
Fanny, D.	Ivory Coast. Ministère de l'Agriculture

Fisher, C.T.H.	Rhodesia. Department of Agriculture
Freeman, J.A.	United Kingdom. Ministry of Agriculture, Fisheries and Food
Giles, P.H.	Nigeria. Nigerian Stored Products Research Institute
Griffiths, D.A.	United Kingdom. Pest Infestation Laboratory
Henderson, S.M.	United States. University of California
Hobbs, W.W.	Ethiopia. Haile Selassie I University
Howe, R.W.	United Kingdom. Pest Infestation Laboratory
Kockum, S.	Kenya. National Agricultural Laboratories
Lefebure, H.	Dahomey. Institut de recherches agronomiques tropicales, Paris
Lepigre, A.	Dahomey. Centre national de recherches agronomiques, Versailles
Ministero dell'Agricoltura e Foreste	Italy. Rome
Neves, Professor Baeta	Angola. Ministerio do Ultramar, Lisboa
Ott, C.U.	Dahomey. FAO specialist on commercialization
Pearson, J.D.	Rhodesia. Grain Marketing Board
Pest Infestation Laboratory	United Kingdom. Slough
Plant Protection Ltd.	United Kingdom. Fernhurst
Prevett, P.F.	Nigeria. Nigerian Stored Products Research Institute
Proctor, D.L.	Zambia. Department of Agriculture
Quagraine, K. A.	Ghana. Ministry of Agriculture
Rawnsley, J.A.	Ghana. FAO specialist on stored products

Riley, J.	Nigeria. Nigerian Stored Products Research Institute
Rose, D.J.W.	Rhodesia. Ministry of Agriculture
Southgate, B.J.	United Kingdom. Pest Infestation Laboratory
Sweeney, R.C.H.	Malawi. Agricultural Research Services
Taylor, K.D.	United Kingdom. Ministry of Agriculture, Fisheries and Food
Tropical Products Institute	United Kingdom. London
Tremlett, R.K.	Tanzania (Zanzibar). Department of Agriculture
Tropical Stored Products Centre	United Kingdom. Slough

Appendix B

A SELECTION OF STORED PRODUCTS[1] LEGISLATION IN TROPICAL AND SUBTROPICAL COUNTRIES

(Quality, Pests, Treatments)

1. Quality

Aden

Produce Marketing Ordinance, 1958

Rules may be made for the grading, inspection and packing of cereals, legumes and oilseeds.

Argentina

Resolution 558 issued by the Dirección Nacional de Granos y Elevadores DNGE in November 1947

For all grades there is a tolerance of 5 percent for degermed grain (germen roido); tolerance for weevil holed grain (granos picados) is also prescribed (see Res. 808). Defines the obligatory grading standards for wheat.

Places in sample grade, *inter alia,* all wheat which is heating, which exceeds 14 percent moisture content, has unfavourable commercial odours, has been processed or treated with materials likely to alter its natural condition, and which has more than reasonable numbers of living weevils.

Definitions

Granos picados includes all grains or pieces of grains which show perforations caused by pests which attack grain in store.

Granos con germen roido includes all grains or pieces of grains of which the germs have been eaten by pests.

[1] Here relates to cereals, oilseeds and legumes.

Argentina (*continued*)

Moisture content shall be determined in an air oven at a temperature of 130°C ± 3 for 1 hour or by such other method as DNGE shall determine. (In practice the Brown-Duvel water distillation method is widely used.)

NOTE - The obligatory standards for oats, barley and rye (Resolution 584 of November 1948) contain no reference to insects, but prescribe a basic tolerance of 1 percent of picado (Art. 9).

DNGE Resolution No. 852 of 23 March 1954

Defines certain temporary standards for the marketing of maize.
Maize for export must not exceed 15.2 percent moisture content (naturally dried) or 14.0 percent (artificially dried) respectively.

DNGE Resolution No. 808 of 5 July 1951

Regulates the tolerance of picado in cereals (see above for definition).

1. Establishes for deliveries of wheat, oats, barley and rye a fixed tolerance for picado of 2 percent, for compulsory receipt, without price deduction, of the harvest of the corresponding crop year.
2. As 1), but prescribes 5 percent for maize.
3. As 1) and 2), but raises tolerances to 4 percent and 10 percent respectively for deliveries of grain of previous harvest. Cereal year for wheat, etc., starts on 1 December and for maize on 1 April.
4. Seasonal tolerances may be established by DNGE with price reduction of ½ percent for wheat, oats, barley and rye and of ¼ percent for maize for each 1 percent tolerance above the basic minimum prescribed in 1) 2) 3) above.
5. Prescribes further price penalities for badly damaged grain.
6. Maximum tolerance for export shipment shall be that prescribed for obligatory receipt for the period.

British Solomon Islands

Copra Ordinance, 1954. Regulation of 1954; Rules of 1961

Controls the quality of exported copra. The rules give details of the criteria for grading copra and how sampling shall be done by inspectors.

Cocoa Ordinance, 1961; Rules, 1962

Regulates the purchase of cocoa beans (in the pod or wet) for processing; provides for the registration of persons operating processing units; lays down certain standards for buildings used for storing graded cocoa beans. The rules prescribe the grades of cocoa for export, the grading procedure and the marking of bags of cocoa for export.

Cameroon (Southern)

Cocoa (Control of Preparation) Law, 1958; Southern Cameroon Produce Inspection Law, 1960

Applies to cocoa, palm kernels, palm oil and coffee for export and provides for inspection, grading, condition of premises used, adulteration, containers used.

China (Taiwan)

Agricultural Products Inspection Law, 1954

Includes provision for the inspection of rice for export.

Cyprus

Agricultural Export Law (original enacted 1933)

Enables a thorough inspection to be made of exported produce at time of packing and at shipment. Inspection is supervised by Produce Inspection Service which is responsible to the Ministry of Commerce and Industry.

The Gambia

Groundnuts (Standard of Quality) Act, Cap. 139; Standard of Quality Regulations, 1965; Water Transport Regulations, 1965

Prescribes certain quality standards for groundnuts including percentage limits of mouldy, blackened, discoloured, insect-infested and damaged nuts.

The Gambia (*continued*)	*Gambia Oilseeds Marketing Ordinance, 1948* Board secures most favourable arrangements for purchase, *grading*, transport, export and sale of groundnuts and oil palm kernels. *Adulteration of Produce Ordinance, 1951* Palm kernels (Standard of Purity) Order, 1951 Groundnuts (Cleaning for Export) Regulations, 1951
Guyana	*Rice Marketing Law, Cap. 249* Provides for inspection and for certain quality standards of rice on arrival at Georgetown from mills and after blending for sale. *Rice Milling Law, 19* Public health inspectors issue licences to each rice mill on basis of siting of drains, toilets, etc., and little account is taken of the hygienic standards in relation to the produce being handled.
India	*Prevention of Food Adulteration Act, 1954; Rules of 1955; Second Amendment Rules of 1964* Provides for the prevention of the adulteration of food, i.e., food not of the nature, substance or quality demanded by the purchaser and to his prejudice. This includes food which is injurious to health as a result of improper and insanitary storage. The Second Amendment Rules, 1964 define certain standards of quality of food grains. *Agricultural Produce (Grading and Marking) Act, 1937* Fixes grades and defines quality of some agricultural products (including cereals, oilseeds and legumes). Specifies type of packaging to be used for such products. Also, ensures better buying and selling of agricultural produce by establishing regulated markets. Features of such markets include: regulation of market practices, licensing of market functionaries, use of standard weights and measures, and arrangements for the settlement of disputes regarding quality, weight and deductions.

India (*continued*)

Rice Milling Industry (Regulation) Act, 1958

Under this Act, the Rice Milling Industry (Regulation and Licensing) Rules, 1959 require that millers should be licensed. Also, that they should take adequate measures to ensure that paddy and rice are stored so as to prevent damage by ground moisture, rain, insects, rodents, birds and other causes.

Export (Quality Control and Inspection) Act, 1963 and Rules of 1964

Wherever, for the development of the export trade of India, the Central Government thinks that any food commodity should be subjected to quality control or inspection or both prior to export, it may require that the necessary steps be taken.

Kenya

Food and Drugs (Adulteration) Ordinance, 1931

Restricts mixing of food with other ingredients and prohibits sale of food not of the nature, substance or quality demanded. Inspectors empowered to sample.

1. *Food and Drugs (Grain, Flour and Seed) Regulations, 1956*

Prohibits presence in these scheduled commodities of any insecticide or miticide other than:
pyrethrum powder at not more than 2 500 ppm, pyrethrins at not more than 25 ppm, lindane at not more than 1 ppm, and malathion at not more than 8 ppm.

Agricultural Produce (Export) Act, Cap. 319

The grading of maize rules (1937 and 1940) made under the Act regulate the quality of maize exported from Kenya, also its method of packaging and the assignment of grades. The grading of wheat rules (1929 and 1930) and the grading of beans rules (1937 and 1940) do more or less the same for wheat and beans as for maize above.

Wheat Industry Ordinance, 1952

Prescribes conditions under which wheat, flour and wheat feed are inspected, distributed, imported and

Kenya (*continued*)	exported; the grades of flour and wheat feed milled for sale and the type and specification of machinery, etc., installed in mills.
	Seeds Ordinance, 1955
	Controls testing, sale, import and export and use of seeds. Lists impurities and gives powers including inspection and sampling of premises where they are stored.
	Maize Marketing Ordinance, 1959
	Board regulates, controls and improves collection, storage, marketing and distribution of maize and maize products. Prescribes standards and is empowered to inspect maize and maize premises, take samples, grade and define manner of handling, storing, etc.
Nigeria	*Public Health Ordinance, 1917*
	Health officer may inspect provisions exposed for sale for the use of man if it appears to be diseased or unwholesome or unfit for man, and may condemn same and order it to be destroyed.
	Produce (Enforcement of Export Standards), Ordinance 1959
	Scheduled produce intended for export in federal territory of Lagos and ports of shipment; enables inspection and grading according to quality, purity, condition of storage premises, types of containers; controls adulteration, provides for cleaning. (Inspection carried out by Western Region Produce Inspection Services).
	1. *Cocoa (Inspection for Export) Regulations, 1961* 2. *Palm Produce (Inspection for Export) Regulations, 1961* 3. *Groundnuts (Inspection for Export) Regulations, 1961*
	Produce Inspection (Northern Region) Law, 1961
	Scheduled produce intended for export, and gives same powers as in above, inspection being carried

Nigeria (*continued*)	out by the Produce Inspection Division of the Ministry of Agriculture, Northern Region.

1. *Produce Inspection (Benniseed)*[2] *Regulations, 1962*
   Define adulteration, provide for inspection, testing, sealing of bags and sifting provisions.
2. *Produce Inspection (Cocoa) Regulations, 1962*
   Define adulteration and provide for inspection, riddling, sampling, bagging, grading, sealing and storage.
3. *Produce Inspection (Groundnuts) Regulations, 1962*
   Define adulteration, provide for exemption from inspection, substandard and unmerchantable groundnuts, inspection, testing, bagging and sealing, storage.

Malawi

Marketing of African Produce Ordinance, 1957

Rules may be made prescribing grade or quality of any specified African produce and providing for inspection of same. Scheduled produce listed.

Control of Foodstuffs Ordinance, 1960

Rules may be made for regulating or prohibiting the production, treatment, storage, etc., of foodstuffs and for inspection of same.

Produce Marketing Ordinance, 1961

Rules may be made for prescribing grade or quality of any specified produce (including maize, rice/paddy, groundnuts, barley, wheat and any of their products).

Pakistan

West Pakistan Pure Food Ordinance, 1960

States that food which is unsound, unwholesome, injurious to health or unfit for human consumption shall not be stored or sold for human consumption.

West Pakistan Foodstuffs (Control) Act, 1958

Under this Act, the West Pakistan Paddy and Rice Control Order, 1964 restricts the processing of paddy into rice to authorized rice mills. Further, such rice millers may only process paddy into

[2] Benniseed is also known as sesame

Pakistan (*continued*)	rice of the type and kind which is scheduled under this Order. The schedule concerned includes the tolerance limits and rejection limits for admixtures and impurities. *East Pakistan Warehouses Ordinance, 1959 and Rules of 1964* Provides for licensing of warehousemen on condition (among many others) that warehouses are kept in a sanitary state and that any deterioration in the stored produce should be controlled.
Senegal	*Plant Protection Decree, 60 - 121* Plant Protection Service reserves right to inspect goods exported and imported and take samples; some products are compulsorily inspected, some are not restricted, and some are inspected on request from importers to exporters.
Tanzania	*Produce Export Ordinance, Cap. 137* No scheduled produce to be exported until it has been inspected as laid down in rules. Provides for prevention of export of unsound produce, treatment to ensure produce in good condition for export. Rules may be made as to percentage of impurity, maximum moisture, standards of composition, containers used, storage, grading, percentage to be inspected. *Copra Ordinance, Cap. 139* Provides for drying and storage for improving quality of copra; conditions for licensing buyers, millers and exporters, and for inspection, grading, sampling treatment. *Wheat Industry Ordinance, 1960* All millers to be licensed and provides for grading, inspection of mills and machinery. *African Agricultural Products (Control and Marketing) Ordinance, Cap. 284* Provides for harvesting, drying, storage, processing and grading of specified agricultural products in areas declared by the Government.

Tanzania (*continued*)

Food and Drugs Ordinance, Cap. 93

Provides for additives and abstraction of constituents to and from foods; sale of foods not of nature, substance, quality demanded; prevents importation, preparation, storage of foods not clean, unwholesome, unsound or not free from disease, infection and contamination; quality standards; sampling, inspection, condition of storage premises, etc.

Standards of Quality Regulations

1. *Dried pulses* shall be sweet, sound, free from extraneous matter and shall not contain more than 5 percent damaged beans.
2. *Maize meal* shall be free from insect infestation and limit of cold water acidity given.
3. *Red palm oil* - gives required acid value and colour.

Markets Ordinance, Cap. 106

Provides for inspection, adulteration, grading; articles likely to attract flies to be protected.

Thailand

Rice Standard Regulations, 1957

Includes provision for the inspection of rice prior to export.

Uganda

Food and Drugs Ordinance, Cap. 229

Provides for safe, satisfactory storage of produce; committee set up to draft rules for the safe storage of food. Provides for adulteration and food unfit for human consumption; inspection, seizure, sampling, controlling treatments and processes used in the preparation of food, quality standards.

Public Health Ordinance, Cap. 98

Medical officers can enforce the safe storage and protection of foodstuffs, and can direct seizure of unwholesome food. They also have powers of entry, inspection and sampling.

Uganda (*continued*)	*Produce Marketing Ordinance, Cap. 139* Types of stores in which controlled produce can be held may be specified; provides for grading and inspection.
Zambia	*Public Health Ordinance, 1930* Sale of food in tainted, adulterated, diseased or unwholesome state prohibited; measures must be taken to prevent this. *Markets Ordinance, 1937* Provides for the inspection of specified produce, fixing grades and prohibition of adulteration. Market master has right to refuse the sale of goods he considers unfit for consumption.
Zanzibar	*Food and Drugs Decree, 1956* Restricts addition to and abstraction from foods; prohibits sale of food not of nature, substance or quality demanded, prohibits sale of unsound food. Provides for inspection and seizure, sampling, prescribing quality standards. *Public Health Decree, Cap. 60* Provides for inspection and destruction of unsound food, storage of food and its manufacture. *Agricultural Produce Export Decree, Cap. 111* Prohibits export without inspection of declared produce including cloves and copra. Prescribes specific designation under which produce may be exported including percentage impurities, maximum moisture, manner of storage and treatment, grading and sampling.

2. Pests

Antigua	*Plant Protection Ordinance, 1941* (No. 14 of 1941); *Animals (Diseases and Importation) Ordinance, 1953* (No. 3 of 1953) Includes control of insects on imports.

Argentina	*Resolution 558 issued by the Dirección Nacional de Granos y Elevadores, November 1947* Gives tolerances for weevil holed wheat grains (see under Quality - Argentina). *Resolution 808 of DNGE of July 1951* Limits insect-damaged cereal grains present in a consignment (see under Quality - Argentina).
Australia	*Commonwealth Government's Export Grain Regulations, 1963* Provides for inspection of export wheat prior to loading and observance of a nil tolerance for live insects.
British Solomon Islands	*Copra Ordinance, 1954; Regulation of 1954; Rules of 1961* Restricts export of copra containing insects and moulds, the presence of which are sought by inspectors.
Cameroon (Southern)	*Southern Cameroon Produce Inspection Law, 1960* Empowers inspection for pests in general.
The Gambia	*Quarantine Ordinance, 1932* Merchandise coming from an infected local area and likely to harbour plague-infected rats may be unloaded early on condition that the necessary precautions are taken to prevent the escape of rats and to ensure their destruction. Sanitary authority may prohibit storage of goods likely to harbour or attract rats in any store, etc., which cannot be made ratproof. *Prevention of Damage by Pests Ordinance, 1962; Amendment Ordinance, 1964; Amendment Act, 1965* Provides for the control of rats, mice, insects, mites or fungi in food in premises, vehicles, vessels, equipment and containers.

Guyana

Plant Protection Ordinance, 1942, Cap. 245; Conditions of Importation Regulations, 1958; Conditions of Exportation Order, 1958

Provides for the control of plant pests and diseases in plants imported, exported and within Guyana, although no stored product pests have as yet been scheduled under this ordinance. Plants here include cereals, oilseeds and legumes.

Quarantine Ordinance, 1947, Cap. 148

Includes provision for keeping the number of rats on board ships arriving at Guyana ports down to the minimum.

India

Prevention of Food Adulteration Act, 1954; Rules of 1955 and Second Amendment Rules of 1964

Provides (among other things) for controlling the import into India or the storage, manufacture or sale in India of insect-infested food. No specific insects appear to have been scheduled although the rules of 1964 restrict the amount of uric acid present in food grains; also, damages by fungi to food grains are restricted.

Rice Milling Industry (Regulation) Act, 1958

Licensed millers to store paddy and rice so as to prevent damage by insects, rodents and birds; this is stipulated in the Rice Milling Industry (Regulations and Licensing) Rules of 1959.

Kerala Agricultural Pests and Diseases Act, 1958

Makes provision for preventing the spread of agricultural insect pests and plant diseases within the State of Kerala. Insect pests and plant diseases may be scheduled as such from time to time by the Government when it is considered they are dangerous to health or injurious to crops. There is no notification that storage insects and moulds are recognized as pests under this Act.

India (*continued*)

Destructive Insects and Pests Act, 1914

This Act governs plant quarantine work in India. There is no indication that storage pests are regulated under this Act.

Jamaica

Food Storage and Prevention of Infestation Law, 1958; Amendment of 1962

Regulates the storage, sale or transportation of any food which is infested with insects, mites, rodents and fungi.

Kenya

Plant Protection Ordinance, 1937

1. *Importation Regulations* (*Zanzibar*) *Order, 1956* To prevent entry of *Trogoderma granarium* or any other pest from Zanzibar into Kenya.
2. *T. granarium* and *Araecerus fasciculatus* declared pests in 1957 under Ordinance.
3. *Importation* (*Malt and Malt Bags*) (*Trogoderma*) *Order, 1957* To prevent entry of *T. granarium* on malt and malt bags into Kenya.
4. *Plant Protection* (*Amendment*) *Order, 1963* A large number of stored products insects declared pests.

Agricultural Produce (*Export*) *Act, Cap. 319*

The grading of maize rules (1937 and 1940) made under this Act restrict the amount of weevily maize which may be exported and how and where such maize shall be stored and dealt with.

Malawi

Plant Protection Ordinance, Cap. 126

The following storage insects declared pests:

Cadra cautella, Lasioderma serricorne, Stephanoderes hampei, Plodia interpunctella, Sitotroga cerealella, Corcyra cephalonica, Anagasta kuhniella, Acanthoscelides obtectus, Callosobruchus chinensis, C. maculatus, Sitophilus oryzae, Trogoderma granarium, Tribolium confusum, T. castaneum, Rhizopertha do-

Malawi (*continued*)

minica, *Gnathocerus cornutus*, *G. maxillosus*. Also others in list of the principal noxious insects existing in Africa south of the Sahara published by the Inter-African Phyto-Sanitary Commission, 1958.

Malaya

Agricultural Pests and Noxious Plants Ordinance, 1953

Provides for the control of plant pests (insects, rodents and fungi) on plants imported, exported and moved within the then Federation of Malaya. No specific storage pests appear as yet to have been scheduled under this ordinance. Plants here include cereals, oilseeds and legumes.

Nigeria

Public Health Ordinance, 1917

Provides for making rules for the destruction of rats, mice and other vermin in order to render houses ratproof.

Produce (Enforcement of Export Standards) Ordinance, 1959

In the event of an outbreak of serious pest infestation, steps may be taken in Lagos to combat such infestation and prevent its spread.

Produce Inspection (Northern Region) Law, 1961

No specific pests listed but left to produce officers' discretion.

Produce Inspection (Groundnuts) Regulations, 1962

No person shall introduce into or near any groundnuts any pests or pest-infested nuts.

Pakistan

East Pakistan Warehouses Ordinance, 1959 and Rules of 1964

Rats and other pests likely to damage or injure stored agricultural produce to be controlled.

Pakistan (*continued*)	*Destructive Insects and Pests Act, 1914* Prevents the introduction into the provinces and the transport from one province to another of any insect, fungus or other pest which is or may be destructive to agricultural crops (includes cereals, legumes and oilseeds).
Rhodesia and Zambia	*Plant Pests and Diseases Act, 1958* 1. *Plant Pests and Diseases (Pests and Alternate Hosts) 1958* Pests – *Stephanoderes hampei, Ephestia elutella, Lasioderma serricorne* and *E. elutella* 2. *Plant Pests and Diseases (Pests and Alternate Hosts) (Amendment) Order, 1961* (No. 1)
Sarawak	*Agricultural Pests Ordinance, Cap. 124, Revised Edition, 1958* Provides for the control of pests (includes insects, rodents and fungi) destructive or injurious to cultivated plants (includes cereals, oilseeds and legumes). No storage pests appear to have been scheduled so far under this ordinance.
Senegal	*Plant Protection Decree, 60 - 122* Compulsory control of pests. The following must be controlled by definite measures in certain places, e.g., collection centres, storage centres, silos, ports and warehouses: *Calandra, Tribolium, Trogoderma, Caryedon, Araecerus fasciculatus, Lasioderma serricorne, Hemiptera, Sitotroga cerealella, Corcyra cephelonica, Ephestia elutella* and *Cadra cautella.*
Tanzania	*Plant Protection Ordinance, Cap. 133* 1. *Plant Protection (Pests) Order, 1956* *Trogoderma granarium* declared a pest. 2. *Plant Protection (Import) Order, 1960* Designation of insects as pests left to inspector.

Uganda	*Plant Protection Ordinance, Cap. 136* *Trogoderma granarium* declared a pest. *Public Health Ordinance, Cap. 98* Rules provide for ratproofing of all storage buildings. *Factories Ordinance, Cap. 229* Under the Building Rules, ratproofing is enforced.
Zambia	*Plant Pests and Diseases Act, 1958* See under Rhodesia. *Public Health Ordinance, 1930* Warehouses, etc., used for food storage to be constructed so that they are ratproof. *Markets Ordinance, 1937* Foodstuffs offered for sale must be protected from flies.
Zanzibar	*Plant Protection Decree, 1937* *(Declaration of Pests) Order, 1956* *Trogoderma granarium* and other species of *Trogoderma* declared as pests. Provides for the declaration of other pests.

3. Treatments

Argentina	*DNGE Resolution No. 844, 15 December 1953* Instructions for the warehousing of grain and rules for conservation and disinfestation (extended on 23 August 1954 to goods stored in oilseed crushing mills and in flour mills). *DNGE Expte. 3.010/53, 27 November 1953 and amended 13. 8. 54* Compulsory insecticidal treatment of transport vehicles and ships used for carriage of cereals, oilseeds and their products.

Argentina (*continued*)	*DNGE Cir. No. 2211/54 of 1954* Rules concerning the construction of warehouses to be used for the storage of government grain.
Australia (Queensland)	Certified maize and sorghum seed required by law to be dusted with a 0.5 percent and 1 percent lindane dust respectively.
Bahama islands	*Plant Protection Act, Cap. 244, Revised Edition, 1957* Provides for the control in imported plants (includes cereals, oilseeds and legumes) of insects and moulds (unnamed). Inspectors may be appointed to ensure the Act is adhered to. No details of which methods to be used are available.
Brazil	*Regulamento de Defesa Sanitario Vegetal, 2nd Ed. 1935, Cap. 7* Makes obligatory the disinfection or fumigation of cereals, pulses and cottonseed intended for export and provides for them to be accompanied by the appropriate official certificates. States that a certificate of disinfection or fumigation shall be valid for a period of 90 days from the date of treatment. States that no responsibility shall be incurred by any organization which carries out the treatment for any infestation or contamination which may occur to certificated goods after they have been delivered from the place of fumigation if they are: – Stacked with other untreated goods. – Placed in untreated warehouses. – Transported with other infested or contaminated goods. – Transported in wagons, holds of ships, etc., which have not been disinfested.
Cameroon (Southern)	*Southern Cameroon Produce Inspection Law, 1960* Regulations may be made to prevent occurrence and spread of pest infestation in stored produce and the produce officer may make orders for treatment as he thinks necessary.

The Gambia

Prevention of Damage by Pests Ordinance, 1962; Amendment Ordinance, 1964; Amendment Act, 1965; Rice Importation Regulations, 1964

Directions may be given for the treatment (unspecified) necessary for preventing or remedying infestation in food, containers and premises. The Rice Importation Regulations require that rice be free from insect infestation at the time of loading for export to The Gambia; this may entail insecticidal treatment.

Guyana

Plant Protection Ordinance 1942, Cap. 245; Conditions of Importation Regulations, 1958; Conditions of Exportation Order, 1958

Provides for the disinfection, treatment or destruction of any plant and of any article likely to infect any plant with a pest or disease. This applies to plants being imported, exported and those being moved within Guyana. No specific control measures have, as yet, been scheduled under this ordinance.

Quarantine Ordinance, 1947, Cap. 148

If the number of rats on ships arriving at Guyana ports is above the minimum considered safe by a Health Officer, he may order the ship to be deratized in a manner specified or approved by him.

India

Destructive Insects and Pests Act, 1914

Although no storage pests appear to have been scheduled under this Act, it does provide for the fumigation or other methods of disinfestation of infested produce imported into India.

Kerala Agricultural Pests and Diseases Act, 1958

Provides for the control of agricultural insect pests and plant diseases within the State of Kerala. In particular, the Government may prescribe the preventive or remedial measures which should be taken although none appear to have been scheduled. Also, there is no indication that storage insects and moulds are recognized and dealt with as pests under this Act.

India *(continued)*	*Rice Milling Industry (Regulation) Act, 1958* Rules of 1959 made under this Act require that trained personnel should use approved fumigants (unnamed) for controlling insects in stored paddy and rice. *Indian Export Promotion Council, 1964* After 31 July 1964, fumigation of rice bran prior to loading (for export) was enforced.
Jamaica	*Food Storage and Prevention of Infestation Law, 1958, and Amendment of 1962* Amendment enables disinfestation work to be done by an inspector without owners' consent. Enables regulations to be made for the use of chemicals for controlling infestation.
Kenya	*Plant Protection Ordinance, 1937* 1. *Plant Protection Rules* – treatments (insecticidal) in general terms. 2. *Plant Protection Order* – (for produce imported into Kenya) treatments in general terms. 3. *Importation (Malt and Malt Bugs) (Trogoderma) Order, 1957* Malt not allowed into Kenya unless certificate shows malt has been fumigated within 7 days before shipment and treated and held at a temperature lethal to *T. granarium.*
Madagascar	*Decree* authorizing the use of nontoxic insecticides for protection of dried starchy vegetables, maize and dried cassava destined for export; also fixing maximal dose for products based on benzene hexachloride, for disinfestation of rice, maize, starchy vegetables and dried cassava; also authorizing the use of the insecticide Gammagrain at 1 percent concentration (lindane quality); also Lindex grain, Saindane and Geigy 33 all at 0.6 percent concentrations for protection of above commodities destined for export or as cargo; also authorizing the use of an insecticidal product named Granalise.

Malawi	*Plant Protection (Export) Rules, 1963* Empowers inspectors to order disinfection, fumigation and treatment of plants (except oil, tea, and coffee); vehicles, if infested with any pests scheduled; also to order that only one of following fumigants may be used and at the dosage he directs: methyl bromide, aluminium phosphide, carbon bisulphide, carbon tetrachloride, ethylene dichloride, ethylene oxide.
Malaysia	*Agricultural Pests and Noxious Plants Ordinance, 1953* Makes provision for control, within the then Federation, of pests (includes insects, rodents and moulds) of plants (includes cereals, oilseeds and legumes) by measures considered expedient by the Inspecting Officer. No specific control measures appear to have been scheduled under this ordinance. Rules may be made under the ordinance for governing the import or export of plant pests.
Nigeria	*Produce (Enforcement of Export Standards) Ordinance, 1959* Produce officers empowered to require fumigation or treatment of produce and premises in Lagos, if produce is infested or suspected of being infested with any pest. *Produce Inspection (Northern Region) Law, 1961* Where any produce, including that in transit through the Northern Region and local crops stored in the vicinity of produce, is found or suspected to be infested with any pest, a produce officer may make such orders as he deems necessary for the treatment of such pest. *Produce Inspection (Groundnuts) Regulations, 1962* Produce officers may order fumigation (including precautions to be taken) or other pest control measures to be carried out.

Nigeria (*continued*)	*Quarantine Ordinance, 1926* Sanitary authority may carry out deratization in vessels at Lagos and decide technique to be used.
Pakistan	*East Pakistan Warehouses Ordinance, 1959 and Rules of 1964* States that warehousemen shall take all necessary precautions against rats and other pests which are likely to damage or injure the agricultural produce in the warehouse.
	Destructive Insects and Pests Act, 1914 The Government may make rules for the disinfestation or destruction of any insects infesting agricultural crops (includes cereals, oilseeds and legumes).
Rhodesia and Zambia	*Plant Pests and Diseases (Importation) Regulations, 1960* Provides for the insecticidal treatment of infested seeds only.
Sarawak	*Agricultural Pests Ordinance, Cap. 124, Revised Edition, 1958* Gives powers to agricultural officers to order the destruction or other treatment of plants infested with pests in order to control them. No specific treatments have, as yet, been scheduled.
Senegal	*Plant Protection Decree, 60 - 121* Plant Protection Service may require treatment or destruction of infested foods. Treatment at official station by vacuum fumigation or other effective method.
Tanzania	*Produce Export (Fumigation) Rules, 1965* Lays down the dosages of methyl bromide to be used on scheduled products (includes various cereals, legumes and oilseeds) not more than 7 days before shipment, if required by the contract of sale or any law in force at the time.

Tanzania (*continued*)	*Plant Protection (Import) Order, 1950* Treatments provided for but left to inspectors' discretion. *Plant Protection (Control of Trogoderma granarium) Order*, 1960 *and Control of Trogoderma granarium Rules, 1960* Fumigation and insecticidal dosages laid down against *Trogoderma granarium* on imports and native commodities.
Uganda	*Plant Protection Ordinance, Cap. 136; (Fumigation of Imports) (Trogoderma granarium) Order*, 1957 Fumigation and insecticidal dosages laid down to combat *Trogoderma granarium* on scheduled imports and in vehicles used for transport. *Regulation of Importation of Plants* Provides for the control, disinfection and treatment of any plants (including seeds) which appear to be infected with any pest. Disinfection and treatment of buildings, vehicles, aircraft and vessels is also allowed for where necessary.
Zambia	*Plant Pests and Diseases (Importation) Regulations, 1960* See under Rhodesia and Zambia.
Zanzibar	*Plant Protection Decree, 1937; (Compulsory Fumigation of Imports) Order, 1956* Fumigation dosages laid down for scheduled imported produce; insecticidal dosages for Director of Agriculture to decide. Ordinance provides for rules which may lay down disinfection and treatments for any plants appearing to be infested with any pest, also for the treatment of premises or vehicles.

Appendix C

ASSESSMENT OF INSECT INFESTATION: STANDARDIZED PROCEDURE

The following procedure for assessing infestation is presented for the consideration of organizations handling produce in the tropics and subtropics. It is not intended that this procedure should be adopted per se but perhaps it could form the basis of a standardized procedure for consideration by all countries.

Inspection of commodities in store should be carried out with the aim of assessing the degree of infestation by *all* insect species present, including both beetles and moths. The fabric of the premises housing the commodity should be inspected at the same time as the commodity or, if the store is empty, immediately after discharge of a commodity and before reloading. Since beetles and moths fly readily especially in dark and warm places or when disturbed, cross infestation of commodities and buildings (especially well-ventilated premises) can easily occur. When flying insects are obvious in a building it is reasonably certain that there is a heavy infestation.

Obvious damage to a commodity is an unreliable factor on which to estimate degree of infestation, e.g., holes in grain are made by living insects; if at the time of inspection holes are obvious and insects are not, insects have either migrated or been killed by some treatment, etc. Commodities showing obvious damage by insects and which are known not to have undergone fumigation (or adequate heat) treatment should however be assumed to be actively infested and should be inspected thoroughly.

In these definitions, two sets of letters are used. The first letter indicates the type of inspection made, and the second letter or pair of letters indicates the severity of the infestation.

Inspections are of three kinds, classified as:

G (General)

S (Sampling)

B (Building)

Methods *G* and *B* should be carried out regularly and Method *S* as often as is practical, but at least at the beginning and the end of the storage period. The degree of infestation is indicated by the simple categories light (*L*), medium (*M*), heavy (*H*) and very heavy (*VH*). Many other categories could be used, but it is intended to keep the system as simple as possible, and intermediate degrees of infestation of the above may be shown by hyphenating two groups, e.g.

G/M-H; *B/H-VH*

General inspections (*G*)

The following categories are recommended for use when inspection of goods is carried out, without using sampling methods for investigating within a stack or a sack, by walking round a stack and crawling over the top. Inspection of a stack built in the open (e.g., stacks of produce outdoors often covered with old tarpaulins) should not be carried out during the heat of the day because very few insects will be seen on the parts of a stack directly exposed. Wherever possible, inspection should be carried out in dim light (using a torch) because most insect species are more active in the dark.

G/C	Clear (none)	No insects found in the course of a prolonged search.
G/L	Light	Small numbers of insects occurring irregularly.
G/M	Medium	Insects obvious, occurring regularly (perhaps in small aggregations).
G/H	Heavy	Insects immediately obvious, i.e., large numbers crawling actively over the whole of the outside of the stack. A carpet of insects on the floor round the base of the stack, or on top of the stack.
G/VH	Very heavy	Insects so numerous and active that a rustling sound can be heard inside the stack. A thick wide band of insects or cast skins present on the floor round the base of the stack or on top of the stack.

Sampling inspections (*S*)

The following tentative categories are presented for use when samples of the commodity, taken by "spiking" sacks at different parts of the stack, by opening several sacks and taking samples by hand (e.g., as usually used in grading grain), by taking samples from bulk grain with a grain spear and examining by sieving; or alternatively (and to be preferred) by sieving the contents of whole sacks.

S/C	Clear (none)	No insects obvious before taking samples or after sieving many samples from different parts of the stack.
S/L	Light	Insects not obvious on stack or sack or in sample before sieving. Less than 10 insects per sack of 70 kg or not more than one insect per 3 kg of sample.
S/M	Medium	Insects obvious on stack or sack and in sample before insects sieved from a 10-kg sack of the commodity or not more than 2 insects per 3-kg sample.
S/H	Heavy	Insects obvious in considerable numbers on stack or sack and in numbers before sieving. More than 20 insects and less than 50 insects per sack or between 2 and 10 insects sieved from a 3-kg sample of the commodity.
S/VH	Very heavy	Insects present before and after sieving in very large numbers.

Produce which comes under the categories *S/M*, *S/H* and *S/VH* requires urgent attention.

BUILDING INSPECTIONS (*B*)

The following categories are presented for use when inspecting the fabric of a warehouse and/or a mill for residual and endemic infestations.

B/C	Clear (none)	No insects found either on walls, floors, beams or in any machinery in the building.
B/VL	Very light	One or two insects found in the course of a prolonged search.
B/L	Light	Insects found regularly singly, or in twos or threes, in the course of a prolonged search.
B/M	Medium	Insects occurring regularly and frequently, often in aggregations but nowhere so obvious as to immediately arrest the attention.
B/H	Heavy	Insects obvious immediately on commencing inspection, crawling actively up walls, etc.
B/VH	Very heavy	Insects present in exceptional numbers, forming black covering on fabric.

Appendix D

MAJOR CONSIDERATIONS IN MINIMIZING THE INCIDENCE OF TOXINS IN PRODUCE (PARTICULARLY GROUNDNUTS) BY INSPECTION

This information outlines the care and attention necessary in relation to the handling and storing of groundnuts to minimize the presence of aflatoxin. Similar procedures are relevant to the handling of other crops.

Many countries are concerned about the presence of aflatoxin and similar mycotoxins. They are aware of the need to carry out an appropriate testing procedure so as to be satisfied that this poison is absent in the case of produce for human consumption, or to determine the extent to which the poison is present (in the case of produce intended for oil expressing and the sale of cakes or meal for animal feed).

1. When groundnuts or their products (e.g., peanut butter) are to be used for human consumption, only whole undamaged kernels (i.e., hand-picked selected) must be sold or used during the manufacturing process. Samples from such consignments must show negative toxicity on a chemical test.

2. Groundnuts in shell for sale to the public must be whole, undamaged, clean, healthy pods (preferably originating from regions where termites are not a problem and where drying can be effected quickly).

3. Groundnuts for oil extraction ideally should have as low a toxicity value as is practical in relation to the conditions in the exporting country and the requirements of the animal feed compounder. The latter are to be established on the basis of information available on the veterinary implications of the problem.

4. Care at harvesting and immediately after harvesting can minimize the incidence of aflatoxin:

(*a*) All healthy plants should be harvested as soon as they reach maturity.

(*b*) Plants must be harvested in a way which will prevent breakage of the pods.

(*c*) Nuts from plants which have dried prior to reaching maturity must be discarded.

(*d*) Nuts should be picked from plants as soon as possible and at most within three days of harvesting. It there is no rain after harvest, i.e., dry areas, drying in windrows with the plants inverted on the ridges or on racks in small heaps may continue for one week.

5. Efficient, quick drying methods will minimize the period of time during which conditions are present which allow growth of moulds, e.g., *Aspergillus flavus* and the possibility of the production of mycotoxins including aflatoxin.

(*a*) Sun dry pods (unshelled nuts) on matting (not more than one layer thick) for at least one week.

(*b*) Protect the drying pods during rain and at night by placing them under cover.

(*c*) Artificial drying with air temperatures not over $42^{\circ}C$ may also be used.

6. Prior to sale to traders, care in storing and discarding of suspect nuts is important; all dust, dirt, stones, etc. must be removed.

Nuts for human consumption

(*a*) Remove broken and badly discoloured pods (and discard).

(*b*) Shell only pods which are unbroken and of normal appearance.

(*c*) All broken, shrivelled, mouldy and discoloured kernels must be removed and must not be used for human consumption.

(*d*) Farmers must store only dry nuts in clean, dry places.

Nuts for crushing

(*a*) Remove broken and badly discoloured pods (and discard).

(*b*) Shell only pods which are of normal appearance.

(*c*) Shrivelled, mouldy and discoloured kernels should be removed and stored in bags clearly labelled as reject nuts which if used for oil expressing must not be mixed, either as nuts or cake, with good quality produce.

(*d*) Farmers must store only dry nuts in clean, dry places.

7. Attention by traders can assist in stopping the movement of nuts containing aflatoxin.

Nuts for human consumption

(*a*) Only consignments of groundnuts containing no shrivelled, mouldy or discoloured kernels are acceptable; thus hand picking in an attempt to ensure no defects in the consignment is essential.

(*b*) Traders must store only dry nuts (i.e., below 7 percent moisture content) in clean, dry places; groundnuts must not be stored in direct contact with the ground.

(*c*) Water damage during transportation of groundnuts, cakes or meal must be prevented.

(*d*) Groundnuts which have been wetted during storage and transportation must not be sold or purchased for human consumption.

(*e*) The moisture content of nuts, cake and meal in store must never exceed 7 percent (for nuts) and 16 percent (for cake and meal).

Nuts for crushing

(*a*) Consignments of groundnuts unless intended for crushing for refined oil extraction only should contain only a very low percentage of shrivelled, mouldy or discoloured kernels.

(*b*) Traders must store only dry nuts (i.e., below 7 percent moisture content) in clean, dry places; groundnuts stored in or out of shell in contact with the ground even in dry areas will be mouldy.

(*c*) Water damage during transportation of groundnuts, cakes or meal must be prevented.

(*d*) Groundnuts, groundnut cake or meal which have been wetted during storage or transportation must be clearly labelled as "Water damaged/suspect nuts."

(*e*) The moisture content of nuts, cake and meal in store must never exceed 7 percent (for nuts) and 16 percent (for cake and meal).

8. Consignments should be sampled prior to export in such a manner as to be reasonably certain of obtaining factual data on the presence or absence of aflatoxin; while this is essential for nuts for human consumption (for which a certificate should be provided), it is desirable for nuts for expressing and cake/meal production.

9. Inspection for the presence of aflatoxin has to be effected within the exporting country at buying points and grading depots as well as at the point of export. At rural handling points, inspection by means other than visual assessment is difficult. Therefore, the visual method should be used on all consignments.

10. The level of incidence of the presence of aflatoxin must be determined. This level can be used as a basis for establishing a sampling procedure. In most countries investigations have not been carried out to determine the numbers or percentages of nuts affected and the degree of aflatoxin content of these nuts. It may be that in different countries the following alternatives are involved: large numbers of nuts of low aflatoxin content or small numbers of nuts of high aflatoxin content. It is important for each country to determine its own particular problem.

Sampling procedure

Sampling at primary buying points

(*a*) Sampling of nuts for visual examination for the presence of mouldy, discoloured and shrivelled nuts should be carried out at primary buying points.

(*b*) Each small quantity of nuts delivered by the farmer should be examined carefully; obviously good nuts which are damp (i.e., above 8 percent moisture content) must be rejected and mouldy, discoloured and shrivelled nuts must be removed from the quantity to be purchased.

(*c*) Consignments of nuts purchased should be batched and clearly labelled to made it possible to trace the buying point, purchasing officer and store involved.

Sampling at main collecting and sorting depots

(*a*) All consignments of nuts should be checked for moisture content on receipt at these depots (see 7 above).

(*b*) Nuts for the edible trade require 100 percent check by visual examination of the contents of every bag to remove defective nuts. Nuts for crushing require sampling for visual examination.

(*c*) The following procedure is suggested, in which a ½-lb sample of shelled nuts is taken from each of the bags sampled (e.g., using a spear or by taking handfuls of nuts as the contents are being emptied from the bag, preferably from more than one position of each bag; preferably by using the TSPC sampler/divider). While sampling of every bag is desirable it is unlikely to be practical and therefore the following pattern of sampling could be considered in such cases. (If more extensive sampling can be carried out, e.g., every other or every third bag, then this should always be done).

Consignment size	*No. of bags sampled*
0 — 100	20
100 — 500	25
500 — 1 500	30
1 500 — 5 000	35
5 000 — 7 500	45
7 500 +	55

All bags sampled should be clearly marked. The whole sample should be visually examined for mouldy, shrivelled and discoloured kernels and appropriate action taken on the basis of paragraphs **8** and **9** above.

(*d*) When the nuts have been graded and handpicked selected, further sampling should be carried out, but the composite sample should be dealt with in the following manner:
Pass the sample through a Boerner Divider and obtain four subsamples to be:
— examined visually at the depot,
— kept and labelled,
— bulked and sent for chemical analysis.

(*e*) Consignments received at ports should be sampled prior to export. Since the percentage of defectives will be very low the samples taken for examination should be as large as possible. It is suggested that the sampling should be as outlined above but the sample should be 1 lb from each bag and handled to obtain four subsamples to be:
— kept and labelled,
— sent to the importer,
— sent for analysis,
— inspected visually at the port.

(*f*) Consignments of groundnuts for the edible trade must show nil defective by visual examination of the samples drawn and a negative result in the chemical analysis of the samples drawn at the hand sorting depots and at the port of export.

(*g*) Consignments of groundnuts for crushing can tolerate a small percentage of defective nuts and it is recommended that, if visual examination of the sample at the main collecting points and at the port of export shows the presence of 0.25 percent defective nuts, the result of the chemical analysis must be communicated to the purchaser.

11. The recommendations given in 10 (*f*) and (*g*) for tolerance levels are a guide but each country may consider giving less or greater tolerance according to existing conditions.

12. Ideally all samples should be analysed chemically to provide reliable information about the areas of a country from which aflatoxin-affected consignments are being received, thereby indicating the areas where existing local conditions allow the development of aflatoxin-producing strains of *Aspergillus flavus*.

13. When consignments are known to contain more than the acceptable level of defective nuts (and aflatoxin content) for the trade concerned, they should be subjected to treatments which could be expected to remove nuts likely to contain aflatoxin. Such treatments include removal by selection by eye, electronic sorting machines, or by machines which are adjusted (for the variety being handled) to remove lightweight nuts or to sort by bulk density.

Appendix E

OUTLINE OF MEASURES FOR RODENT-PROOFING STORAGE BUILDINGS

Rodent proofing means the proper closing and protection with rodent-proofing materials of all openings in a building in such a way as to exclude rodents. It includes the prevention of rodents climbing up poles, pipes, wires and any shafts connected with a building by the proper use of suitable guards around any pipe, wire or other installation connected with a building by which rodents might enter. Openings in the foundations, outer walls, floors, roof, eaves, grilles, windows, vents, vent pipes, ventilated gratings in footpaths, and elevators must be suitably guarded to exclude rodents.

The gauges of materials (standard wire gauge) referred to in this discussion are as follows:

	Gauge	*mm*
Perforated sheet metal	18	1.22
Wire gauze	19	1.0
Expanded metal	18	1.22
Sheet metal	24	0.56

PRIMARY STRUCTURES

1. Where foundation walls do not extend more than 0.75 metre below ground level, a concrete curtain wall should be provided unless the foundations are seated directly on hard rock. This wall should extend 0.75 metre below ground level and should have an exterior lip projecting at least 30 centimetres and at least 10 centimetres thick.

2. Buildings erected on piers which provide a clearance of at least 0.6 metre between the underside of the lowest floor and the ground surface should have all piers fitted with rodent guards. In buildings where this clearance is less than 0.6 metre, spaces under the lowest floor should be enclosed by a continuous screen of wire gauze or perforated or expanded metal. Openings in the screen should not have a dimension exceeding a 1/4 inch or 0.6 centimetre. The screen may be applied around the perimeter of the building, in which case the material should be corrosion-resistant so that it may be extended into the ground 0.6 metre and have a 0.3-metre horizontal lip at the bottom.

3. Where loading platforms are separate from a building, their supports should not be boxed in and there should be a clearance of at least 0.6 metre between the underside of the platform and the ground surface, or the space beneath the platform should be enclosed as with buildings built on piers (see above).

4. Enclosed spaces between upper ceilings and roofs should be rodent-proofed and easily accessible for inspection. If the walls are not built up between ceiling joists and rafters, the ceiling boards should be protected from rats climbing the outside wall by continuous sheet metal flashing, extending at least 15 centimetres inward from the edge of the floor or ceiling, downward from the edge between the joists or rafters, and turned in 5 centimetres into the wall.

5. Eaves should be rodent-proofed. Where external walls are not built up by concreting to the underside of the roof, the junction between the roofs and walls should be rodent-proofed with continuous metal flashing turned in at least 5 centimetres under the roof plate and extending at least 15 centimetres along the underside of the roof. Enclosed eave spaces should also be fully rodent-proofed and all gnawing edges flashed with continuous metal sheeting. Any ventilation opening in the eaves should be protected with hardware cloth or expanded metal so that there are no openings larger than a 1/4 inch.

6. Parapet walls should be rodent-proofed with metal flashing which should enter the parapet wall at a distance of at least 15 centimetres above the roof cap and extend at least 5 centimetres into the parapet wall and at least 15 centimetres along the roof away from the parapet wall.

7. If the basement in a building is connected with underground tunnels or other basements, all openings should be completely rodent-proofed.

8. Foundation vents should be completely covered with metal grilles or gratings, or with perforated sheet metal.

SECONDARY STRUCTURES

9. Exterior doors should fit to within 5 millimetres at the top, bottom and sides. Wooden doors should be fitted with metal kickplates at least 30 centimetres high and wooden door-frames should be similarly protected. Rolling, sliding and curtain doors should have continuous double guides at the bottom and sides. Exterior doors, other than the main loading and unloading doors of warehouses, should be fitted with automatic closing devices.

10. Concrete thresholds of all exterior doors should be hardened with a granolithic or cement finish to reduce wear.

11. Skylights and trapdoors should fit snugly into a rabbeted or rebated frame constructed of or covered with metal. Ventilators and skylights which can be opened for ventilation should be screened with perforated or expanded metal or wire gauze with a mesh not greater than 5 millimetres. Windows capable of being opened should, in the following circumstances, be covered with metal framed hardware cloth screens or tight fitting metal fly screens: where the bottom of the window is less than 1 metre above ground level or the level of any adjacent structure; where there are, or are likely to be, trees or shrubbery nearby; where there is any roof or ledge of a building within 2.5 metres (horizontally); where there are service wires nearby; or where there are any other possible ways by which rodents could reach the window.

12. Partition walls should be solid wherever possible. Where a double partition wall is used, the bottom of the wall should be protected by a continuous sheet metal flashing extending across the bottom and at least 15 centimetres up either side. The top of the wall and exposed corners and edges should be similarly protected.

13. Insulated boxed and structural beams should have a sheathing material, of an approved rodent-proof character, installed in a continuous and unbroken manner.

14. Floor drains and all other drains should be fitted with grid plates installed so that no openings are greater than 5 millimetres.

15. Openings in external walls, double walls, floors or ceilings for the passage of pipes, wires or other service lines should be closed by metal collars fastened securely to the adjoining structure or by building in the pipe, wire or other service line with cement mortar.

16. Underground piping should be used wherever possible to bring all service lines into buildings. Wires and pipes attached to the outsides of buildings must be fitted with rodent guards. All openings into utility ducting should be rodent-proofed.

17. Meter boxes should be constructed so that rodents cannot enter a building by following the outside of the service lines.

18. Exhaust fan openings that can be reached by rodents should be protected by wire gauze screening having openings not greater than 5 millimetres or by movable louvres that close automatically when the fan ceases operation.

19. Water and sewer vent stacks should extend at least 1 metre vertically above the nearest building projection or should be capped with wire gauze, with openings not wider than 5 millimetres. Openings into enclosed spaces in ventilation systems should be carefully rodent-proofed.

RODENT GUARDS

20. Rodent guards must be used for preventing rodents climbing into buildings via supports, cables, wires and pipes (except that such guards should not be used directly on high voltage wires or cables, and all other electrical wires should be adequately insulated). Such guards should conform to the following specifications:

(*a*) Cone, half cone, barrel (i.e., cylindrical) and collar guards should be of steel of 24 gauge (0.56 millimetre) or heavier; and flat guards should be of sheet metal at least as heavy as 26 gauge (0.46 millimetre).

(*b*) Half cone guards may be used on vertical pipes or wires running along wall surfaces but should be at least 30 centimetres from base to apex and at the base should stand out at least 22 centimetres from the pipe or wire. The apex should fit to within 5 millimetres of the pipe or wire, and the sides, where attached to the wall, should fit tightly against the surface of the wall.

(*c*) Cone guards may be used on a horizontal pipe or wire at the point at which the pipe or wire meets the wall but should stand out at least 45 centimetres from the pipe or wire, and should fit at the apex to within 5 millimetres of the pipe or wire.

(*d*) Cylindrical guards may be used on pipes or wires running vertically along a wall surface but should be at least 45 centimetres long and should stand out at least 22 centimetres from the pipe or wire and should be closed at the top to within 5 millimetres of pipe or wire.

(*e*) Flat guards may be fitted to pipes smaller than 25 millimetres in diameter or wires running vertically on a wall surface but should be at least 45 centimetres high and should fit to within 5 millimetres of the pipe or wire, and should extend at least 45 centimetres on either side of the pipe or wire, which extensions should fit tightly against the wall and be fastened to it by nails, bolts or screws along the top and bottom edges only.

(*f*) Flat guards may be fitted to a pipe smaller than 25 millimetres in diameter or wire running horizontally on a wall surface but should extend at least 0.6 metre along the pipe or wire and should fit to within 5 millimetres of the pipe or wire, and should extend at least 45 centimetres on either side of the pipe or wire, which extensions should fit tightly against the wall and be fastened to it by nails, bolts or screws along the vertical edges only.

(*g*) Where collar guards are used for rodent-proofing holes in floors or walls through which pipes, cables or wires pass, such guards should extend outward at least 20 centimetres from the pipe, cables or wires and should fit at the neck to within 5 millimetres of the pipes, cables or wires, and should be securely fastened against the floor or wall.

(*h*) Where perforated screens are used to exclude rodents, they should be of expanded or perforated metal or wire gauze with perforations not exceeding 5 millimetres. Under buildings or storage containers erected on piers each pole, pipe, cable, wire, conduit, etc., passing through the wooden ground floor should be protected by a collar of unbroken sheet metal (of the dimensions given in the preceding paragraph) securely fastened to the floor. All other openings in wooden floors through which rodents could enter double walls on the inside of a building should be closed with unbroken sheet metal, concrete or masonry.

Appendix F

BUSHEL AND STANDARD BAG WEIGHTS OF CERTAIN PRODUCE

	Bushel weight	Standard bag weight
	Kilogrammes	
Maize	25–26	90
Barley	22	90
Wheat	27	90
Sorghum	25–27	90
Millet	22–27	100
Rice (paddy)	19–27	64
Milled rice	29–38	45–100
Beans	27–28	90
Soybeans	27	65
Groundnuts:		
Unshelled	10–16	29–45
Shelled	23	74–84
Cottonseed	15	50
Cocoa beans	21	60–90
Coffee	11–16	60–65
Flour	23–24	45
Palm kernels	14–28	82–84

NOTE : See also page 40.

LOADS IMPOSED BY STORED GRAIN

(Canada farm building standards)

DEFINITIONS

1. Shallow bin:

   Depth of grain (H) less than or equal to equivalent diameter (D).

   Or: $\frac{H}{B} \tan\left(\frac{ø}{2} + 45^{o}\right)$

   B = width.

   ø = emptying angle of repose

   (i.e., wheat: ø = 28°, if H = 1.66 B or less use shallow bin design)

2. Deep bin:

   Depth of grain (H) greater than the equivalent diameter (D).

   Or: greater than second definition above.

3. Equivalent diameter (D):

   Grain is a semifluid. Loads both vertical and lateral are a function of depth. In the design of some bins, discussed later, the equivalent fluid density (EED) directly relates load and depth, assuming linearity. From Rankine's development:

   Lateral pressure (L) = EFD X $\frac{H^2}{2}$

   where EFD = r $\tan^2 (45^{o} - \theta/2)$.

   r = density of material

   θ = angle of internal friction

   (Use emptying angle of repose to compute EFD.)

A. SHALLOW BINS

1. Lateral load on vertical walls:

   L = EFD X H.

2. Vertical loads on vertical walls:

   $V = \mu \times L$ where $\mu =$ coefficient of friction, grain on wall.

3. Vertical loads on horizontal floors:

   V = EFD X H.

   Conservative: V = Bulk Density X H.

4. Design values — Equivalent fluid density (EFD):

   Level fill: shelled corn, 30 kg/m^3
   wheat, 27.7 kg/m^3

   Effect of storage time: increase above figures 25 percent for storage longer than one year.
   Effect of surcharge: increase above figures 25 percent for maximum surcharge. (NOTE: These figures have checked out in extensive loading and pressure studies. They also agree with Rankine's formula, using emptying angle of repose for angle of internal friction. See apparent inconsistency with data under Coulomb's theory below.)

5. Inward sloping, or inward curving walls:

   EFD pressures will result in conservative designs.
   Use Coulomb's "wedge" theory.
   (NOTE: With level fill and zero wall friction, Coulomb's theory reduces to Rankine's theory.)

6. Design values — Coulomb's theory:

   The angle of internal friction as determined from loading studies does not equal the unloading angle of repose as commonly used in the EFD method.
   Angle of internal friction: shelled corn, 22°
   wheat, 31°

B. DEEP BINS

Janssen's formula:

1. Lateral load on vertical walls:

   $$L = \frac{wD}{4\mu}\left(1 - e^{-4K\mu H/D}\right)$$

   L = lateral pressure, kg/m^2

   w = material density, kg/m^3

D = bin diameter, or equivalent diameter, m

K = ratio of lateral to vertical internal pressure = (1 — sinø)/(1 + cosø)

ø = angle of repose

μ = coefficient of friction, material on wall

H = depth of fill, m

V = μL = vertical load on wall

2. Vertical load on vertical walls:

   V = $\mu \times$ L.

   (NOTE: Vertical load and horizontal load may never be maximum at the same time).

3. Vertical load on horizontal floors:
   F = L/K

C. HOPPER BOTTOMS

1. Coulomb's theory will work for shallow bins with sloping walls and/or floors.

2. Deep bins — at any given depth, the forces on the hopper surface are:

(*a*) Normal pressure = L $\sin^2 0$ + L/K $\cos^2 0$
where 0 is the angle between the hopper surface and the horizontal. (This formula is reported to be too conservative for deep bins.)

(*b*) Friction force parallel to surface = Normal pressure $\times$ μ.

(*c*) Vertical tensile stress resulting from the lower end of a hopper face providing end reactions to another face.

(*d*) Hoop stress in conical hoppers, or
Horizontal tensile stress resulting from one face of the hopper providing end reactions to other faces.

D. VERTICAL LOADS ON WALLS WITH EXPOSED HORIZONTAL GIRTS

Wall load = F + V

F = vertical load on girts.

V = $\mu \times$ L = vertical load on wall. In computing L, omit those areas " shaded " by the girts.

E. Thermal effects

Coefficient of linear thermal expansion for 9.3 percent maize = = 0.0000187 cm/cm.

Temperature changes of ambient air will result in dimensional changes in the bin, and lower and/or smaller changes in the stored material. Differential changes between the bin and stored material result.

Sun warming of the bin surface, followed by settling of the stored material and subsequent cooling, may result in passive pressures. Because dimensional changes will be relatively small, elasticity of a grain mass (24 to 70 kg/cm^2) will permit yielding to reduce the apparent high stresses.

Yielding of the grain mass is reported to increase the EFD significantly as well as changing the stress patterns in the grain. Repeated cycles may lead to failure.

F. Moisture effects

In commercial warehousing and farm bins with the grain put in at safe moisture contents and with no drying anticipated, moisture changes are not important to structural design.

Wall pressures will increase at least 6 times if the moisture content of dry grain is raised 4 percent. Pressures will increase 10 times with a 10-percent moisture increase.

G. Unloading effects

A number of investigators report varying amounts of overloading during grain discharge.

No design values or procedures seem to be available at this time.

H. Physical properties of stored crops

See coefficients of friction for grains (Table 1) and calculated densities of grains (Table 2).

TABLE 1. — COEFFICIENTS OF FRICTION (μ) FOR GRAINS AT VARIOUS MOISTURE CONTENTS ON VARIOUS SURFACES

Material	Moisture content (percent)	Surfaces										
		Concrete			Wood				Plastic		Metal	
					Oak		Douglas fir					
		Plastic smooth finish	Steel trowel finish	Wood float finish	Grain par.	Grain perp.	Grain par.	Grain perp.	Teflon	Poly-ethyl-ene	Mild steel (cold rolled)	Gal-vanized sheet metal
Oats	10.6	0.276	0.396	0.434	0.202	0.231	0.268	0.294	0.130	0.204	0.197	0.223
	13.0	0.343	0.443	0.435	0.244	0.251	0.289	0.354	0.139	0.239	0.256	0.240
	14.0	0.326	0.514	0.423	0.232	0.248	0.343	0.358	0.126	0.278	0.214	0.180
	16.0	0.292	0.459	0.456	0.314	0.307	0.371	0.366	0.110	0.312	0.204	0.405
	17.3	0.497	0.652	0.639	0.459	0.479	0.480	0.500	0.135	0.502	0.443	0.315
Spheres (Teflon)		0.322	0.398	0.375	0.300	0.323	0.330	0.354	0.243	0.280	0.213	0.248
Wheat	11.2	0.356	0.516	0.506	0.235	0.264	0.307	0.347	0.170	0.269	0.204	0.095
	13.0	0.460	0.520	0.546	0.247	0.291	0.345	0.382	0.156	0.351	0.286	0.142
	15.0	0.503	0.547	0.510	0.353	0.368	0.468	0.457	0.146	0.389	0.269	0.272
	15.7	0.563	0.677	0.689	0.411	0.464	0.482	0.501	0.119	0.448	0.514	0.332
Soybeans	7.1	0.246	0.390	0.391	0.239	0.337	0.290	0.309	0.160	0.246	0.191	0.206
	8.1	0.318	0.554	0.515	0.294	0.336	0.323	0.366	0.174	0.316	0.192	0.205
	9.8	0.308	0.467	0.367	0.281	0.308	0.333	0.314	0.155	0.288	0.202	0.182
	12.2	0.363	0.552	0.515	0.279	0.360	0.353	0.441	0.147	0.430	0.230	0.199
Barley	10.7	0.232	0.557	0.503	0.234	0.285	0.269	0.322	0.169	0.232	0.197	0.198
	12.3	0.248	0.547	0.522	0.214	0.277	0.275	0.306	0.147	0.275	0.247	0.174
	14.3	0.236	0.568	0.508	0.205	0.277	0.297	0.323	0.131	0.278	0.288	0.204
	16.4	0.331	0.619	0.552	0.304	0.330	0.374	0.412	0.105	0.354	0.214	0.342
Rice (rough)	14.0	0.516					0.435	0.500				0.402
		0.611					0.506	0.542				0.449
Shelled maize	7.5	0.268	0.405	0.456	0.238	0.245	0.271	0.288	0.170	0.219	0.255	0.195
	9.9	0.247	0.589	0.615	0.282	0.314	0.314	0.314	0.176	0.270	0.201	0.241
	12.2	0.331	0.677	0.647	0.261	0.291	0.330	0.333	0.160	0.303	0.201	0.246
	13.9	0.345	0.635	0.540	0.294	0.360	0.365	0.380	0.123	0.381	0.238	0.372

TABLE 2. — CALCULATED DENSITIES OF GRAIN

	Bulk density	
	kg/m³	*lb/ft³*
Alfalfa	770	48.0
Barley	615	38.4
Beans:		
Lima, dry	719	44.8
unshelled	411	25.6
Snap	285	24.0
Other, dry	770	48.0
Broomcorn	565–641	35.2–40.6
Buckwheat	615–668	38.4–14.6
Castor beans	590	36.8
Clover	770	48.0
Cottonseed	411	25.6
Cowpeas	770	48.0
Flaxseed	718	44.8
Grain sorghums	718 and 641	44.8 and 40.0
Groundnuts, unshelled:		
Virginia type	282	17.6
Runners, southeastern	359	22.4
Spanish	285	24.0
Hempseed	565	35.2
Hickory nuts	641	40.0
Hungarian millet	615 and 641	38.4 and 40.0
Kafir	718 and 641	44.8 and 40.0
Kapok	499–514	28.0–32.0
Lentils	770	48.0
Maize:		
Ear, husked	449	28.0
Shelled	718	44.8
Green sweet	449	28.0
Millet	615-641	38.4–40.0
Mustard	744–770	46.4–48.0
Oats	411	25.6
Orchard grass		11.2
Perilla	475–514	29.6–32.0
Popcorn:		
On ear	449	28.0
Shelled	718	44.8
Poppy	590	36.8
Rapeseed	641 and 770	40.0 and 48.0
Rice, rough	577	36.0
Rye	718	44.8
Sesame	590	36.8
Sorghum	641	40.0
Soybeans	770	48.0
Spelt (p. wheat)	514	32.0
Sudan grass	514	32.0
Sunflowerseed	308 and 411	19.2 and 25.6
Timothy	577	36.0
Velvet beans (hulled)	770	48.0
Vetch	770	48.0
Walnuts	641	40.0
Wheat	770	48.0

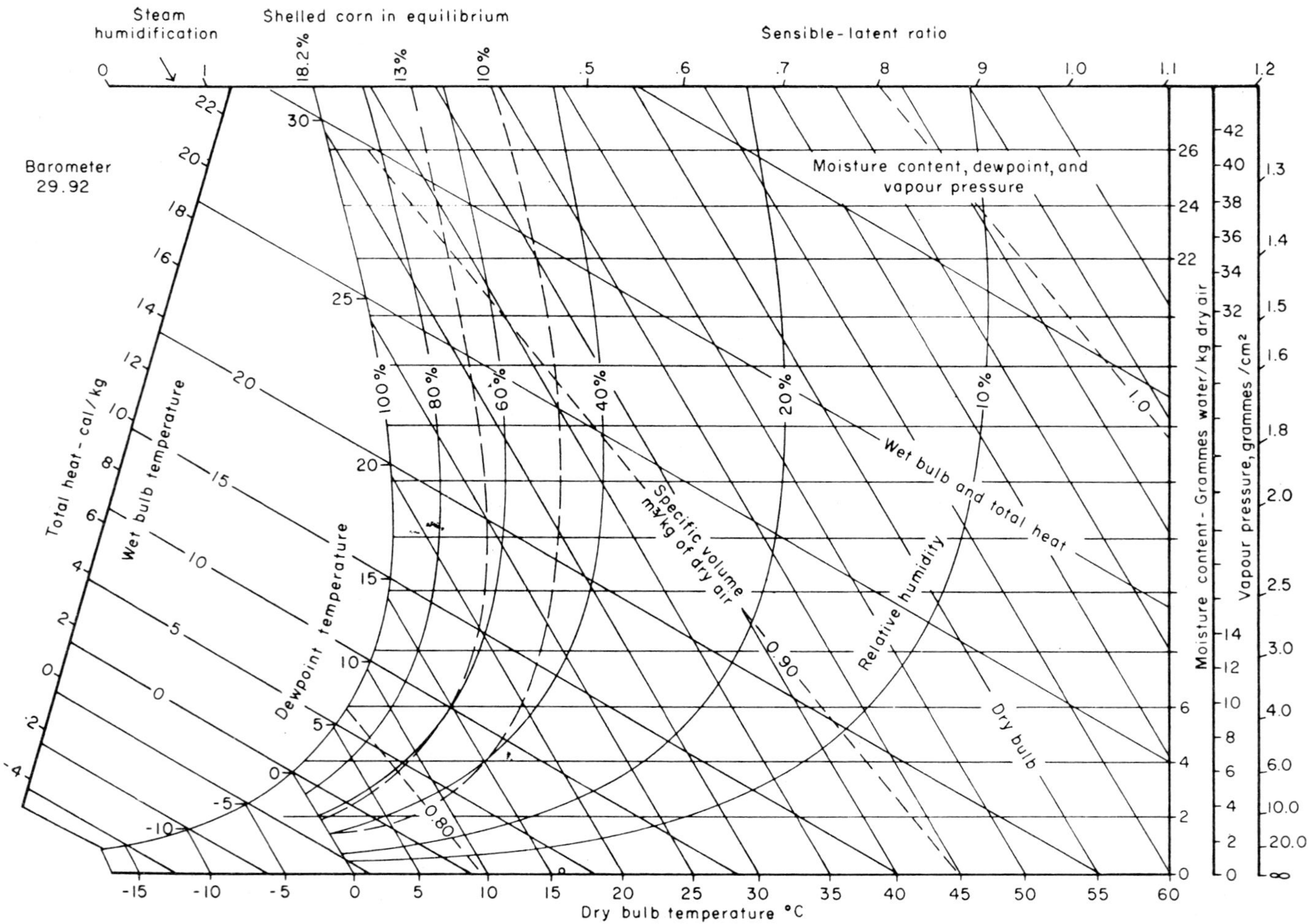

FIGURE 61. Psychrometric chart.

Appendix H

USE OF THE PSYCHROMETRIC CHART IN GRAIN DRYING

The psychrometric chart (Figure 61) has been prepared from experimentally determined temperature humidity values and permits the immediate determination of the relative humidity of air once the wet bulb and dry bulb temperatures are known. Humidity can be measured in several ways. It can be measured in a laboratory by drawing a known volume of air through a series of tubes containing calcium chloride. The calcium chloride absorbs the water vapour and the increase in weight gives the weight of water vapour absorbed.

A more common method in the field is to use the wet and dry bulb thermometers. The principle of operation here being that when a wet cloth is swirled through the air it is cooled by the evaporation of the water from the cloth. The lower the relative humidity of the air, the more rapid is the evaporation of the water and hence the greater the cooling effect giving a wet bulb temperature reading much below that shown on the dry bulb. Wet and dry bulb thermometers are made up into a unit and called sling psychrometers.

The sling psychrometer is used then to determine the wet bulb temperature and the dry bulb temperature. When these temperatures are known the relative humidity can be determined from the psychrometric chart. Relative humidity is a measure of relative saturation of air with water vapour.

Moisture in the air also exerts a vapour pressure dependent on the degree to which air is saturated. Relative humidity is then also the ratio of the actual vapour pressure which occurs at the wet and dry bulb temperatures compared to the vapour pressure which would occur at saturation for the given dry bulb temperature. The lower the relative humidity, the lower the vapour pressure at any given temperature. Therefore, if grain is at a moisture equilibrium point of about 25°C and 70 percent RH and if the RH of the air then drops to 40 percent, there will be a pressure gradient between the grain and the air, so that drying will occur. Moreover, if the actual amount of moisture is held constant and the temperature is increased, the relative humidity is lowered but the vapour pressure of the air remains constant. In these conditions the heat which is supplied to the product by the drying air will increase the vapour pressure of the produce being treated so that there is a transfer of moisture from the grain to the drying air.

For example

1. Determine relative humidity (RH).
   Given air at 25°C dry bulb and 21.6°C wet bulb, the RH will be 80 percent.
2. Determine the change of RH when air is heated to 35°C.
   RH will drop to 47 percent.
3. The vapour pressure in examples 1 and 2 will be 16 g/cm^2.
4. The product when heated will develop a vapour pressure upto 28 g/cm^2 of mercury so that there will be a transfer of moisture from the product to the air.
5. The air as it passes over the product picks up moisture until it approaches saturation and in the process is cooled to about the wet bulb temperature corresponding to 35°C and 47 percent RH, which is 25°C. The vapour pressure of the drying air is also increasing so that it is approaching the vapour pressure of the product at the point of exit. In practice, saturation cannot be reached prior to exhausting the air, or moisture will begin to condense out of the air creating problems by increasing the moisture in parts of the product.
6. The moisture-holding capacity of the air increases from 25.8 g of water/kg of dry air to 32.3 g of water for fully saturated air at 25°C.
7. The amount of heat added will be:
   18.3 — 15.7 = 2.6 calories per kg of dry air (cal/kg) being heated or approximately 2.6 × 1.15 = 3.0 cal/m^3 (where air at 25°C and 80 percent RH weighs 1.15 kg/m^3).

When the data available from the psychrometric chart are combined with grain air equilibrium considerations, some additional factors are presented.

Grain with above 18 to 20 percent moisture content may be considered for all practical purposes to be in equilibrium with air at 100 percent RH.

Reviewing the psychrometric charts, the curved upper boundary line (the saturation line) shows the wet bulb temperature and, horizontally opposite, the number of pounds of moisture a pound of dry air carries at each temperature when saturated (100 percent RH). Roughly paralleling this line are two curves showing the moisture equilibria between air and shelled corn at 13 and 15.5 percent moisture content. These two curves may be taken as approximately representative of moisture equilibria for all grains at these moisture contents.

Once grain has been dried below the level at which the drying air is exhausted in a near saturated state, the efficiency of drying is reduced before the desired equilibrium moisture content or final storage moisture content (whichever is lower) is reached. In practice, when increasing the vapour pressure of the grain above that of the air, energy is lost in heating above the desired storage temperatures. Nevertheless, some of this energy is regained by the moisture removed by extra air movement which is required to provide cooling back to mean storage temperatures. After a period of tempering, the measurement of wet and dry bulb temperatures in the grain will once more permit determination of the relative humidity of the air in the interstices between the grain. This in turn, by reference to the standard moisture-relative humidity curves, will indicate the moisture content of the grain. If the moisture content is still too high for safe storage, further drying will be required.

Appendix I

TEMPERATURE MEASURING EQUIPMENT AND METHODS

Adapted from FAO Informal Working Bulletin No. 21, Portable equipment for sampling and temperature measurement of bulk grain, *by H.J. Griffiths, Engineering Section, Commonwealth Scientific and Industrial Research Organization, Melbourne, Australia*

Several factors govern the design of equipment for the measurement of temperature in grain:

(*a*) The thermal conductivity is low. Oxley (1948) [1] gives values for wheat, maize and oats which are only about three times the value for cork (a good insulator). The transfer of heat to or from a temperature sensing device inserted in the grain is, therefore, very slow. Although the time the sensing device will take to approach the equilibrium value, to within a specified error, will depend on the initial temperature difference, it is convenient in practice to specify an arbitrary period to be observed in all cases: 30 minutes may be regarded as a minimum period for most purposes. Due to poor heat transfer in the grain, it is also necessary to limit heat transfer along the connecting structure of the sensing device, otherwise its insertion may excessively alter the temperature pattern under observation.

(*b*) Changes of temperature over periods of days or weeks are often more important than the actual temperatures themselves; hence rather greater accuracy is required than would otherwise be the case — an accuracy of $\pm$ 1°F is desirable.

(*c*) It is preferable that temperatures be measured at a grid of points in three dimensions through the bulk being examined. This involves a large number of measurements, some at considerable depths.

---

[1] Oxley, T. A., 1948: *The scientific principles of grain storage.* Northern Publishing Co. Ltd., Liverpool, England.

METHODS OF TEMPERATURE MEASUREMENT

The numerous methods which have been used to measure temperatures in bulk grain may be divided into two groups according to whether they measure at one point, or at a number of points simultaneously.

Single-point methods

Examples of the single-point group are: mercury in glass thermometers placed in the tips of wooden or steel probes or lowered down metal pipes inserted into the grain; long stem thermometers in metal sheaths; and electric resistance thermometers placed in the tips of metal probes, the reading being made with an instrument at the surface.

Methods of this type usually exhibit slow response; in fact, there appears to be no sensing device which has both fast response and adequate robustness for insertion deep into grain. The measurement of temperature at a large number of points in a reasonable time therefore requires a large number of sensing points, all of slow response but all in use simultaneously. In addition, many of the methods of this group are liable to error because the sensing device must be removed for reading, or as a result of heat conduction along the probe. Some are limited to depths of 5 to 10 feet (1.5 to 3 metres).

Multipoint methods

A large number of points can be obtained by using a large number of single-point probes. It is more convenient, however, to use a few probes having a number of equally spaced sensing elements, the consequent restriction of positions of measurement to a series of straight lines being no great disadvantage.

Two methods in this group have been described by Oxley and Henderson. The first uses thermocouples placed at intervals along a 43-inch (110-centimetre) long wooden spear which is inserted using wooden extensions. The second and more versatile method uses thermocouple ropes with nine thermocouples spaced at intervals of 10 to 118 inches (25 to 300 centimetres) as required. A rope is formed by attaching copper wires at intervals along a full length constantan wire, and then covering the whole with two layers of cotton braid for strength.

The thermocouple rope method enables nine temperatures to be measured in little more time than is required for one measurement; namely, the time required for equilibrium of the rope with the grain. Further reduction in the average time per measurement can be achieved by the

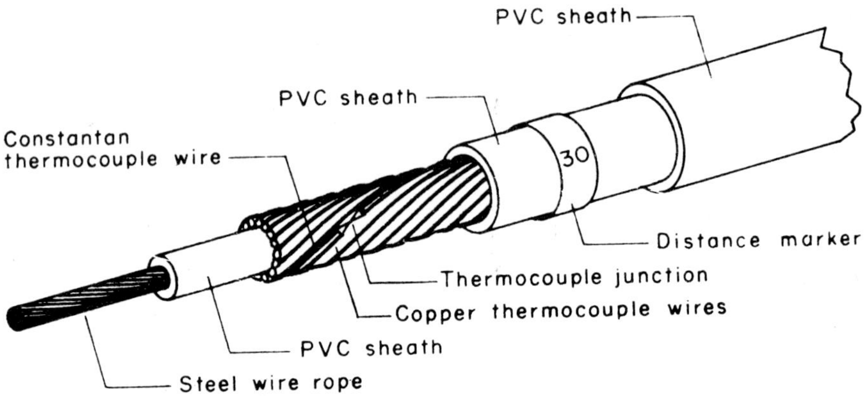

FIGURE 62. Details of thermocouple cable construction.

use of several ropes. The heavy tubes used for insertion are immediately removed, thus reducing conduction of heat along the rope. This method, therefore, meets the requirements for a satisfactory temperature measurement system.

The equipment to be described in detail below uses thermocouple cables differing only in construction from those of Oxley and Henderson. Thermocouples have been retained as the sensing elements because a neater, more robust cable can be constructed at lower cost than would be possible with thermistors or metallic resistance thermometers. The greater complication and cost of the measuring instrument required for thermocouples are offset by the fact that a number of cables can be read conveniently with one instrument. The construction of the cable is shown in Figure 62.

The cable consists of a plastic covered steel core about which are closely wound an insulated constantan thermocouple wire, and 9, 10, or 11 insulated copper thermocouple wires. The thermocouple wires are of 30 B and S gauge covered with polyvinyl chloride (PVC) to an outside diameter of 0.05 inch (1.2 millimetres). Each thermocouple wire follows a helical path of about 1 inch (2.5 centimetres) pitch around the steel core. Thermocouple junctions are formed at the required intervals along the cable during the winding process by parting the PVC insulation on the constantan wire and on an adjacent copper wire, twisting the two wires (including all of them not yet wound) 1½ turns and soft soldering the joint. When winding is continued, the constantan wire has crossed over the copper wire at the junction. The next junction is formed between the constantan wire and the adjacent copper wire to which it has not yet been connected. Thus the constantan wire crosses over the copper wires in turn, making a thermocouple junction with each at a different depth. The uniform helical construction is maintained except where the insulation is parted at the junction itself. Clearly, as much as half the copper wire used performs no electrical function; however, the cost of the wire is small, and only in this way is the neatness and strength of the construction maintained. Due to the short pitch helical construction, only small strains are imparted to the thermocouple wires during flexing of the cable.

The thermocouple wires are protected and held in place by one or two thin plastic sheaths shrunk into place. Although PVC tube dilated with a suitable solvent has been used successfully for cables 35 feet (10 metres) long, specially treated PVC tube which shrinks when heated to a temperature of 130°C appears more suitable, as there is then unlimited time to thread the wound cable into the tube. Distances are marked along the cable using special PVC marking inks, or by placing adhesive cable numbering strips under the outer clear sheath. The cable is terminated at one end in a brass plug carrying a transverse stainless steel pin, and at the other end in an aluminium bush; in each case the steel core, wires, and covering are anchored into the fitting by an epoxy-resin adhesive. The aluminium bush is clamped to a multicontact plug which is used to connect the cable to the measuring instrument. The plug and receptacle are fitted with constantan contacts for the constantan wire, in order to reduce errors resulting from temperature gradients which occur when a hot plug is connected to a cold receptacle, or vice versa. Dust caps are fitted in order to keep the connector contacts clean.

Multipoint thermocouple cables are manufactured in a number of similar forms. Specific limitations on lengths, spacing of thermocouples and methods of placement are available from the manufacturers.

Cables are strong, flexible and robust. Two men can usually insert the cable into wheat to a depth of 34 feet (10.4 metres), the limit for the longest cable yet constructed. Cables have been inserted easily to a depth of 22 feet (6.7 metres) in paddy rice. The time required is approximately 6 minutes. The thermocouples are inserted into the grain by means of screwed chrome-plated steel rods to which they are attached by a special coupling. The coupling permits the rods to be removed without risk of fouling the cable in the process. Details of one type of inserting rod are presented in Appendix J.

The thermocouples are inserted in the grain by the following procedure.

A thermocouple cable is attached to an inserting rod by the claws of the cable coupling. The rod, coupling, and cable are then pushed vertically down, slight tension being maintained on the cable for the first few feet to ensure that it does not slip from the coupling. The cable is inserted to the required depth by adding rods one at a time and pushing them into the grain, the inserting clamp being used when hand pushing becomes difficult. The rods and coupling are immediately removed, with the aid of the inserting clamp if necessary. It is convenient to insert the cable too far and to withdraw it, at this stage, to the required position. As the cables in use do not exceed 35 feet in length and have nine thermocouples at 2-foot (0.6-metre) intervals, the first cable is inserted to a depth of 34 feet and a second is then inserted, in a similar manner, to a depth of 16 feet (5 metres). A delay, which will permit grain sampling to be carried out, is required before temperatures are read. After approximately 30 minutes the thermocouple cables are connected in turn to the direct-reading potentiometer. Each is measured after a delay of two minutes or more which allows temperature gradients through the plug and receptacle to decay.

INSTRUMENT FOR TEMPERATURE MEASUREMENT

In installations where the sensing cables are all brought to one central control room, a potentiometer operated by central power and a switching device to handle a large number of circuits may be used. In grain storage facilities, where the cables are not brought to a central point, a portable unit will be needed.

A measuring instrument, for use by unskilled personnel in the conditions of difficult access and dark, dusty environment found in many grain storages, should be robust and reliable, easily portable (battery powered), simple to operate and read, and should not require levelling.

Of the two types of instrument commonly used with thermocouples — the moving-coil current meter and the potentiometer — the first may be readily rejected for this type of application on the grounds of insufficient robustness, particularly if it is to have sufficient sensitivity to render unnecessary the fitting of individual thermocouple-circuit equalizing resistances. However, the usual portable thermocouple potentiometer which is more suitable requires the following procedure when making a measurement.

(*a*) Adjust the potentiometer current to a standard value by reference to a standard cell — the "standardizing" operation.

(*b*) Read the temperature of the thermocouple reference junction on a thermometer.

(*c*) Adjust the measuring dial until balance is indicated by the galvanometer.

(*d*) Determine the temperature by reference to tables (in some instruments the temperature is read directly).

In order to meet the requirements for field use by unskilled personnel, at least one instrument has been designed in which this procedure has been considerably simplified. The adjustment of the potentiometer current and the compensation for the reference junction temperature have been made automatic, and the measuring dial for made direct reading in degrees. To make the whole unit sufficiently robust and quick to use, the usual sensitive galvanometer for balance detection has been replaced by a chopper-type DC amplifier driving a robust pivoted meter.

The potentiometer incorporates the receptacle for connexion of the thermocouple cable, and a multiposition switch for selection of the required thermocouple junction. A noteworthy contribution to ease of reading is made by the in-line numerical readout on the temperature dial. The potentiometer has a range of 0 to 60°C. This instrument has an accuracy of ± 1°C, but another is being constructed with a range of 40 to 140°F, and with more careful adjustment this should have an accuracy better than ± 1°F.

The complete series of operations necessary to determine a temperature with the new potentiometer is as follows:

(*a*) Switch on.

(*b*) Select required thermocouple.

(*c*) Move key switch to balance position.

(*d*) Rotate temperature dial until meter pointer is restored to original position, and read temperature.

(*e*) Move key switch to "battery test" position. If meter pointer moves in "replace" direction, disregard reading and replace or recharge battery. This operation is a very rapid one and need be made only occasionally.

The resulting instrument is a direct-reading potentiometer of great robustness. It is simple to use and no knowledge of the principle of operation is required. For the sake of completeness, however, a few details of the circuit of the potentiometer follow.

A zener diode operating in the high-voltage avalanche-breakdown region in which voltage depends linearly on both temperature and current is connected in a bridge network which provides compensation for temperature and current changes. The constant voltage output of this bridge is fed to another bridge circuit, one half of which incorporates a resistance thermometer, and provides compensation for the temperature of the thermocouple reference junction. The copper resistance thermometer in use at present gives an approximately linear output which results in errors of compensation of the nonlinear thermocouple characteristic; however, published resistance-temperature tables for nickel show that very good compensation can be obtained with this material.

The other half of the second bridge incorporates a rheostat-connected precision linear helical potentiometer. As the rheostat resistance is decreased, the current in this half of the bridge increases nonlinearly and causes a corresponding nonlinear voltage to resistances; this voltage can be made to follow closely the copper-constantan thermal electromotive force (EMF) corresponding to the temperature indicated by the linear digital dial attached to the rheostat shaft.

The out-of-balance signal is amplified by a transistor amplifier using an electro-mechanical low-noise chopper driven by a transistor multivibrator. The synchronously rectified output of the amplifier drives a DC milliammeter.

The potentiometer can be powered by mercury cells or sealed rechargeable nickel cadmium accumulators.

Thermocouple cables placed in bulk grain permit the rapid determination of grain temperature in bulk grain storages by making it possible to take a large number of readings with a direct-reading potentiometer.

Appendix J

SAMPLING GRAIN STORED IN BULK

Two basic sampling probes of the type in particular use in Australian grain storage structures are described here.

1. The more common probe takes samples at 6-inch (15-centimetre) intervals, usually to a depth of 6 feet (1.8 metres). It consists of two tubes, one fitting closely inside the other, and each containing a series of holes at 6-inch intervals along its length. The holes in the tubes may be closed off or made to overlap by rotating one tube against the other; in this way the probe can be inserted into, and removed from, the grain with the holes closed off, and can be opened for entry of the samples after insertion to the required position. The inner tube is usually divided into compartments 6 inches long.
2. The other sampling probe is similar in principle to that described by Oxley and Henderson. Here, a tube with one closed end is pushed into the grain by means of a rod and extensions. During this time, grain is prevented from entering the open top end of the tube by the presence of a sealing cap attached to the inserting rod, but at the required point the rod is raised allowing grain to enter. An internal rod or strip prevents the probe cavity becoming separated from the inserting rod by a distance greater than 1 or 2 inches (2.5 to 5 centimetres). Oxley states that his 1-ounce (0.3-hectogramme) spear can be used to a depth of 20 feet (6 metres) or more, a greater depth than can be reached with some probes of larger construction.

In addition, Anderson and Martin (1943)[1] have described an auger-type probe which consists of 3-foot (90-centimetre) lengths of pipe, assembled together by means of cap screws as the probe is inserted. Rotation of the section at the surface is transmitted to the auger attached to the first section, the whole probe being thereby pulled into the grain. This probe has been used frequently at a depth of 36 feet (11 metres) and has been tested at a depth of 76 feet (23 metres).

---

[1] Anderson, J.A. and Martin, U.G., 1943. Probe for sampling deep grain bins. *Grain Research Laboratory Bulletin No. 3.* Canada.

The probe designed as part of the equipment described here is of the second type; it consists basically of a single cavity inserted by a rod and extensions. However, it possesses certain advantages over the other probe types described.

Its advantage over other types (which may be regarded as deep sampling probes) is that of being sealed as it is withdrawn from the grain. It is therefore not necessary that the top layer of the sample be scraped off and discarded in case of contamination by the grain through which the probe has travelled since it was filled. This is considered to be important when tests such as insect population counts are to be performed, as the sample is often removed through a heavily infested surface layer. As a consequence of this design, the probe cracks some of the grain which enters. This may be a disadvantage for some purposes. On the other hand, it has the advantage of being more easily emptied, and more easily cleaned.

The probe in use has an outside diameter of $1^{3}/_{16}$ inches (30 millimetres), an overall length of 10 inches (25.4 centimetres), and a capacity of 2 ounces (0.6 hectogramme) of wheat. Two men can usually insert it to a depth of 34 feet (10.4 metres) or more in wheat, and have inserted it without difficulty to a depth of 22 feet (6.7 metres) in paddy rice.

The probe consists of two parts only, a brass head which is screwed to the inserting rod, and a hollow brass body into which the sample falls. Over part of its length the body is reduced in diameter so as to slide neatly into the head. Two stainless steel pins fixed diametrically opposite in the head engage the body by means of two slots shaped in such a way that a "bayonet" action is required to assemble the probe; this sliding movement followed by rotation results in the pins entering the long closed-end slots, and only a reversal of this movement can separate the probe parts. While the pins are positioned at either end of the main slots, the four holes in the head and the corresponding four holes in the body do not overlap.

In order to take a sample, the probe is inserted to the required depth using screwed rods. The pins during this time are at the lower ends of the slots and no grain can enter the cavity. The rods and the head which is attached to them are then moved up and down within the limits imposed by movement of the pins in the main slots, thus admitting grain through the overlapping holes. When the probe is removed, the pins register in the tops of the main slots and no grain can enter the probe.

Slight modification of the probe has been found necessary for use in rice. During tests in paddy, filling was often prevented by jamming of the probe body in the head, apparently as a result of the presence of hard particles of husk. In addition, the greater friction between the grains (as shown by the angle of repose) appeared to cause the formation of a marked tunnel where the probe had been pushed through the rice, consequently reducing the frictional force between the rice and the body of the probe. However, the addition of two wedge-shaped rings to the probe body resulted in increased grip, and the probe then operated satisfactorily. Another consequence of the friction between the grains was the increased number of up-and-down movements of the head required to fill the cavity — 50 cycles for rice compared with 25 cycles for wheat. A rather more satisfactory probe for this purpose could be made by slightly increasing the outside diameter and the hole size for easier entry of the grain, and by turning wedge-shaped recesses in the body in place of the added rings.

A little care during use of the probe is required in order to ensure that samples are not contaminated, and that the probe body is not lost in the grain. The sample will be contaminated by grain from another level if, during insertion or withdrawal of the probe, the direction of motion of the rods is reversed: actually a movement of $^1/_8$ inch (3.2 millimetres) in the case of the present probe is needed before overlapping occurs. Similar care must be taken while inserting the other types of probe described above, although none is needed during withdrawal of these probes as they are not then sealed. Overlapping of the holes occurs before the pins can leave the main slots via the circumferential ones, so that avoidance of contamination is sufficient to prevent separation of the probe parts in the grain. An independent requirement for separation is anticlockwise rotation of the head via the inserting rods; thus, if care is taken to avoid both contamination of the sample and anticlockwise rotation of the rods, the chance of accidental separation of the probe parts is negligible.

A procedure which guards against contamination and probe body loss is easily observed. Further details are given in the section on procedure for using the inserting rod.

Auxiliary equipment

The basic items of equipment — sampling probe (and also thermocouple cable, direct-reading potentiometer as described in Appendix I) — have been described. However, several other items of equipment are used with them in an auxiliary capacity.

The most important items are the rods used for inserting both the thermocouple cables and the sampling probe. Each rod (or more accurately, tube) at present in use consists of a chrome-plated hard-drawn mild steel tube into which threaded stainless steel inserts are fixed with epoxy-resin adhesive. The tube is of ½-inch (12.7-millimetre) outside diameter and 14-gauge wall thickness, the length of the rod between butting faces is 5 feet (1.5 metres) and the threads are $^3/_8$-inch (9.5-millimetre) diameter of British Standard Whitworth form.

This rod construction provides a satisfactory compromise of properties in the following groups.

(*a*) Small diameter for ease of insertion, but large section modulus and moment of inertia for resistance to bending and buckling. Light weight for ease of transport.

(*b*) Easy coupling of rods but small chance of accidental uncoupling.

(*c*) Smooth low friction surface for ease of insertion, high yield point material for resistance to permanent bending, and long life, but low cost, particularly as rods are occasionally bent during use.

The threaded inserts are drilled to allow air samples to be drawn up through the rods. The volume of air contained within a rod is quite large so that sampling points cannot be close together; in fact, the air from an 8-inch (20.3-centimetre) diameter sphere of rice or wheat would be required in order to replace the air in 30 feet (9 metres) of rods three times. The rods have not yet been used for sampling the intergranular atmosphere.

The coupling device used in combination with these rods in order to insert the thermocouple cables consists of a brass body into the top of which is screwed one of the inserting rods. Two claws, clamped tightly together by means of a socket head screw, can rotate freely in a transverse hole, but the extent of rotation is limited by machined recesses in the body. Removal of the socket head screw enables the coupling to be dismantled for cleaning and lubrication.

To insert a cable the claws are turned so as to project from the coupling and engage the transverse pin of the brass plug of the thermocouple cable. Only when the inserting rods and coupling are withdrawn is the cable released by the claws of the coupling. During withdrawal the grain will force the claws alongside the body of the coupling, thus preventing fouling of the cable on the claws.

Finally a rod inserting clamp, although not essential in principle, has been found to be of very great value for this work. Figure 63 shows a diagram of this device. The clamp consists basically of two arms carrying small rod clamping shoes on short rigidly attached cranks. The pins on which arm and cranks rotate are held in the correct relative position by two plates.

In use, the clamp is slipped over the top of the rod with the clamping shoes down for insertion, or up for withdrawal. Downward forces applied at the ends of the arms are transmitted to the rod without slip, pro-

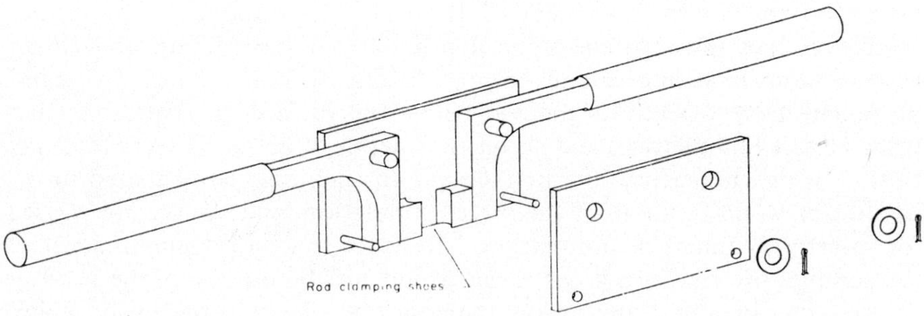

FIGURE 63. Rod inserting clamp (exposed view).

vided the lever ratio exceeds the reciprocal of the coefficient of friction of the shoe material on the rod. During the process of insertion, an upward movement of the handles immediately unclamps the shoes and no force is transmitted to the rod. A similar situation occurs during withdrawal. Insertion and withdrawal can then proceed by a series of short strokes, thus providing one of the following advantages of the method over the fixed "T" handle and hand gripping.

(*a*) Force is applied close to the grain surface — the small unsupported length reduces the tendency of the rod to buckle.

(*b*) The operators are in comfortable positions and can apply greater force; in fact, practically their total weight.

(*c*) The clamp need not be removed before rods are added or removed.

(*d*) The device is also useful as a clamp to prevent movement during unscrewing of rods.

PROCEDURE FOR USING INSERTING ROD

Sufficient information has already been given for the use of the equipment to be visualized; however, a few details of the procedure which has been used for the periodic observation of wheat in cylindrical silo bins may be of interest. The procedure for the insertion of the thermocouple cables has been described. Sampling can take place while the thermocouples are coming to equilibrium.

A sampling probe is screwed to the inserting rod in place of the coupling, and is cleaned by lightly tapping the inverted probe body against the head, or by use of a bottle brush. The probe is then inserted 1 foot (30 centimetres) below the surface (the first depth to be sampled), filled by an up and down movement of the rod, and withdrawn. A second sample is then taken at the same depth. It has been found convenient to take samples at intervals of one rod length, so that the next two samples come from 6 feet (1.8 metres) below the surface, the two after that from 11 feet (3.4 metres), and so on to a depth of about 34 feet (10.4 metres). In the laboratory, the first sample in each case is incubated in order to obtain an estimate of the insect population, and the second is used for moisture content determination. In order to avoid contamination of the sample, the rods are given a sharp pull just before the probe is withdrawn, thus breaking any grains that may be blocking the probe holes. Some caution is also necessary as the probe is withdrawn and the rods are removed, particularly whenever a rod is removed to ensure that the joint which unscrews is above the grain surface and not below it.

TYPICAL TIMETABLE FOR OBSERVATIONS OF WHEAT IN SILO BINS

	Depth	Time taken	Progressive time total
	Feet	*Minutes*	
Insert thermocouple cable 1	34	6	6
Insert thermocouple cable 2	16	4	10
Prepare for sampling	—	4	14
Take sample:			
1	1	2	16
2	1	1.5	17.5
3	6	2	19.5
4	6	1.5	21
5	11	2.5	23.5
6	11	2	25.5
7	16	3.5	29
8	16	3	32
9 [1]	22	4.5	36.5
10	22	4	40.5
11 [1]	28	4.5	45
12	28	5	50
13 [1]	34	5.5	55.5
14	34	4.5	60
Read temperatures of two cables		12	72

[1] 6-foot rods are added at these points.

The extra care required during sampling is ensured by the following procedures. After each upward lift on the rod clamp and rods, the rod is grasped in order to prevent downward movement as the clamp is lowered. After the next screwed joint is raised sufficiently, the clamp is lowered to the surface. One operator then maintains an upward force on one arm, the other arm being supported by the grain surface. The lower rod is thus securely clamped against rotation or downward movement, and the upper rod may be safely unscrewed by the other operator. When little force is required for withdrawal, it is more convenient to lift by hand, but the clamp may still be left on the grain surface ready for action while rods are unscrewed. A hand-over-hand method of raising the rods is used to prevent them falling under their own weight, or being accidentally pushed downward as they are grasped.

One operator is able to apply the clamp with one hand while he unscrews the rods with the other, but it is desirable to have two operators, and is indeed necessary for deep measurements where the additional weight is required. Use of the inserting clamp by a single operator is unwise, due to the likelihood of injury should the clamp slip while he supports his weight over a rod.

The transfer of the sample from probe to container is performed in the following way, in order to minimize contamination from conditions at the surface, such as a heavy insect infestation. One operator, holding the probe and attached rod in one hand, cleans the outside of the probe and removes the probe body. The other operator then places a bottle upside down over the probe; and both probe body and bottle together are inverted. The probe body is then raised leaving the sample in the bottle, which is then sealed.

The table shows typical times taken for the combined thermocouple placement and sampling which has been described. As is to be expected, the time required to take a sample varies markedly with depth. The times apply to a team of two, and include the placing of samples in bottles and the recording of the necessary data. An average labour time of 6.6 man-minutes per sample was required for this work. This compares quite favourably with the figure of 5.4 man-minutes per sample which has been calculated from data given by Anderson and Martin (1943) for use of their multipoint auger probe to a depth of 36 feet (11 metres). It should be noted, however, that the latter probe takes larger samples.

REFERENCES

A'Brook, J. Artificial drying of groundnuts: a method for the small farmer. *Trop.*
1963 *Agric. Trin.*, 40: 241-245.

Ahmadu Bello University. Institute for Agricultural Research. *Annual re-*
1963 *port 1962/63.* Samaru, Northern Nigeria.

Amaro, J. P. & Cancela de Fonseca, J. P. Panorama actual dos problemas fito-
1957 sanitarios dos produtos armazenados en Africa. *García de Orta*, 5 : 675-699.

American Cyanamid Co. Agricultural Department. *Malathion insecticide : protec-*
1962 *tion of stored grains, seeds, and other food products.* Wayne, N. J., 24 p.

Anon. A warning from the scientists. *World Health*, April 1967, p. 3. Meet the
1967 rat. *World Health*, April 1967, p. 4-6.

Anthonio, Q. B. O. The economics of cowpea storage in a concrete bin. Lagos,
1963 West Africa Stored Products Research Unit. Technical Report No. 19. *In* West Africa Stored Products Research Unit. *Annual report 1962*, p. 94-95.

Asem, A. K. Our daily bread. Part V. (Results of malnutrition). *Ghana Fmr*, 6:
1962 99-101.

Ashman, F. Factors affecting the abundance of the copra beetle, *Necrobia rufipes*
1963 (Deg) (Col., Clearidae). *Bull. ent. Res.*, 53: 671-680.

Austwick, P. K. C. & Ayerst, G. Toxic products in groundnuts: groundnut micro-
1963 flora and toxicity. *Chemy Ind.*, 2: 55-61.

Autrey, H. S. *et al.* Effect of milling conditions on breakage of rice grains. *J.*
1955 *agric. Fd Chem.*, 3: 593-599.

Bailey, C. H. Respiration of seeds. *Plant Physiol.*, 15: 257-274.
1940

Bailey, P. H. & Williamson, W. F. Some experiments on drying grain by solar
1965 radiation. *J. agric. engng Res.*, 10 (3): 191-196.

Bailey, S. W. Airtight storage of grain, its effects on insect pests. 2. *Calandra ory-*
1956 *zae* (small strain). *Australian J. agric. Res.*, 7: 7-19.

Bailey, S. W. Airtight storage of grain, its effects on insect pests. 3. *Calandra ory-*
1957 *zae* (large strain). *Australian J. agric. Res.*, 8: 595-603.

Bailey, S. W. The effects of percussion on insect pests of grain. *J. econ. Ent.*, 55:
1962 301-305.

Barker, T. W. Cocoa: storage and treatment of some food materials in the African
1960 tropics. *Agric. vet. Chem.* 1 (3) : 141-145.

Barnes, J. M. Toxic fungi with special reference to aflatoxin. *Trop. Sci.*, 9: 64-74.
1967

BECKLEY, V. A. The protection of grain against weevils. *Pyrethrum Post*, 1 (1) : 1948 8-10.

BILLS, G. T. Equipment for indoor pest control 1. *Int. Pest Cont.*, 8 (4): 6-11. 1966 Equipment for indoor pest control. 2. *Int. Pest Cont.*, 8(5): 15-21.

BISHOP, G. W. The comparative bionomics of American *Cryptolestes* (Coleoptera-1959 Cucujidae) that infest stored grain. *Ann. ent. Soc. Amer.*, 52. 657-665.

BLANE, M. A. & FORSYTH, J. Co-operative maize storage: Ashanti. *Ghana Fmr*, 1: 1957 216-217.

BLATCHFORD, S. M. & HALL, D. W. Methods of drying groundnuts. I. Natural meth-1963a ods (Literature survey). *Trop. Sci.*, 5: 6-33.

BLATCHFORD, S. M. & HALL, D. W. Methods of drying groundnuts. II. Artificial 1963b methods (Literature survey). *Trop. Sci.*, 5: 82-98.

BOWDEN, J. Uganda: review of agricultural entomology. *Report of the seventh Com-1960 monwealth Entomological Conference, London*, p. 353-360.

BOYCE, D. S. Aspects of in-bin drying of padi in Malaya utilising the waste heat of 1956 an internal combustion engine. *Malay. agric. J.*, 39 : 277-292.

BRAUER, O. & GENEL, M. R. El totomoxtlo como protector de la masorca. *Agric.* 1960 *téc. Mex.*, (10): 39-40

BREESE, M. H. Studies on the oviposition of *Rhyzopertha dominica* (F.) in rice and 1963 paddy. *Bull. ent. Res.*, 53 : 621-637.

BREESE, M. H. Factors governing the infestibility of paddy and rice. *Trop. stored* 1964 *Prod. Inf.*, (8): 289-299.

BROWN, W. B. *Fumigation with methyl bromide under gas-proof sheets.* London, 1959 Department of Scientific and Industrial Research. Pest Infestation Research Bulletin No. 1. 38 p.

BURGES, H. D. & BURRELL, N. J. Cooling bulk grain in the British climate to con-1964 trol storage insects and to improve keeping quality. *J. Sci. Fd Agric.*, 15: 32-50.

BURMEISTER, H. R. & HARTMANN, P. A. Yeasts in ensiled high moisture corn. *Appl.* 1966 *Microbiol.*, 14: 35-38.

CABRAL, A. L. & MOREIRA, I. S. Da cocorrencia de algunas pragas de produtos ultra-1960 marinos en poroes de navios mercantes (carreira da Guiné). *García de Orta*, 8: 47-57.

CALDERON, M., BENYAMINI, N. & SHAAYA, E. *Grain storage studies.* Hakirya, Tel-1961 Aviv, Department of Agriculture, Extension Authority. Publication No. 34. 28 p. (In Hebrew with English summary)

CASWELL, G. H. The infestation of cowpeas in the Western Region of Nigeria. *Trop.* 1961 *Sci.*, 3: 154-158.

CASWELL, G. H. & CLIFFORD, H. T. Effect of moisture content on germination of 1960 fumigated maize grain. *Emp. J. exp. Agric.*, 28: 139-149.

CCTA. *See* Commission for Technical Cooperation in Africa South of the Sahara.

CENTRAL FOOD TECHNOLOGICAL RESEARCH INSTITUTE. *Rice in India: atechno-economic* 1965 *review.* Mysore. (Abstract, *Rice J.*, 69 (2): 34-35.)

CHRISTIANSEN, P. M. & KAUFMANN, H. H. Deterioration of stored grains by fungi.
1965 *A. Rev. Phytopath*, 3: 69-84.

CHRISTIANSEN, P. M. & LOPEZ, L. C. Pathology of stored seeds. *Proc. int. Seed*
1963 *Test. Ass.*, 28: 701-711.

COAKER, T. H. " Insack " treatment of maize with insecticide for protection against
1959 storage pests in Uganda. *E. Afr. agric. J.*, 24 (4): 244-250.

COGBURN, R. R., TILTON, E. W. & BURKHOLDER, W. E. Gross effects of gamma
1966 radiation on the Indian-meal moth and Angoumois grain moth. *J. econ. Ent.*, 59 : 682-685.

COLLINGS, H. Hermetic sealing of a stack of maize with bituminous roofing felt. *Trop. Agric., Trin.*, 37: 53-60.

COMMISSION FOR TECHNICAL COOPERATION IN AFRICA SOUTH OF THE SAHARA/FAO. *A*
1961a *provisional list of insects infesting various stored products in Nigeria*, by M. A. Cornes and J. Riley. Paper read at the CCTA/FAO Symposium on Stored Food, Freetown, February 1962. 8 p. (Mimeo)

COMMISSION FOR TECHNICAL COOPERATION IN AFRICA SOUTH OF THE SAHARA/FAO. *Stor-*
1961b *age of cereal seed in the humid tropics with special reference to rice*, by E.H. Roberts. Paper read at the CCTA/FAO Symposium on Stored Food, Freetown, February 1962. 9 p. (Mimeo)

COMMISSION FOR TECHNICAL COOPERATION IN AFRICA SOUTH OF THE SAHARA/FAO. *Grain*
1962 *storage methods employed by certain Bantu tribes in South Africa*, by M. J. Oosthuizen. Paper read at the CCTA/FAO Symposium on Stored Food, Freetown, February 1962. 4 p. (Mimeo)

COMMISSION FOR TECHNICAL COOPERATION IN AFRICA SOUTH OF THE SAHARA. SCIEN-
1958 TIFIC COUNCIL FOR AFRICA SOUTH OF THE SAHARA. *Stored food products. Meeting of specialists on stored food products, Salisbury*, 1957. London. Publication No. 31. 200 p.

COMMISSION FOR TECHNICAL COOPERATION IN AFRICA SOUTH OF THE SAHARA. SCIEN-
1962 TIFIC COUNCIL FOR AFRICA SOUTH OF THE SAHARA. *Appareils à traction animale: traitement des récoltes au Sénégal*, par A. Bonlieu. Communication MEC. AG 62-4, Troisième réunion du Comité interafricain du machinisme agricole, Lagos, novembre 1962. 8 p. (Mimeo)

CORBY, H. D. R. *Report of a study of a pest* (Pachymerus longus *Pic*) *causing damage*
1941 *to groundnuts in the Wurkum District of the Muri Division of Adamawa.* Samaru, Zaria, Nigeria, Agriculture Department. Report No. 9302/167. 15 p.

CORNES, M. A. A revised listing of the insects associated with stored products in Nigeria. Lagos, Nigerian Stored Products Research Institute. Technical Report No. 19. *In* Nigerian Stored Products Research Institute. *Annual report 1964*, p. 96-119.

COURSEY, D. G. & EGGINS, H. O. W. Origine de la contamination microbiologique
1961 de l'huile de palme du Nigeria. *Oléagineux*, 16: 541-547.

COURSEY, D. G. & SIMMONS, E. A. Observations sur l'influence de la température
1963 de stockage sur l'altération lipolytique de l'huile de palme. *Oléagineux*, 18: 161-166.

CRANHAM, J. E. Insect infestation of stored raw cocoa in Ghana. *Bull. ent. Res.*,
1960 51: 203-222.

CRAUFURD, R. Q. *Breakage of rice during milling.* Rokupr, West African Rice Re-
1960 search Station. Periodic Scientific Report No. 11. 3 p. (Mimeo)

CRAUFURD, R. Q. Moisture changes in raw and parboiled paddy in West Africa and
1962 their influence upon milling quality. II. Changes during drying. *Emp. J. exp. agric.*, 30 (120): 321-329.

CUTLER, J. R. *et al.* Maize storage in 44-gallon oil drums. *In* West Africa Stored
1958 Products Research Unit. *Annual report 1957*, p. 42-43. Lagos.

DAVEY, P. M. The groundnut Bruchid, *Caryedon gonagra* (F.) *Bull. ent. Res.*, 49 :
1958 385-404.

DAVEY, P. M. The acceptability and fitness of maize for human consumption. *Trop.*
1961 *Sci.*, 3 : 163-172.

DAVEY, P. M. & ELCOATE, S. Resistance of two varieties of sorghum to *Sitophilus.*
1962 *Pest Infest. Res.*, 1961, p. 66.

DAVEY, P. M. & ELCOATE, S. *Sitophilus oryzae* infestation of different varieties of
1963 sorghum. *Pest Infest. Res.*, 1962, p. 75.

DAVEY, P. M. & ELCOATE, S. Moisture content/relative humidity equilibria of trop-
1965 ical stored produce (Part 1, Cereals). *Trop. stored Prod. Inf.*, (11): 439-467.

DAVEY, P. M. & ELCOATE, S. Moisture content/relative humidity equilibria of trop-
1966 ical stored produce (Part 2, Oilseeds). *Trop. stored Prod. Inf.*, (12): 495-512.

DAVEY, P. M. & ELCOATE, S. Moisture content/relative humidity equilibria of trop-
1967 ical stored produce (Part 3, Legumes, spices and beverage). *Trop. stored Prod. Inf.*, (13): 15-34.

DAVIES, J. C. Aluminium phosphide for bulk grain fumigation in Uganda. *E. Afr.*
1958 *agric. J.*, 24 : 103-105.

DAVIES, J. C. A note on the control of bean pests in Uganda. *E. Afr. agric. J.*, 24:
1959 174-178.

DAVIES, J. C. Coleoptera associated with stored products in Uganda. *E. Afr. agric.*
1960a *J.*, 25: 199-201.

DAVIES, J. C. Experiments on the crib storage of maize in Uganda. *E. Afr. agric.*
1960b *J.*, 26: 71-75.

DAVIES, J. C. Storage of maize in a prefabricated aluminium silo in tropical condi-
1960c tions. *E. Afr. agric. J.*, 25: 225-228.

DAVIES, J. C. A note on in-sack storage of beans using 0.04% gamma BHC dust.
1962 *E. Afr. agric. for. J.*, 27: 223-224.

DOGGETT, H. The breeding of sorghum in East Africa. I. Weevil resistance in sor-
1957 ghum grains. *Emp. J. exp. Agric.*, 25 (97): 1-9.

DOGGETT, H. The breeding of sorghum in East Africa. II. The breeding of weevil-
1958 resistant varieties. *Emp. J. exp. Agric.*, 26 (101): 37-46.

DROGAT, N. *The challenge of hunger*, tr. by J. R. Kirwan. London, Burns and
1962 Oates. 151 p.

EDSON, E. F., SANDERSON, D. M. & NOAKES, D. N. Acute toxicity data for pesticides.
1966 *World Rev. Pest Cont.*, 5: 143-151.

FAO. *The state of food and agriculture 1958.* Rome. *1958* 222 p.
1958

FAO. *World crop harvest calendar*. Rome, 299 p.
1959

FAO. *Food supplies and consumption in Africa*, by B. F. Johnston. Rome. 103 p.
1961a (Mimeo) (Restricted)

FAO. *Report to the Government of Ghana on foods and nutrition*, by F. Aylward. Rome.
1961b FAO/EPTA Report No. 1449. 76 p.

FAO. *FAO Africa survey: report on the possibilities of African rural development in*
1962a *relation to economic and social growth*. Rome. 168 p.

FAO. *The state of food and agriculture 1962*. Rome. 198 p.
1962b

FAO. *Production yearbook 1965*. Vol. 19. *1965* Rome.
1966

FAO. *The state of food and agriculture 1968*. Rome. 200 p.
1968

FAO. *Manual of fumigation for insect control*. Rome. 381 p.
1969

FAO. *Pesticide residues in food: report of the 1968 joint meeting of the FAO Working*
1969 *Party of Experts on Pesticide Residues and the WHO Expert Committee on Pesticide Residues*. Rome: FAO Agricultural Studies No. 78; World Health Organization Technical Report Series No. 417.

FORGACS, J. & CARLL, W. T. Mycotoxicoses. *Advanc. vet. Sci.*, 7: 273-382.
1962

FORSYTH, J. Ghana. I. Review of entomological work of the Ministry of Agricul-
1960 ture. *Report of the seventh Commonwealth Entomological Conference, London*, p. 279-282.

FORSYTH, J. Major food storage problems. *In* Wills, B.J., ed. *Agriculture and land*
1962 *use in Ghana*, p. 394-401. London, Oxford University Press.

FORSYTH, J. *Agricultural insects of Ghana*. Accra, Ghana University Press. 163 p.
1966

GARG, O. P. & AGRAWAL, N. S., *Bull. Grain Tech., Harpur, U. P.*, 4.
1966

GEERTSEMA, F. K. DE. Handling of maize demands investigation. *Fmg S. Afr.*, 39
1962 (11): 21-23.

GHOSE, R. L. M., GHATGE, M. B. & SUBRAHMANYAN, V. *Rice in India*. Rev. ed. New
1960 Delhi, Indian Council of Agricultural Research. 474 p.

GILES, P. H. Lindane contamination in stored sorghum and millet in Northern Nige-
1964 ria. *Trop. Sci.*, 6: 113-121.

GOLUMBIC, C. Fungal spoilage of stored food crops. *In* Massachusetts Institute of
1965 Technology. *Mycotoxins in foodstuffs*, p. 49-67. Cambridge, Mass.

GOLUMBIC, C. & DAVIS, D. F. Radiation disinfestation of grain and seeds. In *Food*
1966 *irradiation: proceedings of the International Symposium on Food Irradiation* jointly organized by the International Atomic Energy Agency and the Food and Agriculture Organization of the United Nations and held in Karlsruhe, 6-10 June 1966, p. 473-488. Vienna, International Atomic Energy Agency.

GRAHAM, W. M. & KOCKUM, S. Admixture of malathion and lindane with bagged
1961 maize. *Bull. ent. Res.*, 52: 727-739.

GREEN, A. A., KANE, J. & GRADIDGE, J. M. G. Experiments on the control of *Ephes-*
1966 *tia elutella* (Hb.) (Lepidoptera, Phycitidae) using dichlorvos vapour. *J. stor-ed Prod. Res.*, 2: 147-157.

HALL, D. W. The quality of groundnuts from the Gambia with special reference to
1954 insect infestation. *Colon. Pl. Anim. Prod.*, 4 : 227-235.

HALL, D. W. *Problems of food storage in tropical territories.* Paper read at the Jubilee
1955 Conference of the Association of Applied Biology, London, 1954. *Ann. appl. Biol.*, 42: 85-97.

HALL, D. W. & STEPHEN, J. V. *Steel and the storage of agricultural produce in the*
1966 *tropics.* Paper read at meeting of European Coal and Steel Community, Luxembourg, October 1966.

HALLIDAY, D. Persistence of insecticide dusts used as insect barriers. Lagos, West
1962 Africa Stored Products Research Unit. Technical Report No. 24. *In* West Africa Stored Products Research Unit. *Annual report 1962*, p. 110-112.

HAYWARD, L. A. W. Losses associated with groundnuts infested with *Trogoderma*
1955 *granarium* Everts. *J. Sci. Fd Agric.*, 6: 337-340.

HAYWARD, L. A. W. Infestation control in stored groundnuts in Northern Nigeria.
1963 *World Crops.*, 15 (2): 63-67.

HEUSER, S. G. Behaviour of components of an ethylene dibromide-methyl bromide
1964 mixture during fumigation of flour. *J. Sci. Fd Agric.*, 15: 114-119.

HILL, S. T. Dependence of the foreign grain beetle on nutrients in fungi. *Pest Infest. Res.*, 1962, p. 17-18.

HOWE, R. W. Entomological problems of food storage in Northern Nigeria. *Bull.*
1952 a *ent. Res.*, 43: 111-144.

HOWE, R. W. Miscellaneous experiments with grain weevils. *Ent. mon. Mag.*, 88:
1952b 252-255.

HOWE, R. W. The biology of the two common storage species of *Oryzaephilus* (Coleop-
1956 tera, Cucujidae). *Ann. appl. Biol.*, 44: 341-355.

HOWE, R. W. Losses caused by insects and mites in stored foods and feeding stuffs.
1965a *Nutr. Abstr.* 35 : 285-293.

HOWE, R. W. A summary of estimates of optimal and minimal conditions for popu-
1965b lation increase of some stored products insects. *J. stored Prod. Res.*, 1: 177-184.

HOWE, R. W. & CURRIE, J. E. Some laboratory observations on the rates of develop-
1964 ment mortality and oviposition of several species of Bruchidae breeding in stored pulses. *Bull. ent. Res.*, 55: 437-477.

HYDE, M. B. Airtight storage of grain. *Ann. appl. Biol.*, 50: 362-364.
1962

INTERNATIONAL RICE COMMISSION. *Report of the first meeting of the Working Party*
1960-62 *on the Agricultural Engineering Aspects of Rice Production, Storage and Processing, Saigon, 10-15 November 1960.* 44 p. *Report of the second meeting of the Working Party on Agricultural Engineering Aspects of Rice Production, Storage and Processing, Kuala Lumpur, 3-8 September 1962.* 36 p.

JOFFE, A. Moisture migration in horizontally stored bulk maize: the influence of
1958 grain infesting insects under South African conditions. *S. Afr. J. agric. Sci.*, 1: 175-193.

JOFFE, A. The effect of physical disturbance or "turning" of stored maize on the
1963 development of insect infestation. I. Grain elevator studies. *S. Afr. J. agric. Sci.*, 6: 55-64.

JOFFE, A. & CLARKE, B. The effect of physical disturbance or "turning" of maize
1963 on the development of insect infestation. II. Laboratory studies with *Sitophilus oryzae* (L.). *S. Afr. J. agric. Sci.*, 6: 65-84.

JOHNSTON, B. F. *The staple food economics of western tropical Africa.* Stanford,
1958 Stanford University Press. 305 p. (Studies in Tropical Development)

JOTWANI, M. G. & SIRCAR, P. Studies on the extent of insect damage and germina-
1964 tion of seeds. 1. Germination of pea seeds damaged by *Callosobruchus maculatus* (F.). *Indian J. Ent.*, 26: 130-133.

KAMEL, A. E. H. & SHAHBA, B. A. *Protection of stored seeds in Egypt.* Cairo, Minis-
1958 try of Agriculture, Extension Department. Bulletin No. 295. 16 p.

KHALIFA, A. The relative suceptibility of some varieties of sorghum to *Trogoderma*
1962 attack. *Emp. J. exp. Agric.*, 30 (118): 133-136.

KIK, M. C. Thiamin in products of commercial rice milling. *Cereal Chem.*, 20:
1943 103-109.

KIRITANI, K. Insect infestation of stored rice in Japan. *Proc. 12th int. Congr. Ent.*,
1964 London, p. 630.

KIRKPATRICK, R. L. & HAREIN, P. K. Inhibition of reproduction of Indian-meal moths,
1965 *Plodia interpunctella*, by exposure to amplified sound. *J. econ. Ent.*, 58: 920-921.

KOCKUM, S. Control of insects attacking maize on the cob in crib stores. *E. Afr.*
1958 *agric. J.*, 23: 275-279.

KOCKUM, S. & GRAHAM, W. M. Prevention of insect infestation of bagged maize.
1962 *Trop. Agric., Trin.*, 39: 231-245.

KONDO, M. & OKAMURA, T. [Storage of rice. VI. Physical and biochemical studies
1932 of hulled rice stored in straw bags.] *Ber. Ohara Inst.*, 5: 395-406. (In Japanese) (*Chem. Abstr.*, 27: 4284)

KONDO, M. *et al.* [Storage of rice in concrete silos. III. Storage of insufficiently
1941 dried rice for over 4 years after desiccation by heating.] *Rep. Ohara Agric. Inst., Japan*, 32: 95-113. (In Japanese) (*Biol. Abstr.*, 23 (7): 20768, 1949)

KURTZ, O'D. L. & HARRIS, K. L. *Micro-analytical entomology for food sanitation*
1962 *control.* Washington, D. C., Association of Official Agricultural Chemists. 576 p.

LAUDANI, H. *Technology of grain irradiation.* Washington, D.C., U.S. Department
1967 of Agriculture, Agricultural Research Service, Market Quality Research Division. 8 p.

LEMON, R. W. Laboratory evaluation of malathion bromophos and fenitrothion for
1967 use against beetle infesting stored products. *J. stored Prod. Res.*, 2: 197-210.

LE PELLEY, R., comp. *Agricultural insects of East Africa.* Nairobi, East Africa High
1959 Commission. 307 p.

LE PELLEY, R. & KOCKUM, S. Experiments in the use of insecticides for the protec-
1954 tion of grains in storage. *Bull. ent. Res.*, 45: 295-311.

LUCA, Y. DE. *Contributions à l'étude morphologique et biologique de* Bruchus lentis
1956 *Fröhl.: essais de lutte.* Annales de l'Institut agricole et des services de recherches et d'expérimentation agricoles de l'Algérie, Vol. 10, No. 1. 94 p.

MACMASTERS, M. M., comp. *Cereal laboratory methods.* 7th ed. St. Paul., Minn.,
1962 American Association of Cereal Chemists. 814 p. (Loose-leaf)

MATTHEWS, G. A. A preliminary investigation into the insect infestation of cargoes
1958 from West Africa. *Ann. appl. Biol.*, 46: 259-263.

MCCLOY, J. *The artificial drying of groundnuts: Tanganyika 1955.* Silsoe, Beds.,
1955 National Institute of Agricultural Engineering. 18 p. (Mimeographed)

MCFARLANE, J. A. An annotated record of Coleoptera, Lepidoptera, Hemiptera and
1963 Hymenoptera associated with stored produce in Jamaica. *Trop. Agric., Trin.*, 40: 211-216.

NELSON, A. *Medical botany.* Edinburgh, Livingstone. 544 p.
1951

NICHOLLS, L. *Tropical nutrition and dietetics.* 3rd ed. London, Baillière, Tindall and
1951 Cox. 476 p.

NORTHERN NIGERIA. MINISTRY OF AGRICULTURE. *Annual report 1961-62.* Kaduna.
1962

OCHSE, J. J. *et al. Tropical and subtropical agriculture.* New York, Macmillan. 2 v.
1961

OXLEY, T. A. *The scientific principles of grain storage.* Liverpool, Northern Publishing
1948 Co. 103 p.

OZBURN, G. W., EFFIONG, E. A. & FAYINKA, O. A. Hermetic storage of cowpeas. *In*
1959 West Africa Stored Products Research Unit. *Annual report 1958*, p. 64-65. Lagos.

OZBURN, G. W. *et al.* Hermetic storage of guinea corn. Lagos, West Africa Stored
1961 Products Research Unit. Technical Report No. II. *In* West Africa Stored Products Research Unit. *Annual report 1960*, p. 45-47.

PAGE, A. B. P. & LUBATTI, O. F. Fumigation of insects. *A. Rev. Ent.*, 8: 239-264.
1963

PARKIN, E. A. Insects and stored food : world losses and control measures surveyed.
1959 *Food Manuf.*, 34: 164-168.

PARKIN, E. A. The onset of insecticide resistance among field populations of stored
1965 product insects. *J. stored Prod. Res.*, 1: 3-8.

PARKIN, E. A. & LLOYD, C. J. The grain weevil and pyrethrum. *Pest Infest. Res.*,
1963 1962, p. 37.

PAWLEY, W. H. *Possibilities of increasing world food production.* Rome, FAO. FFHC
1963 Basic Study No. 10. 231 p.

PERTI, S. L. Control of insect infestation in foodstuffs by fumigation. *J. Sci. Tech-*
1965 *nol., Kanpur, India*, 3 (1): 64-65.

PINGALE, S. V. Effect of damage by some insects on the viability and weight of stored
1953 grain. *Bull. cent. Fd tech. Res. Inst., Mysore*, 2: 153-154.

PINGALE, S. V. Report from the Grain Storage Research and Training Institute, Hapur.
1963 *Grain Storage Newsletter* (FAO), 5 (3): 4.

PINGALE, S. V. *Maintenance of buffer stacks of cereals under the tropical conditions*
1964 *of India.* Paper presented to the twelfth International Congress of Entomology, London, 1964.

PINGALE, S. V., RAO, M. N. & SWAMINATHAN, M. Effect of insect infestation on stor-
1954 ed wheat. I. Studies on soft wheat. *J. Sci. Fd Agric.*, 5 : 51-54.

PINGALE, S. V. *et al.* Effect of insect infestation on stored grain. II. Studies on
1957 husked hand-pounded, milled raw rice and parboiled milled rice. *J. Sci. Fd Agric.*, 8: 512-516.

PLATT, B. S. *Tables of representative values of foods commonly used in tropical coun-*
1962 *tries.* London, Medical Research Council. Special Report Series No. 302. 46 p.

PRADHAN, S., MOOKHERJEE, P. B. & SHARMA, G. C. Pusa bin for grain storage. *In-*
1965 *dian Fmg*, 15 (1) : 14-16.

PREVETT, P. F. *An investigation into the storage of rice in Sierra Leone.* London,
1959 Colonial Office. Colonial Research Studies No. 28. 52 p.

PREVETT, P. F. Field infestation of cowpea (*Vigna unguiculata*) pods by beetles of
1961 the families Bruchidae and Curculionidae in Northern Nigeria. *Bull. ent. Res.*, 52 : 635-645.

PREVETT, P. F. An investigation into the bulk storage of sorghum in five cylindrical
1962 a aluminium silos. Lagos, West Africa Stored Products Research Unit. Technical Report No. 13. *In* West Africa Stored Products Research Unit. *Annual report 1961*, p. 73-82.

PREVETT, P. F. *The reduction of Bruchid infestation of cowpeas by post-harvest storage*
1962 b *methods.* Lagos, West Africa Stored Products Research Unit. 7 p.

RAI, L., SARID, J. N. & PINGALE, S. V. Fumigation of food grains in India with
1963 hydrogen phosphide. *Bull. Grain Tech., Hapur, U.P.*, 1, pt 1-2: 3-17; 1, pt 3: 43-49.

RANSOM, W. H. *Buildings for the storage of crops in warm climates.* London, Depart-
1960 ment of Scientific and Industrial Research. Tropical Building Studies No. 2. 24 p.

RAYMOND, W. D., SPICKETT, R. G. W. & WARD, J. B. The estimation of insect frag-
1954 ments in maize. *Colon. Pl. Anim. Prod.*, 4: 334-348.

RHIND, D. The breakage of rice in milling : a review. *Trop. Agric., Trin.*, 39 : 19-28.
1962

RILETT, R. O. The biology of *Laemophloeus ferrugineus* (Steph.). *Canad. J. Res.*,
1949 D, 27 (3) : 112-148.

ROMER, J. *Report on pest control in Hong Kong*, p. 2.
1965

ROTH, L. M. & WILLIS, E. R. *The medical and veterinary importance of cockroaches.*
1957 Washington, D. C., Smithsonian Institution. Smithsonian Miscellaneous Collections Vol. 134, No. 10. Publication No. 4299. 147 p.

ROWLANDS, D. G. The degradation of malathion on stored maize and wheat grains.
1964 *J. Sci. Fd Agric.*, 15 : 824-829.

SALMOND, K. F. *A report on investigations into grain storage problems in Nyasaland*
1957 *protectorate with special reference to maize* (Zea mays *L.*). London, Colonial Office. Colonial Research Publications No. 21. 49 p.

SARID, J. N. & KRISHNAMURTHY, K. Storage structures for large scale handling and
1965 preservation of food grain. *Bull. Grain Technol.*, 3 (2) : 62-69.

SAWAF, S. K. EL-. Some factors affecting the longevity, oviposition and rate of develop-
1956 ment in the southern cowpea weevil, *Callosobruchus maculatus* F. (Coleoptera, Bruchidae). *Bull. Soc. ent. Egypte*, 40: 29-95.

SCOTT, DE B. Toxigenic fungi isolated from cereal and legume products. *Mycopath.*
1965 *Mycol. appl.*, 25 (3/4) : 213-222.

SINHA, R. N. Insects and mites associated with hot spots in farm stored grain. *Canad.*
1961 *Ent.*, 93 : 609-621.

SINHA, R. N. & WALLACE, H. A. H. Ecology of a fungus-induced hot spot in stored
1965 grain. *Canad. J. Pl. Sci.*, 45 : 48-59.

SNOW, O. W. The economics of agricultural research. *Ghana Fmr*, 6 : 111-113, 116.
1962

SOUTHGATE, B. J. Plastics films for the bulk storage of food. *Plast. Inst. Trans. &*
1965 *J.*, 33 (103) : 11-15.

STRONG, R. G. & LINDGREN, D. L. Germination of cereal, sorghum and small le-
1960 gume seeds after fumigation with hydrogen phosphide. *J. econ. Ent.*, 53: 1-4.

STRONG, R. G. & LINDGREN, D. L. Effect of methyl bromide and hydrocyanic acid
1961 fumigation on the germination of corn seed. *J. econ. Ent.*, 54 : 764-770.

SWEENEY, R. C. H. *Insect pests of stored products in Nyasaland.* Zomba, Department
1962 of Agriculture. 50 p.

TILTON, E. W., BURKHOLDER, W. E. & COGBURN, R. R. Effects of gamma radiation
1966 on *Rhyzopertha dominica*, *Sitophilus oryzae*, *Tribolium confusum* and *Lasioderma serricorne*. *J. econ. Ent.*, 59 : 1363-1368.

UNITED KINGDOM. INTERDEPARTMENTAL WORKING PARTY ON GROUNDNUT TOXICITY
1962 RESEARCH. *Report. Toxicity associated with certain batches of groundnuts.* London. 8 p.

UNITED KINGDOM. MINISTRY OF AGRICULTURE, FISHERIES AND FOOD. *Farm grain*
1966 *drying and storage.* 3rd ed. London. Bulletin No. 149.

UNITED NATIONS. *The handling, storage and processing of agricultural produce: some*
1962a *important aspects of improvement of storage facilities in the less developed areas*, by D. W. Hall and FAO officers. Paper read at United Nations Conference on the Application of Science and Technology for the Benefit of the Less Developed Areas, Geneva, February 1963. 7 p. (E/CONF. 39/C/472) (Mimeo)

UNITED NATIONS. *The technical development in grain harvesting and storage problems*
1962b *related to combining in humid areas*, by T. T. Pedersen. Paper read at United Nations Conference on the Application of Science and Technology for the Benefit of the Less Developed Areas, Geneva, February 1963. 5 p. (E/CONF. 39/C/253) (Mimeo)

UPTON, M. W.A.S.P.R.U./U.C.I. grain storage project. 2. Costs of maize storage
1963 1959-60. Lagos, West Africa Stored Products Research Unit. Technical Report No. 17. *In* West Africa Stored Products Research Unit. *Annual report 1962*, p. 89-90.

U.S. DEPARTMENT OF AGRICULTURE. *Losses in agriculture.* Washington, D.C. Agri-
1965 culture Handbook No. 291. 120 p.

U.S. DEPARTMENT OF HEALTH, EDUCATION AND WELFARE. *Clinical handbook on eco-*
1963 *nomic poisons.* Washington, D.C. Public Health Service Publication No. 476.

U. S. ECONOMIC RESEARCH SERVICE. *The world food budget 1962 and 1966.* Wash-
1961 ington, D. C. Foreign Agricultural Economic Report No. 4. 78 p.

VENKAT RAO, S. *et al.* Effect of insect infestation on stored grain. III. Studies on
1958 Kaffir corn (*Sorghum vulgare*). *J. Sci. Fd Agric.*, 9 : 837-839.

VENKAT RAO, S. *et al.* Effect of insect infestation on stored field bean (*Dolichos*
1960 *lablab*) and black gram (*Phaseolus mungo*). *Food Sci.*, 9 : 79-82.

WATTERS, F. L. Effects of grain moisture content on residual toxicity and repellency
1959 of malathion. *J. econ. Ent.*, 52 : 131-134.

WATTERS, F. L. Physical methods of insect control. *Proc. ent. Soc. Manitoba*, 21 :
1965 18-27.

WEST AFRICAN RICE RESEARCH STATION. *Annual report for 1961.* Rokupr. 42 p.
1963

WOLPERT, V. Rats in store, India. *Far Eastern econ. Rev.*, 53 (10) : 439.
1966

WOLPERT, V. Needless losses. *Far Eastern econ. Rev.*, 55 : 411-412.
1967

WRIGHT, F. N. *Report on food storage in Malaya, Federation of Malaysia.* London,
1963 Tropical Products Institute.

WRIGHT, F. N. New storage, transportation and handling techniques for tropical,
1965 agricultural produce. *C. r. Trav. Prot. Cult. trop., Chambre de commerce et d'industrie de Marseille, 23-27 mars 1965*, p. 93-98.

WRIGHT, F. N. & SOUTHGATE, B. J. The potential uses of plastics for storage with
1962 particular reference to rural Africa. *Trop. Sci.*, 4 : 74-81.

INDEX